ELECTRONICS SERVICING
VOL. 1 (Electronic Systems and Science Background)

This book is to be returned on or before the last date stamped below.

ELECTRONICS SERVICING VOL. 1 (Electronic Systems and Science Background)

K. J. Bohlman
I.Eng., F.I.E.I.E., A.M.Inst.E.

Dickson Price Publishers Ltd
Hawthorn House
Bowdell Lane
Brookland
Romney Marsh
Kent TN29 9RW

Dickson Price Publishers Ltd
Hawthorn House
Bowdell Lane
Brookland
Romney Marsh
Kent TN29 9RW

First published 1987
Second edition 1991
© K. J. Bohlman 1987

British Library Cataloguing in Publication Data
Bohlman, K. J. (Kenneth John)
    Electronics servicing. Vol. 1: Electronic
    systems. — 2nd ed.
    I. Title
    621.381

    ISBN 0-85380-162-2

Photoset by
R. H. Services, Welwyn, Hertfordshire
Printed and bound in Great Britain

CONTENTS

Other Books of Interest

Electronics Servicing Vol 1
Electronics Servicing Vol 2
Electronics Servicing Vol 3
Electronics Servicing 500 Multiple Choice Questions and Answers for Part 1
Electronics Servicing 500 Questions and Answers for Part 2
Colour and Mono Television Vol 1
Colour and Mono Television Vol 2
Colour and Mono Television Vol 3
Principles of Domestic Video Recording and Playback Systems
Video Recording and Playback Systems 500 Q & A
Closed Circuit Television Vol 1
Closed Circuit Television Vol 2
Radio Servicing Vol 1
Radio Servicing Vol 2
Radio Servicing Vol 3
Digital Techniques
Control Systems Technology
Fault Location in Electronic Equipment

Inspection Copies

Lecturers wishing to examine any of these books should write to the publishers requesting an inspection copy.

Complete Catalogue available on request.

PREFACE

IN THE NEW edition of this popular book further chapters have been added to cover the Science Background element of the Part 1 syllabus for the City & Guilds 224 course in Electronics Servicing. Worked examples are used throughout the Science section and there are over 170 multi-choice questions with answers for self-assessment.

The lucid and full descriptive style of the previous edition has been retained to provide the reader with essential background information to supplement lecture notes received at college. Modern methods of communication using both analogue and digital signals are introduced to allow a clear understanding of communication principles to be acquired at an early stage of the course, which is one of the important aims of the book.

CHAPTER ONE

WAVEFORMS

Objectives
1 Determine the following sine wave measurements and their relationships to one another: amplitude; peak-to-peak; average; r.m.s; periodic time and frequency.
2 Identify d.c. level, fundamental frequency and harmonics of speech, triangular, sawtooth and rectangular waveforms.
3 Determine pulse repetition frequency and mark-to-space ratio of pulse waveforms.
4 Distinguish between analogue and digital waveforms.

ALL OF THE Electronic Systems described in this book rely, for their correct operation, on the generation or processing of waveforms of various types. A knowledge of the basic features of the waveforms to be handled by the electronic units which make up complete systems is an essential requirement of your course and will be considered in this chapter.

Sine Waves

The **sine wave** is the most common and useful waveform encountered in electronics. It is the waveshape of the supply voltage produced by electric power stations. In the largest modern power station generators, electricity is generated at about 25,000 volts, but for efficient transmission over large distances the voltage is increased to 132,000, 275,000 or 400,000 volts by transformers and fed over the **grid** system for national use. The voltage is reduced by transformers to consumers at suitable voltages: 33,000 volts for heavy industry, 11,000 volts for light industry, and 240 volts for homes and other places where the power demand is relatively small.

The normal domestic supply of 240V from the substation, see Fig. 1.1(a) is fed to the user

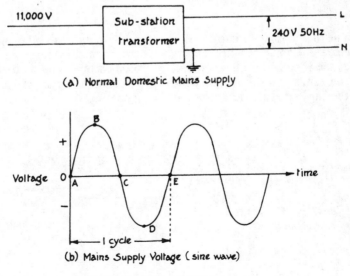

(a) Normal Domestic Mains Supply

(b) Mains Supply Voltage (sine wave)

Fig. 1.1 Mains supply.

via two wires, LIVE and NEUTRAL. The neutral is connected to earth at the substation and should not be earthed at other points. It is substantially at zero voltage relative to earth but a small voltage may be present due to voltage drop in the cable.

The voltage waveform of the mains supply is given in Fig. 1.1(b). This is an alternating voltage (a.c. voltage) since it acts in two directions, unlike d.c. voltage which acts in one direction only. During the period ABC, the voltage is positive whilst during the period CDE the voltage is negative, with the positive and negative sections repeating themselves at regular intervals. The variation of voltage ABCDE is called a **cycle** and the number of complete cycles produced per second is the **frequency** which is measured in **Hertz** (Hz). The frequency of the mains supply in this country is 50Hz, *i.e.* 50 cycles per second.

Shape

The sine waveform of Fig. 1.1(b) is very

important; it occurs in nature and a simple example is the pendulum. A pendulum displaced from its central position swings backwards and forwards, and if we plotted its position against time we would find that its shape was like that of the mains voltage waveform. When moving through the central position it is changing position rapidly and slows down towards its limit of swing in one direction until it stops, and then swings in the other direction. Another example is a weight attached to the end of a vertical spring, which if pulled down and released, will move up and down with a sinusoidal motion.

If one considers an arm AB as shown in Fig. 1.2, moving in an anticlockwise direction, and then if we plotted the vertical distance from B to the horizontal line against the angle ϑ we would also obtain a sine wave as shown. The length BC (known as the **instantaneous value**) is proportional to the sine of the angle ϑ, hence the name **Sine Wave**.

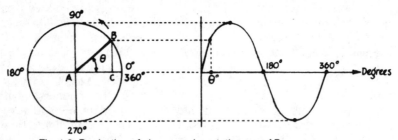

Fig. 1.2 Production of sine wave by rotating arm AB.

Peak Value

The **peak value** of a voltage or current sine wave is the **maximum value** reached during each half cycle, see Fig. 1.3. As the two half cycles are of the same shape, the two peak values are of the same magnitude but one is

positive and the other negative. Peak values are normally measured with the aid of an oscilloscope and are more important in electronics than in electrical power engineering.

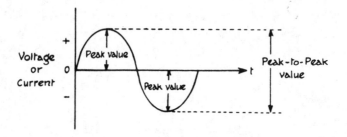

Fig. 1.3 Peak value of sine wave.

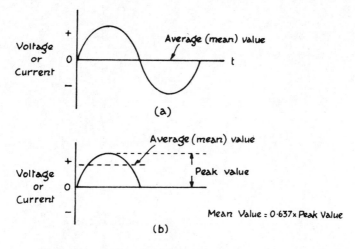

Fig. 1.4 Mean value of sinusoidal waveform.

Mean Value

The **mean** or **average** value of an a.c. is the mean height of the waveform. If the positive and negative half cycles are similar, the average taken over a whole cycle is zero, see Fig. 1.4(a). For this reason, the mean or average value is always taken over a half cycle, see Fig. 1.4(b).

For a sine wave the ratio of

$$\frac{\text{average}}{\text{peak value}} = 0.637.$$

The most important application of average values is to circuits in which rectication takes place.

R.M.S. Value

The **effective** or **r.m.s. value** of an alternating voltage or current is the most commonly used value. The use of the r.m.s. value allows a direct comparison to be made between d.c. and a.c. circuits, see Fig. 1.5. A d.c. supply of 240V will produce the same heating effect in R as an a.c. supply of 240V r.m.s. (assuming R is the same value in both circuits).

The value of a.c. which produces the same heating effect as d.c. of the same value is called the r.m.s. (root-mean-square) value for the following reason. When a d.c. voltage (V) is applied to the circuit, the power in R is given by V^2/R (or I^2R), see Fig. 1.6(a). However, when a.c. is applied to the circuit the voltage (v) changes from instant to instant, see Fig. 1.6(b). The corresponding power in the a.c. circuit is given by v^2/R (or i^2R). If v^2/R is plotted against time over a full cycle the curve shown is obtained, from which it will be seen that the power is unidirectional but pulsates at twice the supply frequency (thus a lamp connected to a 50Hz supply flickers at 100Hz). The average or mean power due to the a.c.

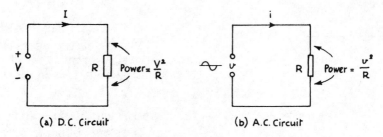

Fig. 1.5 Comparison of D.C. and A.C. circuits.

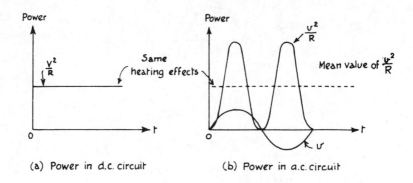

Fig. 1.6 Root-Mean-Square value.

supply is given by the mean of v²/R. If the mean value of v²/R is equal to V²/R then the power would be the same in both circuits, *i.e.*

$$\frac{V^2}{R} = \text{mean value of } \frac{v^2}{R}$$

or V^2 = mean value of v^2

or V = $\sqrt{\text{mean value of } v^2}$

Or the effective value is given by the square root of the mean of the square (root-mean-square). The ratio of

$$\frac{\text{r.m.s. value}}{\text{peak value}}$$

depends upon the shape of the waveform. For a sine wave, see Fig. 1.7, it is $1/\sqrt{2}$ or 0.707.

Unless otherwise stated, r.m.s. values should be assumed when dealing with a.c. voltages or currents. Thus the 240V quoted for the mains supply is 240V r.m.s.

Periodic Time

The **periodic time** of an a.c. waveform is the time taken to complete one whole cycle of the waveform, see Fig. 1.8. The frequency (f) is related to the periodic time (p) by

$$f = \frac{1}{p}$$

where f is in Hertz and p is in seconds. Thus if the periodic time is 1 ms, then

$$f = \frac{1}{1 \times 10^{-3}} \text{ Hz}$$

$$= 1000\text{Hz}$$

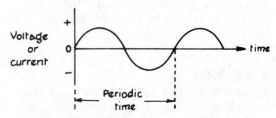

Fig. 1.8 Periodic time of an A.C. waveform.

COMPLEX WAVEFORMS

Waveforms that are not sinusoidal in shape are called complex waveforms and there are several main types encountered in electronics.

Speech and Music Waveforms

Speech and music waveforms are quite complex and differ greatly from a sine

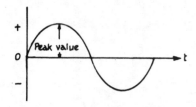

R.M.S. Value = 0·707 x Peak Value

also Peak Value = 1·414 x RMS Value

Fig. 1.7 R.M.S. value of sinusoidal voltage or current.

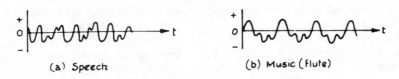

(a) Speech   (b) Music (flute)

Fig. 1.9 Speech and music waveform (constant notes).

waveform, see Fig. 1.9. If we sing or whistle a constant note, the frequency will be constant and all of the cycles will usually be alike. The exact shape of the waveform will, however, depend upon the source of the note and this variation in shape enables us to distinguish one persons voice from another. The same note played on two different musical instruments sounds quite different although the frequency and amplitude are the same. This is because the wave shapes produced by the instruments are different.

It can be shown that where a waveform is not sinusoidal (like those given in Fig. 1.9) it can be split up into a number of sine waves or, put another way, any complex wave can be produced by adding together a number of pure sine wave components. The sine wave components consist of one at the same frequency of the waveform being considered known as the **fundamental**, together with frequencies which are multiples of the fundamental, *e.g.* 2 × fundamental, 3 × fundamental, 4 × fundamental *etc*. These multiples of the fundamental are called **harmonics**. Twice the fundamental is known as the **second harmonic**, three times the fundamental is called the **third harmonic** and so on. For example, suppose that we have a complex waveform which is repeated regularly at 2000Hz. This waveform may consist of sine waves at 2000Hz (fundamental), 4000Hz (2nd harmonic), 6000Hz (3rd harmonic) and 8000Hz (4th harmonic). If the shape of this complex waveform is to be

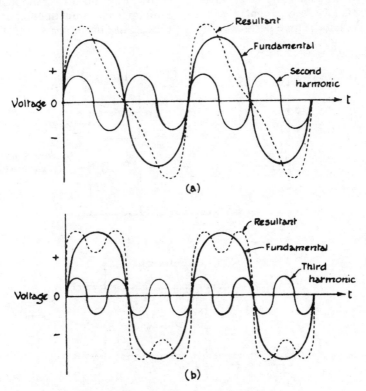

Fig. 1.10 Effect of adding harmonics to a sine wave.

faithfully reproduced, all of these frequencies must be preserved.

The resultant shape of adding a second harmonic to a fundamental is shown in Fig. 1.10(a) and the effect of adding a third harmonic is given in Fig. 1.10(b). The exact shape of the resultant waveform depends upon the amplitude of the harmonic relative to the fundamental; the greater the amplitude of the harmonic the more the resultant will differ from a pure sine waveform. Also the resultant shape will depend upon the position (or phase) of the harmonic relative to the fundamental.

Rectangular Waveforms

Examples of rectangular type waveforms which have numerous applications in electronics are given in Fig. 1.11. When the time period of the waveform A–B is equal to the time period C–D we have a square wave as in Fig. 1.11(a). A square wave may exist as a pure alternating voltage or current, *i.e.* having a mean value of zero as in (1) or have a mean value of either negative or positive polarity as in (2) (which shows a mean value of positive polarity), *i.e.* there is a **d.c. component** present in the waveform. When the time periods A–B

and C–D are unequal the rectangular waveform is commonly referred to as a **pulse** waveform, see Fig. 1.11(b). Again the mean value of the waveform may be zero, *i.e.* no d.c. component present as in (3) or there may be a d.c. component present as in (4).

When describing pulse type waveforms we often speak of the **mark-to-space ratio**. This is a ratio of the time period of the pulse t_m (mark) to the time period between pulses t_s (space). In Fig. 1.12(a) the ratio of $t_m:t_s = 1:3$ and in Fig. 1.12(b) it is 1:5. A square wave has a mark-to-space ratio of 1:1. The periodic time of the waveform is $t_m + t_s$ and the **pulse repetition frequency** (p.r.f.) is the number of pulses occurring per second.

A rectangular wave can be produced by the addition of a fundamental sine wave and a number of harmonics of the fundamental. In the case of a square wave where the mark-to-space ratio is 1:1, it is made up of a fundamental sine wave and a series of **odd** harmonics.

Suppose that we consider the square wave shown in Fig. 1.13(a) which has a mean value of zero, *i.e.* no d.c. component. This can be built up from a fundamental sine wave as in (b) plus a third harmonic as in (c) together with a

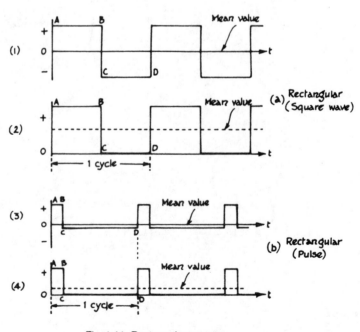

Fig. 1.11 Rectangular waves.

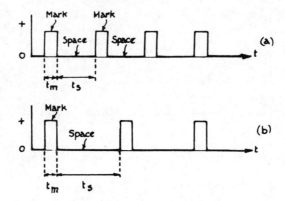

Fig. 1.12 Mark-To-Space ratio.

fifth harmonic as in (d). If these are added together the waveform shown at (e) is obtained which is seen to approximate that given at (a). In theory, an ideal pulse with vertical sides and sharp corners as in (a) can only be produced by an infinite number of harmonics. In practice, we cannot have an instantaneous change of voltage (as implied by the vertical sides of the waveform), hence a pulse can be produced by a finite number of

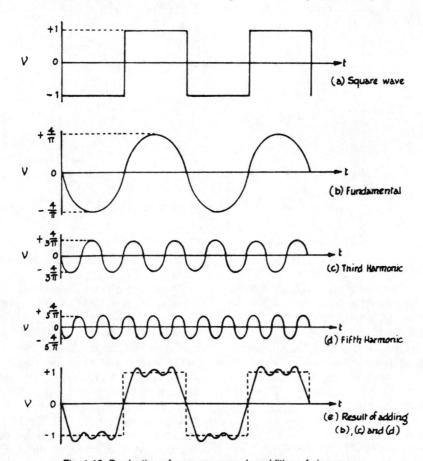

Fig. 1.13 Production of a square wave by addition of sine waves.

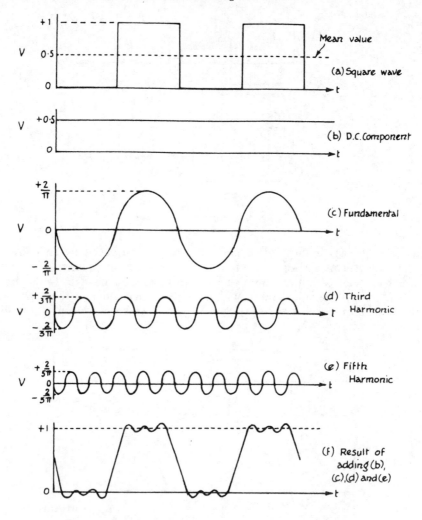

Fig. 1.14 Production of square wave with a D.C. component.

harmonics in the same way as in Fig. 1.13. If the square wave has a d.c. component it may be built up in the same way but there will be an additional component to be added equal to the mean value of the waveform, see Fig. 1.14.

Thus if we wish to faithfully reproduce a complex rectangular waveform, all of the components must be preserved. When the waveform is **asymmetrical** like the pulse waveforms of Fig. 1.11(b), there will be **odd and even** harmonics present.

Sawtooth and Triangular Waveforms

Two further examples of complex waves which are frequently used in electronics are shown in Fig. 1.15.

The sawtooth waveform of Fig. 1.15(a) is an asymmetrical waveform where the voltage rises (or falls) relatively rapidly over the section A–B but falls (or rises) more slowly over the section B–C, the change in voltage being linear over both sections of the waveform. As for the rectangular wave, the mean value may be zero as in (1) or there may be a d.c. component present as in (2). The triangular waveform of Fig. 1.15(b) is a symmetrical waveform where the voltage changes at the same linear rate over the section A–B as it does over the section B–C.

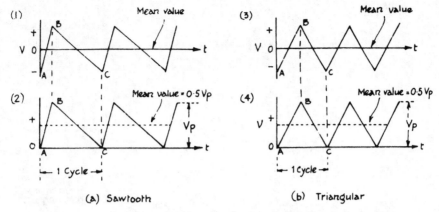

(a) Sawtooth   (b) Triangular

Fig. 1.15 Sawtooth and triangular waveform.

Again, the mean value of the waveform may be zero as in (3) or there may be a d.c. component present as in (4). For both the sawtooth and the triangular waveforms when there is a d.c. component present, the mean value of the waveform is equal to half the peak amplitude V_p.

Examples showing the production of sawtooth and triangular waves by the addition of harmonics to a fundamental sine wave are illustrated in Figs. 1.16 and 1.17. In the case of the **asymmetrical** sawtooth wave, both **odd** and **even** harmonics are present whereas for the **symmetrical** triangular wave only **odd**

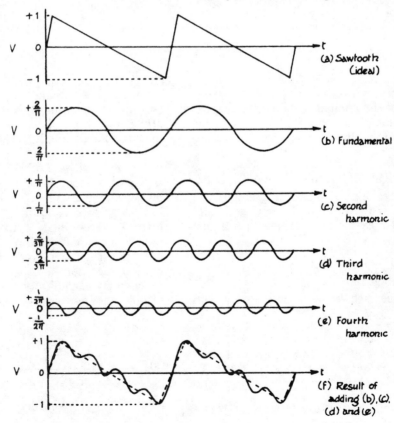

(a) Sawtooth (ideal)

(b) Fundamental

(c) Second harmonic

(d) Third harmonic

(e) Fourth harmonic

(f) Result of adding (b), (c), (d) and (e)

Fig. 1.16 Production of sawtooth wave by addition of sine waves.

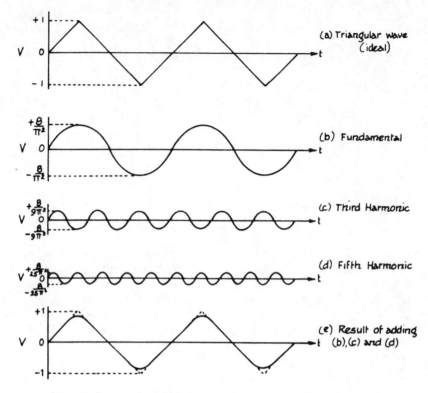

Fig. 1.17 Production of triangular wave by addition of sine waves.

harmonics are involved. For both diagrams, the greater the number of harmonics that are included the closer will be the result of the addition to the ideal.

ANALOGUE AND DIGITAL WAVEFORM

The waveforms or signals encountered in electronic systems can be classied into one of two categories called **analogue** and **digital** signals.

Analogue Signals

Analogue signals vary continuously with time and can assume any amplitude level (within practical limits) and some examples are given in Fig. 1.18. the word analogue means 'similar thing' thus, for example, the speech waveform of (b) may represent the electrical analogue of the sound pressure falling on a microphone, being similar to the pressure in every respect, *i.e.* if the pressure increases the amplitude of the waveform increases accordingly. Analogue electrical signals are used to convey information in radio/television receivers and audio/video cassette recorders.

Everyday examples of analogue quantities include the movement of the hands on a

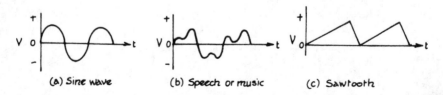

Fig. 1.18 Analogue waveforms.

watch, the level of mercury in a thermometer, the strength of a wind or the amount of light received from the sun.

Digital Signals

Digitals signals, on the other hand, are not continuous but have discrete levels and two examples are given in Fig. 1.19. The digital signal represented in (a) has two discrete levels; one level is zero voltage and the other level is some positive but constant voltage. A six-level signal is shown in Fig. 1.19(b), commonly called a **staircase** waveform. Thus digital signals can only assume the stated levels; any odd level is prohibited.

The **two-level** digital signal is by far the most important and is used in binary digital circuits and systems which are discussed in Chapter Five.

Common examples of two-state devices include, electric lights which are either on of off, railway signals which are up or down or a mouse trap which may be opened or closed.

It may at first be thought that two-state signals would have limited use when compared with analogue signals. This is not so as highly complex information may be represented by coding of the two-state signals. Many complex codes have been devised to serve in applications including telecommunications, computing and automatic process control.

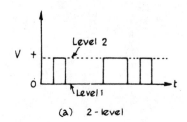

(a) 2 - level

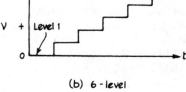

(b) 6 - level

Fig. 1.19 Digital waveforms.

QUESTIONS ON CHAPTER ONE

(1) The frequency of the mains supply in this country is:
    (a) 10Hz
    (b) 50Hz
    (c) 60Hz
    (d) 100Hz.

(2) The mean value of a half cycle of a sine wave is:
    (a) 0·707 × Peak value
    (b) 0·5 × Peak value
    (c) 0·637 × Peak value
    (d) 1·414 × Peak value.

(3) A sine wave has a peak-to-peak value of 20V. Its r.m.s. value is:
    (a) 7·07V
    (b) 10V
    (c) 12·74V
    (d) 14·14V.

(4) The periodic time of a sine wave is 0·01 secs. Its frequency is:
    (a) 0·01Hz
    (b) 1Hz

(c) 50Hz
(d) 100Hz.

(5) The fifth harmonic of a 250Hz sine wave is:
    (a) 50Hz
    (b) 255Hz
    (c) 300Hz
    (d) 1250Hz

(6) The mean value of the waveform shown in Fig. 1(a) over the 4ms period is:
    (a) − 5V
    (b) + 3·75V
    (c) + 5V
    (d) + 7·5V

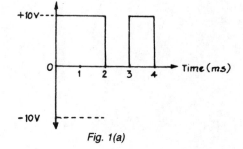

Fig. 1(a)

(7) The mark-to-space ratio of the pulse waveform given in Fig. 1(b) is?:
   (a) 1:1
   (b) 2:1
   (c) 1:2
   (d) 4:6.

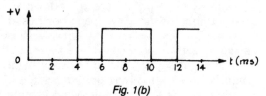

Fig. 1(b)

(8) The p.r.f. of the pulses given in Fig. 1(b) is approximately:
   (a) 166·7 pulses per second
   (b) 249·9 pulses per second
   (c) 499·9 pulses per second
   (d) 66·7 pulses per second.

(9) A sawtooth waveform may be built up from a fundamental sine wave together with:
   (a) Odd and Even harmonics
   (b) Odd harmonics only
   (c) Even harmonics only
   (d) 3rd, 7th and 11th harmonics.

(10) Which of the signals given in Fig. 1(c) is not an analogue quantity?

(a)

(b)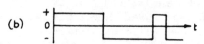

(c)

(d)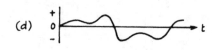

Fig. 1(c)

(Answers on page 219.)

CHAPTER TWO

COMMUNICATION PRINCIPLES

Objectives
1 Understands the basic requirements for intelligent communication.
2 States the nature of sound waves and the relationship between wavelength and frequency.
3 Considers use of sound waves, ultrasonic waves and coded electrical signals in communications.
4 States advantages in using electromagnetic waves for communication. Determines the relationship between frequency and wavelength of e.m. wave.
5 States applications for data communication.

Introduction

THIS CHAPTER IS concerned with the transmission of information or communication between one point and another. People normally communicate with one another using spoken language. Successful communication is only possible if the spoken language is common to both parties. Thus a common language may be regarded as a form of **code** enabling information to be passed from one person to another. Communication using the human voice is limited to short distances. When speech or music is to be conveyed over large distances, electrical speech or music signals may be set up in transmission wires or the signals may be conveyed by radio waves from a transmitter to a remote receiver.

Direct visual communication between people is only possible when one person has a clear visual path to another. At large distances when we can no longer clearly discern the other person, optical aids such as telescopes and binoculars may be used but these become ineffective at larger distances. At one time actors and entertainers could only make visual contact with an audience when a direct visual path existed as in a theatre. Later on, visual images were recorded on film to be viewed at a later date in the cinema and the home. Nowadays, visual contact is possible using an electrical system of creating visual images which are transmitted over great distances using television links. The visual images made

by people, particularly those associated with facial expressions and the attitude of human limbs are another form of **code** which may be regarded as an international communication channel between people.

Written language is another form of **code** enabling one person to communicate with another. Letters, books, newspapers and magazines provide the usual communication channel for written text and graphical information. Transmission of this type of information can be made over very large distances and extremely quickly using an electrical system of digital type signals such as those provided by the Teletext and Prestel services in this country.

Although, so far, we have considered communication as being from one person to another, it is not the only possible interpretation. With the advent of intelligent electronic machines such as the computer, communication between human and machine or machine and human is also possible. For example, a person may communicate with a computer via a keyboard using a **binary code** generated by the keyboard electronics. Computer-to-computer communication is also possible; information sent by one computer may be stored in the **memory** of a second computer providing a common **code** is used. Humans may not be directly involved in a communication process as with automatic computer controlled factory plant. Here the computer acts on information communicated to it from various sensors placed at strategic points around the plant. The brains of the computer provided by its program decides on the necessary action to be taken and then communicates this information in suitable form to operate motors, relays, pumps and heaters *etc* which control the factory process.

SOUND WAVES

It is well known that sound will not travel through a vacuum. Thus there must be **some material**, *i.e.* solid, liquid or gas to allow the passage of sound from one point to another. For speech we are normally concerned with the passage of sound through air. When we speak our vocal cords vibrate producing variations in air pressure which travel through the air. If the variations in air pressure are picked up by the ears of a listener, they produce a similar movement in the ear drum and the sound corresponding to the vibration of the speakers vocal cords is heard.

A sound wave in the air is produced by alternate compression and rarifaction of the air as illustrated in Fig. 2.1. When air close to the source of a sound is compressed so that it is at a higher pressure than the general atmosphere, a force is exerted onto the surrounding air. This in turn is compressed and then acts on the air further away from the source. Thus the compression spreads out from the source. There is not, however, a continual movement of air away from the source, for compression

and rarifaction occur alternately as shown in Fig. 2.1(b). Each molecule of air on average remains in the same position. A similar effect occurs when a stone is dropped into a pond producing ripples which move outwards but the water at any point moves up and down keeping the same average level. The variations in air pressure are thus alternating about the general pressure of the atmosphere as shown in Fig. 2.1(c). In this simple example a sine wave variation has been shown but the waveforms encountered in speech or music are rarely sinusoidal.

The louder the voice or sound or the greater its energy, the greater is the variation in pressure, *i.e.* the larger the amplitude of the waveform in Fig. 2.1(c). It should be noted that the human response to sound energy is not directly proportional to the energy content. About a ten fold increase in sound energy is needed to give the sensation of doubling the loudness to a listener.

Frequency

The sequence of variation in pressure A,B,C,D and E of Fig. 2.1(c) represents 1 cycle of the sound wave and the number of cycles per second is the frequency of the wave. The frequency of a sound wave determines the pitch of a sound, a low note corresponding to a low frequency and a high pitched note to a high frequency. The human ear is only sensitive over a limited range of frequencies of about 20Hz to 20kHz called the **audio frequency range**. In practice, the hearing

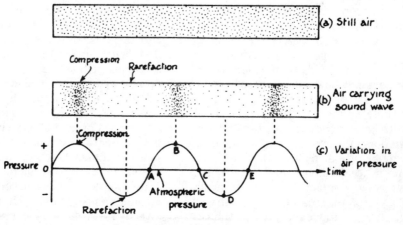

Fig. 2.1 Sound wave in air.

frequency range varies amongst people and as one gets older the upper frequency limit of hearing decreases.

Velocity

A sound wave travels at different velocities in different materials. In air a sound wave travels at about 340 metres per second depending upon temperature. The properties of a material which determines the velocity are its density and elasticity. Some examples are given below:

Material	Velocity (metres/sec.)
AIR	340
WATER	1440
WOOD	3000–4000
BRASS	3500
IRON	5130

Wavelength

When a sound wave is travelling in any material or medium, the distance measured between successive peaks of compression or rarication is called the **wavelength** (λ) of the wave, see Fig. 2.2. For a given frequency the peaks move further apart as the velocity of the wave increases, but closer together as the frequency is increased. The three quantities are related by

$$\lambda = \frac{v}{f} \text{ metres}$$

where λ is the wavelength in metres,
$\quad$ v is the velocity in m/s
and $\quad$ f is the frequency in Hz.

In air where the velocity is 340m/s, the audio frequency range of 20Hz–20kHz corresponds to wavelengths between 17 metres and 1.7cms. Whereas in water, for example, where the velocity is 1440m/s, the audio range corresponds to wavelengths between 72 metres and 7.2cms.

Sound over Distance

Sound waves produced by the human voice are limited in the distance over which they can provide satisfactory communication. As sound energy travels in air from a source it spreads out and its intensity is reduced, the energy at any point being approximately proportional to 1/distance^2. A sound wave in air is also affected by temperature variations which produces changes in the air density. During the day when the air closest to the earth is at a higher temperature than the air above the earth a sound wave is refracted upwards, whereas at night when the air closest to the earth is at the lowest temperature a sound wave is refracted downwards and thus can be received at a greater distance. The distance at which sound can be received is also affected by the wind, the distance increasing with a following wind.

Sound waves may be sent over long distances using wires if the waves are converted into electrical signals at one end and at the other end of the link are converted back into sound waves. This is the principle used in **telephony** and an elementary link for two-way communication is shown in Fig. 2.3.

At each end of the link are identical sets of apparatus comprising a microphone (M), an

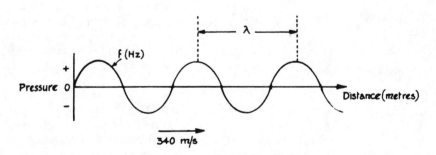

Fig. 2.2 Wavelength of sound wave.

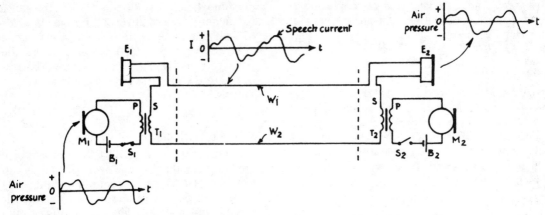

Fig. 2.3 Simple two wire telephone communication link.

earpiece or loudspeaker (E), a battery of a few volts (B), a switch (S) and a transformer (T). The two sets of equipment are linked by a pair of wire conductors (w_1 and w_2).

With S_1 closed as shown in the diagram, current flows from the battery B_1 through the microphone M_1 and the primary of T_1. This direct current causes no effect in the secondary of T_1. When sound waves fall on the diaphragm of the microphone, the resistance of the microphone alters in response to the variations in air pressure causing corresponding variation in current flow through T_1 primary. Similar current variations are then produced in the secondary of T_1 which flow in the conducting wires w_1 and w_2 and the earpiece at the remote end of the link. When the varying (a.c.) current flows in the earpiece, the diaphragm of the earpiece moves producing a sound wave similar to the original sound. With the switch closed at the other end of the link, communication can be established in the opposite direction. In practice, a microphone and earpiece is combined in a handset at either end of the link.

As it is impracticable to provide every user with a separate battery, a central battery system is normally used. Also, it would be impracticable in a national telephone system to connect each user directly to all other users as there would need to be a pair of conducting wires for each link. Thus to reduce the number of interconnections that need to be made, groups of users in each telephone area are connected to one another via a centrally placed local exchange, see Fig. 2.4.

As the telephone is normally only used for speech it has been found that the band of audio frequencies can be greatly reduced before intelligibility of speech suffers. For this reason the telephone deals with a range of frequencies from 300Hz to 3400Hz for commercial speech. Thus, although providing intelligibility of speech, voice recognition is not guaranteed with this restricted range of frequencies. However, by reducing the band of frequencies involved in each telephone conversation, equipment is made simpler and cheaper and more telephone channels may be fitted into a particular bandwidth (a consideration which is important in radio telephony systems).

Ultrasonic Waves

Waves set up in air (or other materials) which produce variations in pressure at frequencies above the upper human audio limit of 20kHz are called **Ultrasonic Waves**.

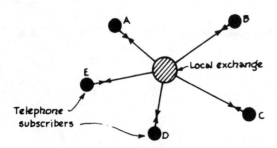

Fig. 2.4 Use of local exchange to reduce number of inter-connections.

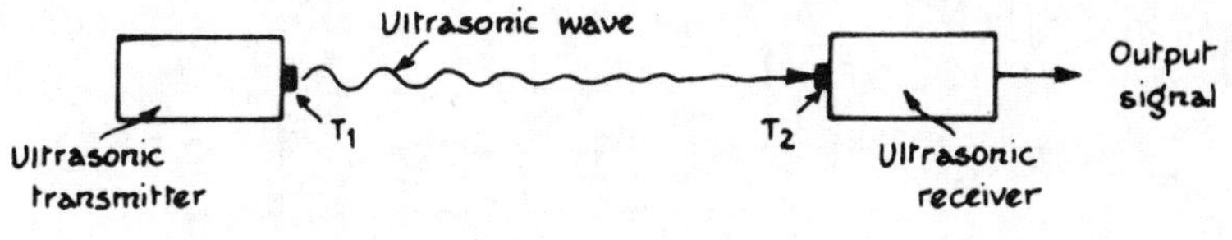

Ultrasonic wave

Ultrasonic transmitter T_1 T_2 Ultrasonic receiver Output signal

Fig. 2.5 Use of ultrasonics for remote control.

These waves have many applications in industry, medicine and science. Special sensors (transducers) are employed to transmit and receive ultrasonic waves but they operate in a similar manner to the loudspeaker and microphone.

One application of ultrasonic waves is in the remote control of television receivers and the basic idea is shown in Fig. 2.5. The system which provides a communication link between a viewer and the television receiver comprises a hand held transmitter and a receiver incorporated into the t.v. receiver. The transmitter generates a high frequency electrical sine wave signal which is converted into an ultrasonic wave by a transmitting transducer T1, operating in a similar way to a loudspeaker. When the ultrasonic wave is picked up by the receiving transducer T2 it is converted back into an electrial signal; the transducer acting in a similar manner to a microphone. The output from the ultrasonic receiver may then be used to provide such facilities as channel change or control of brightness, colour and volume *etc* of the television receiver. Different ultrasonic frequencies may be used to convey the different commands to the t.v. receiver or alternatively a single ultrasonic frequency may be employed but modulated with a code of pulses; a different code is used for each separate command. In such remote control systems the frequencies used for the ultrasonic waves generally lie in the range of 32kHz to 45kHz. The range of the ultrasonic transmitter is quite small being up to about 10 metres maximum.

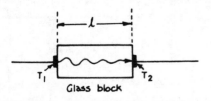

Fig. 2.6 Use of ultrasonics to produce a delay.

When specially required, a time delay may be introduced into a communication link using ultrasonics to produce the delay and the basic idea is shown in Fig. 2.6. An electrical signal at a frequency used by the communication link is applied to a transducer T1 which converts the electrical signal into an ultrasonic wave. The wave which consists of a mechanical vibration at the frequency of the electrical input signal travels though a glass block of known length (l). When the wave falls on the transducer T2 it is converted back into an electrical signal. Since the wave travels relatively slowly in the glass medium, comparatively large delays may be achieved. If the velocity of the wave in the glass block is known, say, 3000 metres/sec and the length of the block is 15cms, the time delay introduced will be

$$\frac{0\cdot15}{3000} \text{ secs} = 50 \text{ micro secs.}$$

Ultrasonic waves can also be used to transmit messages between submarines and are frequently used for obtaining a profile of an ocean floor (depth sounding). Non-communication applications of ultrasonics include the measurement of thickness of materials, detection of flaws in metal casting, welding of plastic components and industrial cleaning.

Telegraphy

Telegraphy was the earliest form of communication using coded electrical signals. A simple arrangement is shown in Fig. 2.7 which comprises at either end of the communication link a battery (B), a key (K) and a sounder (S) connected by a pair of wires w_1 and w_2. In practice only one wire may be used as one wire may be formed by a common earth. One code used is the **Morse Code** where alphabet characters and numbers are represented by a combination of dot and dash signals. The difference between a dot and dash is one of

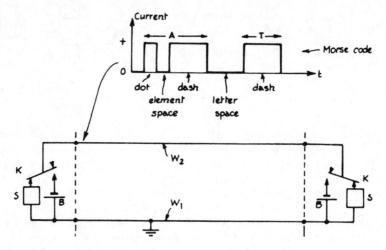

Fig. 2.7 Simple telegraph communication system.

time duration only, a dash being three times the duration of a dot period. Each element (dot or dash) forming the code for a particular character is separated by a space equal to one dot period and each character is separated by a space equal to three dot periods. The space between words is equal to seven dot periods. The sounder in early morse systems was a device in which a hammer was caused to strike a bell when a dot was received and a metal plate when a dash was received. Thus each code element was recognised by its distinctive sound.

Each key in Fig. 2.7 acts as a two-way switch which when not operated connects the sounder to the line w_2. When it is desired to transmit a message the key is depressed which disconnects the sounder at the transmitting station and at the same time connects the battery to w_2. The key is held down for a period corresponding to a dash or dot and released for each element space, letter space or word space as appropriate before it is depressed again. Thus the current flowing in the line between the transmitting station and the sounder at the receiving station is interrupted according to the message to be conveyed.

Apart from coded sound messages, the telegraph system is capable of producing a written record of the message. Originally a Morse printing machine was used which put the dots and dashes onto strips of paper. Later on **teleprinter** or teletypewriter systems were introduced. A teleprinter has a keyboard like

an ordinary typewriter but when the message is typed it is automatically converted into a coded signal which travels over the communication link. At the receiving end the teleprinter converts the coded signal into a printed message. The Morse code is not convenient for use with these automatic printing machines and a common code used is the **Murray Code**. In this code all characters have exactly the same number of signal

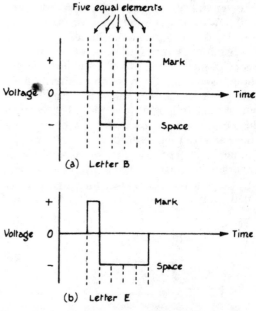

Fig. 2.8 Murray code for letters B and E used with teleprinter system.

elements (five) which are of constant length. Each character is composed of a combination of the five signal elements that may be either a 'mark' or a 'space'. A mark is represented by positive voltage and a space by negative voltage as illustrated in Fig. 2.8 which shows the Murray code for the letters 'B' and 'E'. The different polarity voltages are detected by special polarised relays.

An advantage of telegraphy is that the bandwidth required for a single communication channel is much less than for a telephone channel. The maximum bandwidth for telegraphy is about 120Hz.

Communication Using Electromagnetic Waves

The use of radio waves (electromagnetic waves) for communication has great advantages. They eliminate the use of transmission wires or cables, communication channels may be set up over very large distances and information whether it be speech, music, telegraph, television or data signals can be transmitted to be received almost instantaneously.

A spectrum of electromagnetic waves is given in Fig. 2.9 ranging from radio waves through heat, infra-red, light, ultra-violet and X-rays to gamma rays. All electromagnetic waves consist of an alternating magnetic field existing at right angles to an alternating electric field with both fields disposed at right angles to the direction of propagation as in Fig. 2.10.

Unlike sound waves, electromagnetic waves do not need a medium in which to travel and thus may pass through a vacuum. Electromagnetic waves travel at very high velocity, 300,000,000 metres per second in a vacuum. It is evident that light waves, X-rays and radio waves are all essentially of the same form.

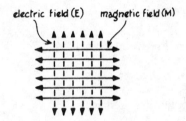

(a) Alternating magnetic field at right angles to alternating electric field

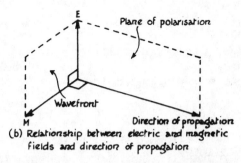

(b) Relationship between electric and magnetic fields and direction of propagation

Fig. 2.10 Representation of electromagnetic wave.

What then distinguishes one type of electromagnetic energy from another? The properties of the different types of e.m. energy are determined by their frequency or wavelength. The wavelength (λ) of an e.m. wave may be found from

$$\lambda = \frac{v}{f}$$

where v is the velocity of e.m. waves (3×10^8 m/s)

and f is the frequency in Hz.

The bands of frequencies used for radio waves and their corresponding wavelengths are given in Table 2.1. The term radio includes waves used for the transmission of television, radar and data type signals *etc.*

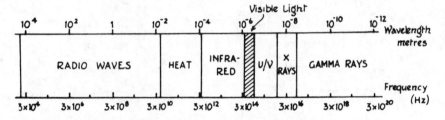

Fig. 2.9 Spectrum of electromagnetic waves.

Nomenclature	Frequency Band	Wavelengths
V.L.F. (Very low frequencies)	10–30kHz	30000–10000 metres
L.F. (Low frequencies)	30–300kHz	10000–1000 metres
M.F. (Medium frequencies)	300–3000kHz	1000–100 metres
H.F. (High frequencies)	3–30MHz	100–10 metres
V.H.F. (Very high frequencies)	30–300MHz	10–1 metres
U.H.F. (Ultra high frequencies)	300–3000MHz	1 metre–10cms
S.H.F. (Super high frequencies)	3–30GHz	10cms–1cm
E.H.F. (Extremely high frequencies)	30–300GHz	1cm–1mm

Table 2.1 Bands of Frequencies used in Radio

RADIO WAVE LINK

A basic communication link using radio waves is illustrated in Fig. 2.11. The transmitter consists of a high frequency power source which feeds a circuit comprising the aerial and earth. It may appear that there is no complete circuit for current to flow in, but the circuit is completed through the capacitance C between the aerial and earth. The high frequency a.c. current flowing in the aerial produces the radio waves which radiate out in all directions from the transmitter. When the radio wave reaches a distant receiver it induces a voltage into its aerial system causing a current to flow between the aerial and earth via its capacitance C. If within the receiver there is a device to indicate when current is flowing, we have a means of detecting the reception of the radio wave and hence complete the communications link.

The frequency of the radio wave radiated from the transmitter will generally lie within one of the frequency bands given in Table 2.1. This frequency is known as the 'Carrier Frequency' since it is used to carry the information from the transmitter to the receiver. There are various ways of impressing the information to be sent onto the carrier wave and these are considered in Chapter Three. For the moment it is sufcient to say that unless the current in the transmitting aerial and hence in the receiving aerial can be varied in some way, no information is transmitted.

Impressing the information to be sent on to

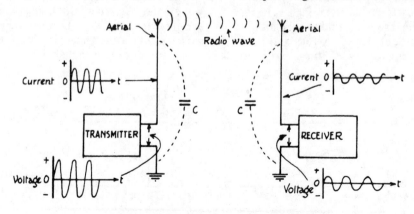

Fig. 2.11 Basic radio wave communication link.

the carrier is known as **modulation** and two methods commonly used are to vary the amplitude of the carrier (amplitude modulation) or the frequency of the carrier (frequency modulation) in accordance with the amplitude of the modulating (information) signal. If telegraph code signals are modulated on to a carrier we have **radio telegraphy** which is widely used commercially for the transmission of messages over large distances. When the information to be conveyed is speech signals from a telephone conversation and are modulated on to the carrier in some way, we have **radio telephony** which may be used over large distances or in a local area for mobile radio telephony links, *e.g.* for police, ambulance and taxis services. On the other hand, if **video** signals from the output of a television camera are modulated on to the carrier we have a **television broadcast** radio link which may be used nationally and internationally for the communication of visual information. According to the nature of the information that is transmitted will depend the type of device used at the receiver output to reproduce the information in the required form, *e.g.* a teleprinter for radio telegraphy, an earpiece or loudspeaker for radio telephony or a display c.r.t. for television.

The size of the aerial used at the transmitter and receiver will depend upon the carrier frequency used. As a rule, the lower the carrier frequency the larger the aerial. In general, the higher the frequency of the current flowing in the aerial the greater the amount of radiation from the aerial and the better is the aerial's efficiency.

Propagation Modes

When a high frequency current flows in the transmitting aerial, a radio wave is radiated in a number of directions which is dependent upon the type of aerial used. The radio wave will arrive at the receiver(s) by one of several different **modes of propagation**. Three of the principal modes of propagation are shown in Fig. 2.12.

(1) Ground Wave

The ground wave which is shown in Fig. 2.12(a) travels along the surface of the earth and partially in it, following the curvature of the earth for some distance of up to several thousands of miles depending upon the carrier frequency. As the wave travels forward it becomes weaker due to attenuation by the earth's surface. The attenuation is least for propagation over sea water and greatest for propagation over rocky and sandy soil. The ground wave will follow undulations in the earth's surface, *e.g.* hills and dales and is mainly used at v.l.f., l.f. and m.f. to provide reliable radio telegraphy, navigational and sound broadcasting links.

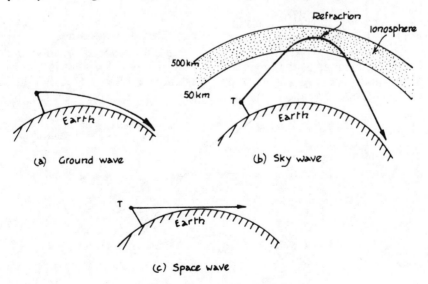

Fig. 2.12 *Modes of propagation for radio waves.*

(2) Sky Wave

Existing some 50–500km above the earth in the upper part of the atmosphere are layers of gas molecules which become ionised by ultra-violet radiation from the sun. The density of the ionised layers (called the 'ionosphere') is greatest at the top of the ionosphere (nearest the sun) and smallest at the bottom of the ionosphere (nearest earth). Due to the variation of density within the ionosphere, radio waves that are directed upwards from a transmitting aerial may be returned to earth at a distant location by the mechanism of **refraction**, see Fig. 2.12(b). The refraction or bending of the radio waves follows the same principle as the refraction of light waves when passing from one medium having a different refractive index from another. Although variations in the density of the ionosphere vary from day to night and between season and season they are predictable allowing a sky wave link to provide a reliable form of communication. The amount of refraction provided by the ionosphere decreases as the frequency of the radio wave increases and at v.h.f. and above no useful refraction is obtained. Thus signals above about 30MHz will normally pass straight through the ionosphere. Sky wave links are mainly used for international radio telephony, sound broadcasting and mobile marine and aero systems.

(3) Space Wave

The space wave of Fig. 2.12(c) travels in almost a straight line path in the space immediately above the earth. The range of the space wave is chiefly governed by the height of the transmitting and receiving aerials and provides **line-of-sight** communication up to the horizon. Obstacles such as buildings, trees and hills *etc* lying in the path of the space wave will limit the useful range (up to about 40–60km in length) and these factors are taken into account when choosing a site for the transmitting aerial.

Space wave propagation is mainly used in the v.h.f., u.h.f. and s.h.f. bands, *e.g.* for f.m. radio broadcasts, television and radar.

The frequency bands and typical uses for the different modes of propagation are summarised in Table 2.2.

Frequency Band	Propagation	Typical Uses
30kHz–3MHz	Ground Wave	L.W. and M.W. sound broadcasting and radio telegraphy.
3MHz–30MHz	Sky Wave	S.W. sound broadcasting and international radio telephony.
30MHz–3GHz	Space Wave	F.M. radio and Television broadcasting, Radar.

Table 2.2 Frequencies used with different modes of propagation.

Satellite Communication

Another important method for the propagation of radio waves is via a communications satellite and Fig. 2.13 shows the basic principle. The frequencies chosen for the **carrier**

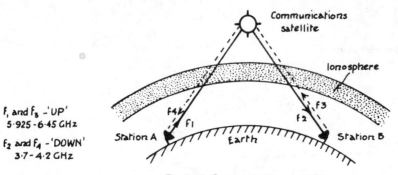

f_1 and f_3 – 'UP'
5·925 – 6·45 GHz

f_2 and f_4 – 'DOWN'
3·7 – 4·2 GHz

Fig. 2.13 Communications satellite.

wave lie in the s.h.f. band and since these frequencies receive negligible refraction by the ionosphere the radio waves travel in virtually straight line paths between the earth stations and the satellite.

Satellite communication enables one earth station to send information to another earth station with the satellite acting as a relay station. For example, station A transmits a carrier wave containing the information to be sent, which is beamed by a large 'dish' aerial at the satellite. The frequency (f_1) of the transmitted wave lies in the frequency range of 5.925–6.45 GHz. When the radio wave is received by the satellite, the signal is amplified and converted to a lower frequency (f_2) lying in the range of 3.7–4.2 GHz. This signal is then transmitted by the satellite to earth station B where it is received. As each earth station incorporates a transmitter and receiver, two-way communication is possible. Thus station B may transmit a carrier wave with a frequency f_3 which is received and amplified by the satellite to be retransmitted as a wave of frequency f_4. This signal will be received by earth station A. Satellite communication provides a very reliable link for international exchange of large numbers of telephone conversations (radio telephony) and television pictures.

Using three suitably positioned communication satellites travelling in circular orbits around the equator at a height of about 36000km, communication around the globe is possible. This particular orbit is known as the **synchronous** or **geostationary** orbit since a satellite travelling in it appears to be stationary over a particular part of the earths surface. Since each satellite can see a large area of the earth, information can be relayed from one earth station to another around the world, see Fig. 2.14.

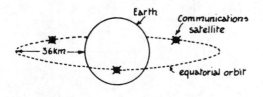

Fig. 2.14 Geostationary orbit.

DATA COMMUNICATION

Data communication is concerned with the sending of the basic facts of information in order to carry out an 'intelligent action'. Data signals which contain the basic facts in either analogue or digital form may be transmitted over telephone lines, special cables or via radio wave links. Some typical applications for data communication are as follows.

(a) Distant Measuring Systems

Often it is necessary to be able to measure a physical quantity such as temperature, pressure, stress, flow rate, vibration *etc* associated with an item of apparatus or industrial product that is located some distance away from where intelligent action can be taken. This **measurement at a distance** is often called **telemetry** and the telemetry information can be transmitted over a directly wired system or by radio waves (radio telemetry) and sometimes by using both methods of transmission.

Telemetry enables, for example, the information relating to the pressure in a remotely installed gas main, the mechanical stresses set up in a space rocket after launch or medical data (blood pressure, heart beat *etc*) taken from a patient to be transmitted over a large distance to initiate an action or for analysis by a specialist or computer. The essential processes involved in a telemetry communications link are illustrated in Fig. 2.15. The transducer converts the quantity to be measured, say, temperature into an electrical signal (voltage or current). The electrical output of the transducer is then prepared for transmission by the block which we will call the 'encoder'. Different functions may be carried out by the encoder according to the transmission method used and whether the data is to be sent in analogue or digital form. If, for example, the communication link uses radio waves, the data from the transducer will be used to modulate a carrier wave and this function will be carried out in the encoder. At the other end of the communication link the received signal is decoded (with a radio wave link the decoding will include demodulation) to produce a signal in suitable form to operate the output device. As it is temperature that is being measured in this example, the output device may take the form of a thermometer, or

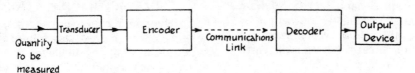

Fig. 2.15 Distant measuring system (telemetry).

the temperature may be displayed in written form on the screen of a visual display unit or on paper from a printer output.

(b) Commercial Data Links

Computers are now used extensively in commerce and industry to perform a variety of tasks which include the calculation of wages, salaries and bills, reservation of airline and theatre tickets, storage of medical and stock records, maintenance of bank records and the solution of engineering problems *etc*. It would not be economic for an organisation to install a computer at each office or factory thus it is usual to install one or sometimes two computers and to connect all branches within the organisation to the computer centre by means of **data links**.

The basic idea of a data communications link using telephone lines is illustrated in Fig. 2.16. The data input (in digital form) may come from a manually operated keyboard and this is fed to a **Modem** (modulator-demodulator) which converts the pulse type data signals into a suitable form for transmission over the telephone lines (usually the two binary states of the digital signal are represented by audio tones of 1300Hz and 2100Hz). At the other end of the link a modem is used to convert the audio tones back into digital signals which are fed to the computer. Here the received data may be analysed, stored if required or have calculations performed on it. Any results of the computer action may them be relayed back to the data terminal for display on paper at a printer output or on the screen of a visual display unit.

The speed at which data can be sent over a communication link is an important factor. Ordinary telephone lines are only suitable for transmitting data at relatively slow speeds. High speed data may be transmitted over **special coaxial lines**, in **waveguides** or via **optical-fibre cables**: An optical-fibre link uses electromagnetic radiation at light frequencies of about 300,000GHz (1000nm) to convey the data, see Fig. 2.17.

The electrical data signal in digital form modulates a light source such as a laser which transmits the light energy along the optical-fibre cable. The cable consists of a bunch of fibres where each fibre is composed of a central core made of glass of high refractive index enclosed by a sheath of low refractive index glass. Light waves from the light source travel along the cable by means of internal reflection. At the remote end of the link the

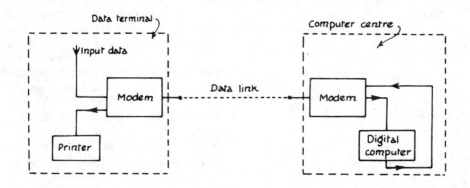

Fig. 2.16 Commercial data link using telephone lines.

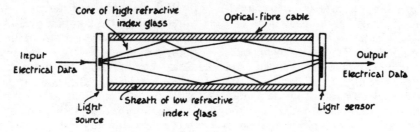

Fig. 2.17 Optical-fibre communications link.

light energy falls on to a light sensitive device which converts the pulses of light back into a digital electrical signal. The losses in the optical fibre cable are small and data may be sent over distances of up to about 30km before the use of a repeater unit (which regenerates the light pulses ready for retransmission) becomes necessary.

(c) Information Data Link

Pages of text and graphical information may be sent in digital form to be displayed on the screen of a modified television receiver. The services provided by the broadcasting authorities (CEEFAX and ORACLE) are given the name **Teletext** and use a radio wave link for sending the data signals which are modulated on to a u.h.f. carrier. In a **Viewdata** system, the data signals are sent to the television receiver via the public telephone network. An example of a viewdata service is Prestel provided by British Telecom.

A basic outline of the data transmission links to the television receiver are illustrated in Fig. 2.18. Teletext pages are assembled by journalists at the television studio centres and provide a whole range of information including news reports, share prices, shipping news, weather maps, t.v. programmes, motorway news, sports reports *etc*. The pages of information are normally stored on a magnetic disc

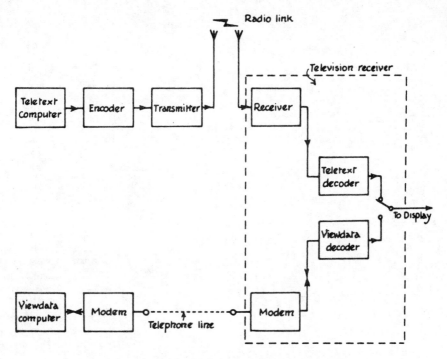

Fig. 2.18 Information data links (teletext and viewdata).

memory before being transferred to a computer to be made ready for transmission. The digital signals relating to each page are fed from the computers memory to an encoder where the digital signals are coded and essential synchronising signals added. The data is then transferred serially (one data pulse followed by the next data pulse) to the transmitter where the data is modulated on to a u.h.f. carrier. The teletext data is actually transmitted along with the normal television picture signal in the unused television lines. At the television receiver, the data is demodulated in the receiver block and then sent to the teletext decoder where the data is assembled to produce a page of teletext. The pages are transmitted one after another and any particular page can be requested by the viewer to be made ready for display after a short waiting time. At present there are several hundreds of teletext pages available.

With the viewdata system each user has a direct link to the computer via the telephone network which enables any particular page of information to be requested and received. Since the computer only transmits information when requested, the page capacity of the system can be increased considerably to several hundreds of thousands. Any page can be made available for display within about 10 seconds of being requested. The serial data signals from the viewdata computer are converted into audio tones of **1300Hz (logic 1)** and **2100Hz (logic 0)** by a modem before being sent over the telephone line to the television receiver. At the t.v. receiver, another modem converts the audio tones back into data pulses which are then sent to the viewdata decoder where they are assembled to produce the requested page for display. Unlike teletext the viewdata system allows two-way communication between the user and the computer.

Summary Diagram

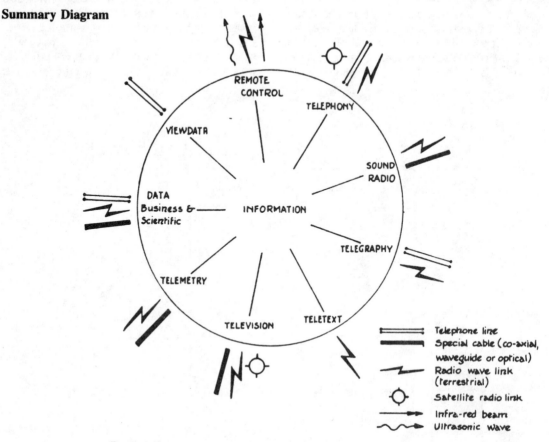

Fig. 2.19 *Communication links used for different types of information.*

QUESTIONS ON CHAPTER TWO

(1) Sound waves in air travel at about:
   (a) 340m/s
   (b) 3500m/s
   (c) 1440m/s
   (d) 300,000,000m/s.

(2) The frequency of a sound wave determines its:
   (a) Amplitude
   (b) Loudness
   (c) Quality
   (d) Pitch.

(3) The wavelength of a 1000Hz sound wave in air is about:
   (a) 0·3m
   (b) 30m
   (c) 300m
   (d) 340m.

(4) The public telephone network deals with speech frequencies in the range of:
   (a) 20Hz–20kHz
   (b) 300Hz–3400Hz
   (c) 30Hz–15kHz
   (d) 15kHz–100kHz.

(5) A common code used with teleprinters is the:
   (a) Binary code
   (b) Morse code
   (c) Gray code
   (d) Murray code.

(6) A common method of remote control of television receivers uses:
   (a) Radio waves
   (b) Sound waves
   (c) Ultrasonic waves
   (d) Heat waves.

(7) With regard to the transmission of radio waves which of the following is correct:
   (a) The higher the frequency, the larger the aerial

   (b) The lower the frequency, the greater is the aerials efficiency
   (c) A medium is required for propagation
   (d) They travel at 3×10^8 m/s.

(8) A radio wave at a frequency of 10MHz will most likely be propagated over a:
   (a) Ground wave link
   (b) Sky wave link
   (c) Space wave link
   (d) Satellite link.

(9) Space wave propagation is normally used for:
   (a) Radio telegraphy
   (b) L.W. sound broadcasting
   (c) Television broadcasting
   (d) Radio telephony.

(10) A communications satellite is used to:
   (a) Amplify the received signal and reradiate at a different frequency
   (b) Provide a one-way communications link between earth stations
   (c) Reflect the received wave to a distant ground station
   (d) Provide a reliable communication link at v.h.f.

(11) Data signals are usually conveyed over the telephone lines in the form of:
   (a) Logic pulses
   (b) Audio tones
   (c) Light pulses
   (d) Ultrasonic signals.

(12) Telemetry is concerned with the relaying of information relating to:
   (a) Bank statements
   (b) Measurements
   (c) Pages of text
   (d) Music and speech.

(Answers on page 219.)

CHAPTER THREE

MODULATION

Objectives

1 Understands the need for a carrier.
2 Distinguishes between amplitude modulation, frequency modulation and pulse modulation.
3 Identifies the main characteristics of each type of transmission.
4 States the frequency range, bandwidth and modulation method used for the transmission of speech, music and television. Considers modulation methods used for satellite communication, telephony, remote control, telemetry and data communication.

NEED FOR A CARRIER

IT WAS SEEN in Chapter Two that communication by sound waves is not practical except over very short distances since sound waves are rapidly attenuated as the distance increases and are affected by air temperature, wind *etc*. There is, however, another difficulty. Suppose that, say, three people are all talking at the same time and are attempting to communicate with others. The result will be chaotic as the sound waves from each speaker will intermingle, since speech signals all occupy the same audio frequency band. Some improvement could be made over short distances by using speaking tubes between the communicating parties as the sound waves of each conversation would be confined to the tubes.

If electrical signals are used to convey speech information, the individual conversations can be kept apart using two methods. One way is to use a pair of conductors for each conversation which is the method used in the telephone system. The other way is to shift the base audio frequency band of each conversation, so that each conversation is 'carried' by a different carrier frequency. The basic idea of shifting a band of frequencies (frequency translation) is illustrated in Fig. 3.1. In Fig. 3.1(a) we have three different conversations occupying the same audio frequency band of 30Hz to 16kHz. If each individual conversation is shifted in frequency to be 'carried' by carriers of different frequency, as in Fig. 3.1(b) the three conversations may be kept apart. By using different carrier frequencies, it is possible to send many conversations

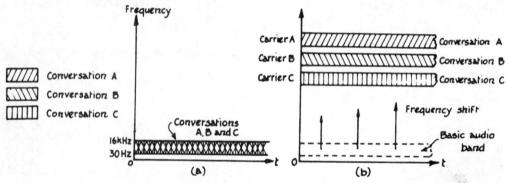

Fig. 3.1 *Idea of frequency shift (translation) of base band audio signals onto carriers.*

(or other information) along a common pair of conductors or to radiate the carriers from a transmitter in the form of radio waves. In either case, the frequency separation between the carriers allows the individual conversations to be detected at the receiving end of the system and the wanted conversation to be accepted, all others being rejected.

The process of frequency shifting the information to be carried, or impressing the information onto the carrier is called **modulation**. There are a number of different modulation methods which will now be considered.

AMPLITUDE MODULATION

With amplitude modulation the amplitude or magnitude of the carrier is varied in accordance with the modulating signal voltage, *i.e.* the information that we wish to transmit. The basic idea is shown in Fig. 3.2. At (a) is shown the radio frequency carrier without any modulation. This voltage which may be obtained from an r.f. generator or oscillator is constant in amplitude and frequency and is of sine waveform. At (b) is shown the modulating signal voltage (or information to be conveyed), assumed to be a sine wave. This has been done for simplicity but generally is not a simple sine wave which makes no difference to the basic principle. If the carrier at (a) is amplitude modulated by the signal at (b) we obtain the modulated carrier as at (c).

At instant A the modulating signal is zero and hence the magnitude of the modulated carrier is the same as that shown in (a). As the modulating signal increases in a positive direction from A to B the resultant modulated carrier increases, at all times its increase in amplitude being proportional to the magnitude of the modulating signal. From B to C the modulating signal decreases and hence the magnitude of the modulated carrier decreases until it reaches its initial amplitude at C, where the modulating signal is zero. From C to D the modulating signal increases in a negative direction and the magnitude of the modulated carrier decreases, the decrease at any instant being proportional to the magnitude of the modulating signal. From D to E the modulating signal decreases and the amplitude of the modulated carrier increases to its original value at E, where the modulating signal is zero. This covers a complete cycle of the modulating signal voltage and the same sequence of events occurs on following cycles.

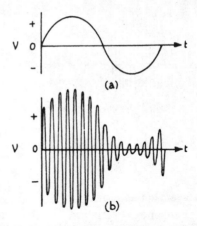

Fig. 3.3 Effect of larger modulating voltage than in Fig.3.2.

If the magnitude of the modulating signal voltage is increased, *e.g.* louder sound into a radio microphone, the greater will be the amount that the modulated carrier varies as in Fig. 3.3. If the frequency of the modulating signal voltage is, say, increased but its amplitude kept the same as in Fig. 3.2, the variations in carrier amplitude will occur more rapidly, see Fig. 3.4. Here two cycles of the modulating signal have been shown which corresponds to a modulating signal frequency of twice that shown in Fig. 3.3.

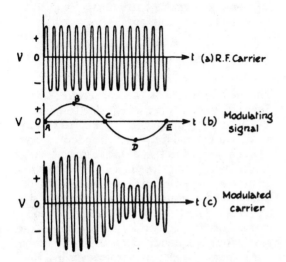

Fig. 3.2 Basic idea of amplitude modulation.

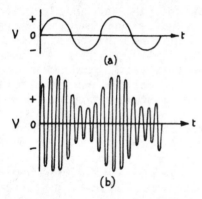

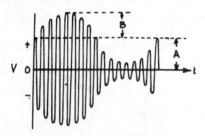

Fig. 3.4 *Effect of higher modulating frequency than in Fig.3.2.*

For efficient detection of the modulating signal at the receiver and for other reasons which cannot be considered here, the frequency of the carrier must be many times that of the modulating signal; at least 20 times the highest modulating signal frequency.

Fig. 3.5 *Diagram to illustrate percentage modulation.*

Percentage Modulation

The percentage variation of the carrier amplitude which takes place due to modulation is called the **percentage modulation** and is illustrated in Fig. 3.5. If A is the magnitude of the unmodulated carrier and B is the variation that takes place either as an increase or decrease, assuming them to be equal then

$$\text{Percentage Modulation} = \frac{B}{A} \times 100\%.$$

There is a limit to the percentage modulation that can be used and this is seen in Fig. 3.6. When the variation B is equal to the unmodulated value A of the carrier, the carrier amplitude is reduced to zero at point P. This corresponds to the maximum permitted

percentage modulation and since B = A, it corresponds to 100% modulation. Any attempt to increase the percentage modulation above this figure causes distortion because although the amplitude can be increased at point Q, it cannot be made less than zero at P. When distortion occurs the output obtained at the demodulator of the receiver will not be a replica of the modulating signal voltage at the transmitter.

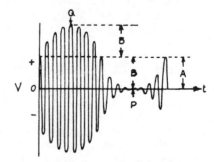

Fig. 3.6 *Result of 100 modulation.*

Side Frequencies

It may at first appear that the only frequency produced at the output of the modulator would be the carrier frequency, but this is not so. Whenever a sine wave is altered in amplitude or shape it can be shown that other frequencies are produced. When we amplitude modulate a carrier of frequency f_c by a modulating signal of frequency f_m, three frequencies are produced:

(1) f_c = the carrier frequency
(2) $f_c + f_m$ = the upper side frequency
(3) $f_c - f_m$ = the lower side frequency

The first term (1) is the carrier frequency. Terms (2) and (3) are called **side frequencies** and differ in frequency from the carrier by the modulating signal frequency. The term (2) is a frequency equal to that of the carrier plus that of the modulating frequency. Since the frequency is therefore higher than that of the carrier, it is referred to as the **upper side frequency**. The term (3) has a frequency equal to that of the carrier frequency minus the modulating frequency and is called the **lower side frequency**, since its frequency is less than that of the carrier.

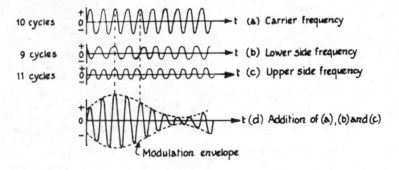

10 cycles — (a) Carrier frequency

9 cycles — (b) Lower side frequency

11 cycles — (c) Upper side frequency

(d) Addition of (a),(b) and (c)

Modulation envelope

Fig. 3.7 Diagram showing graphical addition of carrier and side frequency sine wave components to produce the modulated carrier.

One way of showing that these side frequencies do exist is illustrated by Fig. 3.7. Fig. 3.7(a) shows 10 cycles of the carrier component and (b) and (c) the upper and lower side frequency components. The lower side frequency being less than the carrier frequency is shown with 9 cycles and the upper side frequency being greater than the carrier frequency is shown with 11 cycles. If these sine wave components are added together graphically, the amplitude modulated wave of Fig. 3.7(d) is obtained.

The usual way of showing the carrier and side frequency components of a modulated wave is by means of a frequency-amplitude diagram, see Fig. 3.8. The diagram shows a 1MHz carrier amplitude modulated by a sine wave modulating signal of frequency 10kHz. The amplitude of the side frequency components relative to the carrier amplitude depends upon the percentage modulation. They are, of course, zero when the percentage modulation is zero, *i.e.* no modulation and are each 0·5 of the carrier amplitude with 100% modulation.

Sidebands

In practice the carrier is not usually modulated with a single frequency but rather with a range of frequencies, *e.g.* the audio range. Suppose that a 1MHz carrier is modulated with a band of audio frequencies from 100Hz to 10kHz. For each modulating frequency there will be a pair of side frequencies thus we now have a band of frequencies existing either side of the carrier (**sidebands**) as illustrated in Fig. 3.9. These sidebands extend from 100Hz to 10kHz either side of the carrier. Neglecting the very narrow band (200Hz) in the centre, the modulated carrier now covers a range of frequencies from 0·99MHz to 1·01MHz, *i.e.* a band of 20kHz.

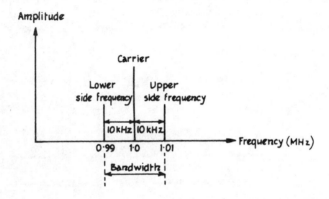

Fig. 3.8 Side frequencies produced when a 1MHz carrier is modulated with a frequency of 10kHz.

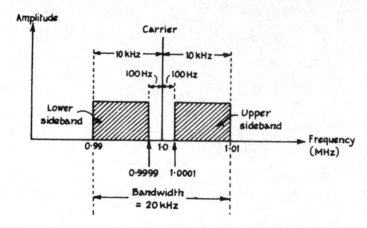

Fig. 3.9 *1MHz carrier amplitude modulated with a band of modulating frequencies from 100Hz to 10kHz.*

Thus when we modulate a carrier in this way, the transmitter covers a band of frequencies equal to twice the highest modulating frequency.

Transmitter Bandwidth

If only one transmitter is in use, the fact that it occupies a band of frequencies is not particularly important, but when a large number of transmitters are in operation it becomes extremely important.

Different transmitters operate on their own carrier frequencies so that we can select one transmission and reject all others at the receiver. This is an example of what is termed **Frequency Division Multiplexing**. Thus if we have three transmitters and they are to be placed as near to one another as regards frequency, they would be as illustrated in Fig. 3.10.

The three transmitters would occupy a total band of 60kHz. If we wished to receive Station Two without interference from Stations One

and Three we would have to use a receiver which accepted a range of frequencies from 0·99MHz to 1·01MHz and rejected all other frequencies. This would be difcult to do, but in practice the position is eased by the fact that transmitters which are adjacent as regards frequency are separated geographically. Thus if Station Two is the local station its signal strength (*i.e.* voltage induced in the receiving aerial) will be much greater than that of Stations One and Three which are situated a long distance away. Therefore, although the tuning of the receiver will include some of the frequencies transmitted by Stations One and Three they will be so small as to be inaudible. In these circumstances it would, of course, be almost impossible to receive Stations One and Three without severe interference from Station Two.

Generally, stations on the medium and long wavebands are separated by 9kHz which would imply a maximum modulating frequency of 4·5kHz. Some overlap is however allowed, use being made of the geographical

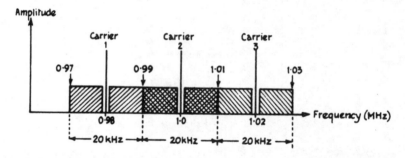

Fig. 3.10 *Three transmitters modulated with frequencies from 100Hz to 10kHz.*

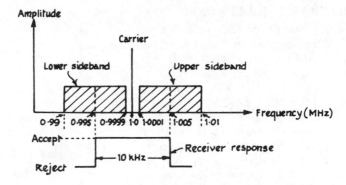

Fig. 3.11 *Effect of insufficient receiver bandwidth.*

separation previously referred to. However, many receivers operating on the L.W. and M.W. only have a station bandwidth of 9kHz.

For a given range of modulating frequencies the band occupied by the transmitter is therefore settled and the sidebands cannot be removed without removing the information being transmitted. For example, if a transmitter is modulated with audio signals from 100Hz to 10kHz giving a transmitter bandwidth of 20kHz, but is used with a receiver having a station bandwidth of only 10kHz then some of the transmitted information will be lost, as illustrated in Fig. 3.11. Side frequencies above 1·005MHz and below 0·995MHz would not be received and accordingly after demodulation there would be no audio frequencies above 5kHz.

The band of frequencies occupied by a transmitter is an extremely important matter particularly in television where the vision modulating frequencies are much higher, up to 5·5MHz. Obviously, much higher carrier frequencies than those discussed must be used because the carrier frequency must be much greater than the highest modulating frequency. Suppose that the carrier frequency is 500HMz; the range of side frequencies would extend from 500 − 5·5 = 494·5MHz to 500 + 5·5 = 505·5MHz as illustrated in Fig. 3.12(a) giving a total bandwidth of 11MHz. In practice, part of one of the sidebands (the lower sideband) is not transmitted as illustrated in Fig. 3.12(b). This type of transmission is known as **vestigial sideband transmission** and is used in television to reduce transmitter bandwidth so that more channels can be accommodated in the bands allocated

to television transmissions. The reasons why it can be done in this case are complex and will not be discussed at this stage of your course.

It is possible to transmit the carrier and one set of sidebands or just one set of sidebands alone. These are known as **single sideband systems** and are used commercially. Details will not be given in this book as the systems are more complicated than when both sidebands are transmitted.

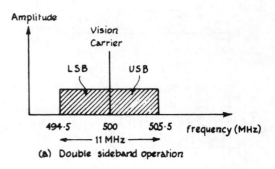

(a) Double sideband operation

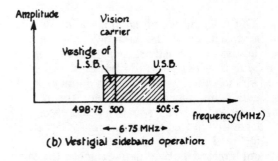

(b) Vestigial sideband operation

Fig. 3.12 *Use of vestigial sideband operation in television to reduce transmitter bandwidth.*

FREQUENCY MODULATION

In frequency modulation the amplitude of the modulated carrier remains constant but its frequency is varied in accordance with the amplitude of the modulating signal. This is illustrated in Fig. 3.13. At A the modulating signal is zero and hence the carrier frequency is at its normal unmodulated value. As the modulating signal increases in a positive direction to B, the frequency is increased in proportion to the modulating signal. As the modulating signal amplitude reduces from B to C the frequency decreases until it is back to its original value at C. From C to D the modulating signal increases in a negative direction and hence the frequency of the carrier decreases to a minimum frequency at D. From D to E the carrier frequency increases until it reaches its original value at E. In practice the ratio of the carrier frequency to the modulating frequency is much higher than is shown in the diagram, *i.e.* there should be many more cycles of the carrier between A and E. Also, the variation in frequency of the carrier is normally much smaller than has been shown.

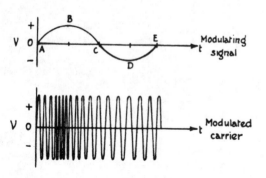

Fig. 3.13 *Frequency modulation.*

If the amplitude of the modulating signal is increased, then the amount of frequency variation or **deviation** from its unmodulated value is increased as illustrated in Fig. 3.14. On the other hand if the frequency of the modulating signal is increased, the rate at which the carrier frequency is increased and decreased in frequency is increased as shown in Fig. 3.15. Here it is assumed that the amplitude of the modulating signal is the same as in Fig. 3.14 thus the actual variation in carrier frequency is the same.

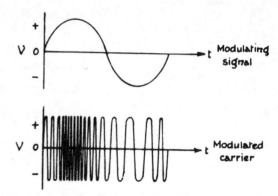

Fig. 3.14 *Effect of larger amplitude of modulating signal than that of Fig.3.13.*

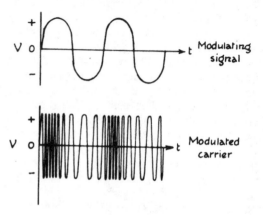

Fig. 3.15 *Effect of higher frequency of modulation signal than that of Fig.3.14.*

Side Frequencies

As will be expected, when we frequency modulate a carrier in this way side frequencies are produced. However, the arrangement of the side frequencies is more complicated than with amplitude modulation.

Amplitude modulation of a carrier by a single tone causes the production of a pair of side frequencies, the upper and lower on either side of the carrier as previously explained. With f.m. a large number of side frequencies are generated whose frequencies differ from the carrier frequency by multiples of the modulating signal frequency. For example when a carrier f_c is frequency modulated by a sine wave signal f_m, the side frequencies produced are

$$f_c \pm f_m, \ f_c \pm 2f_m, \ f_c \pm 3f_m, \ f_c \pm 4f_m,$$
$$f_c \pm 5f_m \ \ldots \ etc.$$

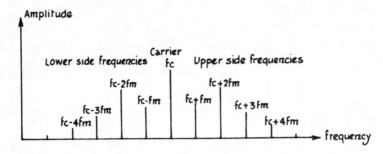

Fig. 3.16 Example of side frequencies produced by frequency modulation.

This is illustrated in Fig. 3.16. The reason for the production of multiple side frequencies is that when the carrier is modulated, the variations in frequency of the carrier do not allow the individual cycles of the carrier to be exactly sinusoidal. As is indicated in Fig. 3.17, the time required to complete consecutive quarter cycles steadily decreases. Thus the actual carrier is a distorted sine wave oscillation. Theoretically, there is an infinite number of side frequencies but many are of negligible amplitude. For practical purposes the significant number of side frequencies involved is determined by the **modulation index** which is defined as

Carrier Frequency Deviation (one way)
_____
Modulating Signal Frequency

The maximum frequency deviation of the carrier frequency is obtained when the modulating signal is at its highest amplitude. The greater the magnitude of the modulation index

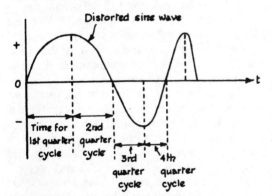

Fig. 3.17 Frequency of F.M. carrier increasing. Carrier is no longer sinusoidal.

the greater the number of side frequencies, but the number is not directly proportional to the modulation index. The way in which the relative amplitudes of the side frequency components and the amplitude of the carrier vary depends on this modulation index. The calculation is very involved and the solution requires taking Bessell functions of the modulation index. In practice tables are used to determine the values.

Since only the frequency is varied when the carrier is modulated, the total power output of the transmitter cannot change. Hence the greater the number of side frequencies and the larger their amplitude, the smaller is the amplitude of the carrier. However, the amplitude of the carrier does not steadily decrease as the number of side frequencies increase but varies in a complex way.

The maximum deviation of the carrier is settled by the performance required and for the BBC v.h.f. radio service this is ±75,000Hz. If a modulating signal frequency of 15,000Hz (the maximum transmitted) is considered then the modulation index is

$$\frac{75,000}{15,000} = 5.$$

With a modulation index of 5, the number of signicant side frequencies is 16 (obtained from tables), 8 either side of the carrier as illustrated in Fig. 3.18(a). These are all spaced 15kHz apart and the total band of frequencies used is

$$16 \times 15\text{kHz} = 240\text{kHz}.$$

If the modulating frequency is lowered the modulation index will be increased. For example, with a modulating signal frequency

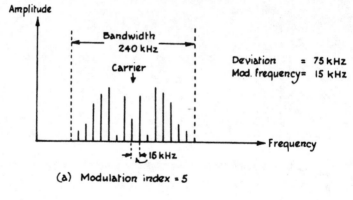

(a) Modulation index = 5

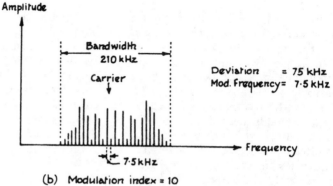

(b) Modulation index = 10

Fig. 3.18 Side frequencies for two values of modulation index.

of 7·5kHz then the modulation index will be

$$\frac{175,000}{7500} = 10.$$

The number of signicant side frequencies is now 28 (obtained from tables) and they are spaced 7·5kHz apart. The total bandwidth is now

$$28 \times 7\cdot5kHz = 210kHz.$$

This is slightly less than previously, see Fig. 3.18(b).

If the amplitude of the modulating signal is reduced, the deviation of the carrier will be reduced as will the modulation index. This will reduce the bandwidth, *i.e.* the bandwidth is dependent upon the amplitude of the modulating signal, whereas with amplitude modulation it is fixed, but the amplitude of the side frequencies vary.

It will be noted that the bandwidth required is much greater than that for amplitude modulation. For a modulating signal frequency of 15kHz, the a.m. bandwidth would only be 30kHz as opposed to 240kHz for f.m. Due to this larger bandwidth it is necessary to use a higher carrier frequency which is the reason why f.m. radio broadcasts are in the v.h.f. band.

The bandwidth of an f.m. transmission may be reduced by reducing the maximum deviation of the carrier but this would however decrease the signal-to-noise ratio in the output of the receiver. Thus the amount of deviation used on the carrier is a compromise between bandwidth and performance.

The main advantage that f.m. has over a.m. is that the noise level at the receiver is reduced. The principal effect of noise or interference is to amplitude modulate the carrier, consequently this appears in the output of the demodulator in an a.m. receiver. However, in an f.m. receiver the demodulator is designed so that it is insensitive to amplitude variations of the carrier thus most of the noise is eliminated.

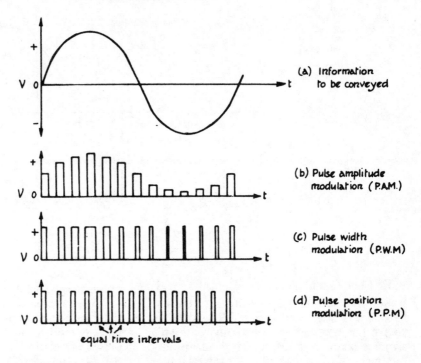

Fig. 3.19 Three types of pulse modulation.

PULSE MODULATION

Information may be conveyed from one point to another by means of pulses by using **sampling** techniques. The information to be sent is sampled at regular intervals and at each interval pulses are formed which are used to represent the amplitude of information at these instants. There are a number of ways in which this can be carried out.

Pulse Amplitude Modulation

Considering Fig. 3.19 where the information to be conveyed is the sine wave of Fig. 3.19(a). If pulse amplitude modulation is used, the result will be as in Fig. 3.19(b). Here a series of pulses of constant width occurring at regular intervals have an amplitude that is proportional to the amplitude of the information to be sent. The number of pulses that are produced per second is known as the **sampling rate**. It is found that if the number of samples taken per second is at least twice the highest frequency contained in the information to be sent, the original wave can be successfully reconstituted from the succession of pulses.

Pulse Width Modulation

When pulse width modulation is used the result will be as in Fig. 3.19(c). It will be seen that when the information is positive, the width of the pulses is increased, the increase being proportional to the amplitude of the information signal. When the information is negative the width of the pulses is reduced, the reduction in width being proportional to the amplitude of the information signal. The magnitude of the pulse waveform being constant at all instants.

Pulse Position Modulation

If pulse position modulation is used the result will be as in Fig. 3.19(d). It will be seen that when the information is positive, the pulses (of constant width) are delayed with respect to their normal time positions but are advanced when the information signal is negative. At all times the change in position of the pulses being proportional to the amplitude of the information signal. The amplitude of the pulses are constant.

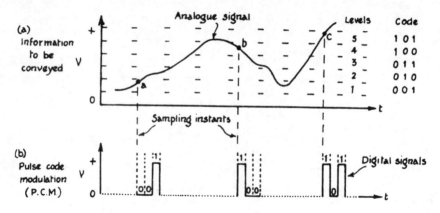

Fig. 3.20 Pulse code modulation.

Pulse Code Modulation

Another method of conveying information by pulses is illustrated in Fig. 3.20. At (a) is shown the information to be conveyed. This signal is sampled as before at regular instants but the peak-to-peak amplitude of the signal is divided up into a number of standard levels (usually 8, 16 or 32) but only five have been shown in the diagram. Each standard level is represented by a code of pulses which is indicated on the diagram using binary notation where binary 1 represents a pulse and binary 0 the absence of a pulse.

Fig. 3.20(b) shows the code of pulses produced at three sampling instants for the amplitude levels a, b and c of the information to be conveyed. In practice the information signal would need to be sampled more often than that indicated to reproduce the original signal. Also, the number of standard levels may be increased for improved fidelity. With 16 standard levels a 4-bit or 4-place code would be required and for 32 standard levels a 5-bit code would be needed. In any event, a certain amount of error is introduced since at each sampling instant the amplitude of the information signal is conveyed at its nearest standard level.

Conveying the Pulses

The pulses produced by any of the four methods described may be transmitted over cables to a remote receiver where the information may be recovered. Alternatively, the pulses may be used to modulate a carrier wave for transmission using a radio wave link. In this case either amplitude or frequency modulation could be employed. The most common pulse modulation systems are P.W.M. and P.P.M. (telemetry) and P.C.M. (modern telephony).

Reasons for using Pulses to convey Information

One may wonder why digital pulses are used to convey analogue information. Why not send the analogue information directly? Clearly, pulse systems must have advantages over analogue systems. One important advantage is that noise has little effect on pulse systems employing constant amplitude pulses (P.W.M., P.P.M. amd P.C.M.) providing the noise is appreciably weaker than the pulses. As long as the presence of a pulse can be detected at a receiver, the pulses may be reconstituted as shown in Fig. 3.21. Thus the effect of the noise is virtually eliminated. An

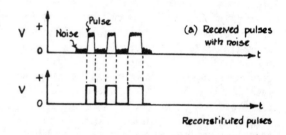

Fig. 3.21 Effect of noise in pulse modulation.

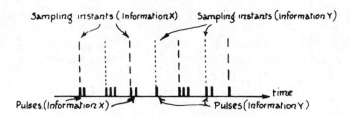

Fig. 3.22 Time division multiplexing.

example of this may be seen by comparing the noise on the screen of a television receiver when displaying a normal colour picture (analogue transmission) with that of a page of teletext information (pulse transmission).

When using sampling techniques with pulse modulation systems, there are periods in between the samples when no pulses are sent. This permits different information to be sent in the periods between samples. The basic idea is shown in Fig. 3.22 where between sampling periods for information X, further samples are taken to convey information Y. This time sharing is known as **time division multiplexing** and allows different items of information to be sent over a common link even though the pulses may cover the same frequency band.

A further advantage of using digital pulses is that the electronic circuits that are designed to handle pulse signals are more reliable and any distortion introduced has small effect on two-level digital type signals.

TYPES OF MODULATION USED

Sound Broadcasting
L.W., M.W. and S.W. — Amplitude Modulation
V.H.F. Radio — Frequency Modulation

Television (625 line)
Vision signal — Amplitude Modulation
Sound signal — Frequency Modulation
Teletext — Amplitude modulation of binary coded pulses

Telemetry
Measurement at a distance — Pulse Width and Pulse Position Modulation

Telephony
Local mobile — Frequency Modulation
Between local exchanges — Pulse Code Modulation

Data Communication
Low speed over telephone lines — Audio tones of 1300Hz and 2100Hz representing binary coded pulse levels of 1s and 0s.

High speed over special cables — Binary coded pulse using time division multiplexing.

Remote Control (of television)
Channel change, brightness, colour *etc* — Binary coded pulse modulation of infra red and ultrasonic waves.

Satellite Communication
Telephony and television — Frequency Modulation using frequency division multiplexing.

QUESTIONS ON CHAPTER THREE

(1) A carrier of frequency 200kHz is amplitude modulated with a 5kHz sine wave. The frequencies present in the output of the modulator will be:
(a) 5kHz and 200kHz
(b) 195kHz, 205kHz and 200kHz
(c) 200 kHz only
(d) 200kHz and 1000kHz.

(2) The maximum percentage modulation without distortion in an a.m. transmission is:
(a) 50%
(b) 100%
(c) 90%
(d) 33·3%.

(3) The bandwidth required by a receiver when tuned to a carrier of 1MHz amplitude modulated by audio signals in the range of 30Hz to 8kHz would be ideally:
(a) 16kHz
(b) 1·008MHz
(c) 1·016MHz
(d) 7·97kHz.

(4) The side frequencies of a frequency modulated carrier are:
(a) Two only, of frequency $f_c + f_m$ and $f_c - f_m$
(b) None
(c) A number depending on the modulation index
(d) 16 in all cases.

(5) When the modulating frequency is increased in amplitude the result on a frequency modulated carrier is to:
(a) Cause the carrier to vary in frequency more rapidly
(b) Cause the amplitude of the carrier to increase
(c) Cause the amount of frequency variation to increase

(d) Cause the amplitude of the carrier to decrease.

(6) The maximum deviation used for f.m. sound broadcasting in the V.H.F. band is:
(a) ±15kHz
(b) ±75kHz
(c) ±50kHz
(d) ±100kHz.

(7) In 625 line television broadcasting:
(a) The vision is a.m. and the sound is a.m.
(b) The vision is f.m. and the sound is f.m.
(c) The vision is f.m. and the sound is a.m.
(d) The vision is a.m. and the sound is f.m.

(8) The type of modulation used on the medium wave for radio broadcasts is:
(a) F.M.
(b) A.M.
(c) P.C.M.
(d) P.W.M.

(9) Pulse Position and Pulse Width Modulation are often used for:
(a) Telephony
(b) Satellite communication
(c) Telemetry
(d) Computer-to-computer communication.

(10) One advantage of using constant amplitude pulses to convey information is:
(a) Pulses are easier to generate than sine waves
(b) Noise has little effect when it is smaller than the pulses
(c) Pulses have less harmonic content than sine waves
(d) The received information is a perfect replica of the original information.

(Answers on page 219.)

CHAPTER FOUR

CHARACTERISTICS OF ELECTRONIC UNITS

Objectives

1 State the main types of electronic units and identify their characteristics to include: (a) Power supplies (b) Oscillators (c) Amplifiers (d) Modulators and demodulators (e) Filters (f) Waveshapers.
2 States the energy transfers for common types of transducers.

COMPLETE ELECTRONIC SYSTEMS, *e.g.* a digital computer, a colour television receiver or an f.m. transmitter are made up from a number of electronic units which may be considered as the 'building-blocks' of the system. In this chapter we will only be concerned with the characteristics of these units; it is not intended at this stage of your course to show what is inside them nor how the particular characteristics are obtained.

POWER SUPPLIES

Most electronic equipment requires a smooth or d.c. supply to allow correct operation. This supply voltage may be obtained directly from batteries or via a power unit fed from the a.c. mains. A **power supply** is thus a unit which converts the a.c. mains into a d.c. supply. In addition to converting the a.c. mains into d.c., the power supply must deliver the d.c. at a suitable magnitude; modern electronic equipment utilising transistors or integrated circuits requires a d.c. supply in the range of; say, 5V to 50V which is a much smaller voltage than the a.c. mains supply. Also, in most power supplies the d.c. output is electrically isolated from the mains input. This feature is desirable in the interests of safety and also for convenience, but there are some exceptions, *e.g.* in certain television receivers. Therefore the main functions of a power supply are to:

(a) Convert the a.c. mains into a d.c. supply.
(b) Provide the correct value of d.c. output voltage.

Transformer Unit

The power supply unit is fed at its input with the mains supply which in this country is a 240V r.m.s. 50Hz sine wave supply. The letters r.m.s. (root-mean-square) are often omitted as it is understood that all voltages are r.m.s. unless otherwise stated. The r.m.s. value of an alternating voltage is that value which produces the same heating effect as d.c. of the same magnitude, *i.e.* 240V r.m.s. a.c. produces the same heating effect as 240V d.c. The peak or maximum value of the supply voltage may be found from

r.m.s. value $\times$ 1·414 = 240V $\times$ 1·414 $\approx$ 340V.

To provide the required magnitude of d.c. at the output of the power supply a **transformer unit** is used. If the required d.c. is less than

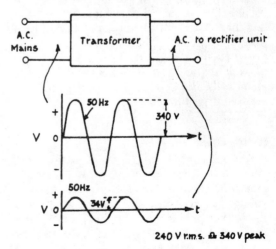

Fig. 4.1 Transformer unit (step-down).

the peak value of the mains supply, a step-down transformer is used as illustrated in Fig. 4.1. Here a voltage step-down ratio of 10:1 is used to provide 34V peak a.c. at the output. Note that the transformer does not alter the frequency of the mains supply voltage, only its magnitude.

On the other hand, if the required d.c. is greater than the peak voltage of the mains supply, a step-up transformer is used as shown in Fig. 4.2. Here a voltage step-up ratio of 1:1·45 is employed to provide 493V peak at the output.

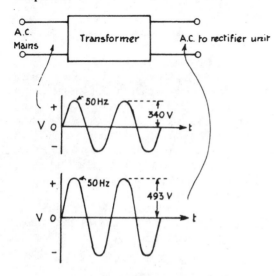

Fig. 4.2 Transformer unit (step-up).

Some items of electronic apparatus, *e.g.* an oscilloscope, require d.c. voltages greater and less than that of the mains peak value to feed different circuits. These voltages may be provided by a single transformer unit employing step-up and step-down ratios in its electrically isolated outputs or by utilising separate transformer units.

Rectifier unit

We have seen that we can adjust the magnitude of the a.c. by means of a transformer unit. The next step is to convert the a.c. voltage output of the transformer unit into d.c. A **rectifier unit** is used for this purpose and there are two basic types, half wave and full wave. Each type may be identified by the nature of its output waveform.

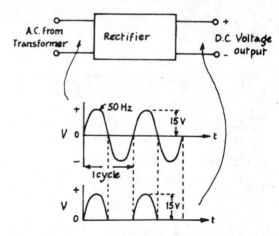

Fig. 4.3 Rectifier unit (half wave).

A half wave rectifier unit is shown in Fig. 4.3 with typical values for a low voltage supply. Although the output is not at a steady level, it is d.c. since it lies in one direction (in this case positive) and is said to be unidirectional. The output consists of one half cycle of voltage followed by an equal period of zero voltage. It will be noted that for every full cycle of the input there is one half sine wave pulse at the output. Thus the pulsation or **ripple** at the output is at the frequency of the input, *i.e.* 50Hz.

A full wave rectifier unit is illustrated in Fig. 4.4 using the same magnitude of input voltage as for the half wave unit. Again the output is d.c. since it lies in one direction but fluctuates from maximum to zero. In this arrangement, however, it is seen that two half cycles are obtained in the output for every full

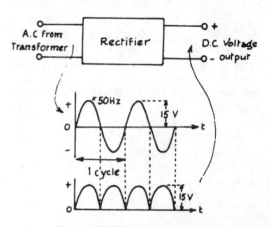

Fig. 4.4 Rectifier unit (full wave).

cycle of the input. It may be regarded that each second half cycle is effectively inverted so that both half cycles of the input are used. The **ripple** at the output is now twice that of the input frequency. *i.e.* 100Hz.

Smoothing Filter

The d.c. output of the basic rectifier units just described is not smooth enough to act as a supply for electronic equipment. The pulsating output voltage would cause a varying performance of the electronic circuits to be fed and would result in the operation ceasing when the rectifier output dropped to a low level, *i.e.* when the voltage approaches zero. To produce an output voltage with only a small amount of fluctuation a **smoothing filter** is required.

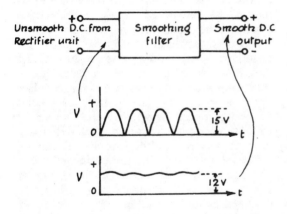

Fig. 4.5 Smoothing filter.

A smoothing filter with a full wave input is illustrated in Fig. 4.5. The effect of the filter is to reduce the fluctuations or ripple to a low level. A certain amount of ripple will always be present in the output but can be made extremely small. The degree of ripple that can be tolerated depends upon the application, *i.e.* the type of electronic circuit to be supplied. The same type of filter arrangement can be used with both half wave and full wave rectifier units. It will be noted that the d.c. output voltage from the filter is less than the peak value of the a.c. input. This is due to voltage drop in the filter unit with the magnitude dependent upon the filter design and the circuits to be fed.

Stabiliser

The magnitude of the d.c. output voltage from the smoothing filter of a power supply has a value which is dependent upon the stability of the mains supply and the current drawn by the load (the electronic circuits fed from the power supply). For example, if the mains voltage increases the d.c. output will rise and conversely for a decrease in mains voltage the d.c. output will fall. Whereas an increase in load current will cause a fall in d.c. output and conversely a decrease in load current will cause a rise in the d.c. output. For some applications these output variations are not important, but in some circuits the operation may be affected if a constant d.c. voltage is not applied.

To maintain a constant d.c. output voltage, a **stabiliser** or **regulator** may be incorporated into the power supply following the smoothing filter as illustrated in Fig. 4.6. The stabiliser prevents any appreciable change in output voltage for mains voltage variations of, say, ±10%. It also maintains a constant output voltage independent of the load current up to the maximum load current for which the power unit was designed to handle.

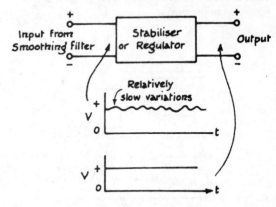

Fig. 4.6 Stabiliser.

Examples of complete power supplies using the features described in this section are considered in Chapter Six.

OSCILLATORS

Oscillators are used to generate alternating waveforms of various types, *e.g.* sine wave, pulse, sawtooth and triangular, which are widely used in electronics. The output power of the oscillator comes from the d.c. supplied to it. Thus an oscillator may be considered as a type of converter, converting the d.c. power supplied to the oscillator into a.c. power in its output.

Sine Wave Oscillator

A sine wave oscillator is illustrated in Fig. 4.7. In common with all oscillators in this section, the oscillator is fed with a d.c. supply without which it will fail to oscillate. The output waveform is sinusoidal and has a frequency which may lie in the range of, say, 5Hz to 20,000MHz depending upon the application. The output may be of a single frequency, sometimes preset to a number of different frequencies or variable over a band of frequencies. Controls are normally included to adjust the frequency to the desired preset or to tune over the required frequency range. In general, the principle of operation of this type of oscillator is the same irrespective of the frequency of oscillation but the actual circuit details may vary. The amplitude of the output waveform is constant (as with all the oscillators in this section) and is called c.w. (continuous wave).

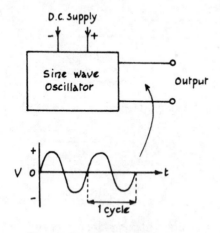

Fig. 4.7 Sine wave oscillator.

Typical applications for sine wave oscillators include master oscillators in signal generators, computer based systems and transmitters and local or reference oscillators in receivers.

Pulse (Rectangular Wave) Oscillator

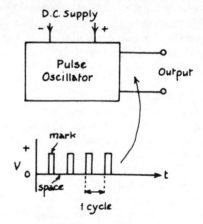

Fig. 4.8 Pulse oscillator.

A pulse oscillator or generator is one which produces a rectangular type waveform at its output, as illustrated in Fig. 4.8. In this example, the oscillator is generating a regular series of short duration positive pulses, but negative pulses could also be produced. The rate at which the pulses are produced (pulse repetition rate) may vary from, say, 5 pulses per minute to 1,000,000 pulses per second depending upon the application. The actual width of each pulse (the mark) relative to the interval between pulses (the space) can be made almost any desired value. In the particular case when a mark-to-space ratio of 1:1 is employed, a square wave output is obtained as shown on Fig. 4.9.

Typical applications for pulse oscillators are to be found in general timing circuits, pulse modulators, computers and colour television receivers.

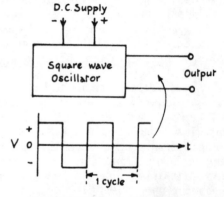

Fig. 4.9 Square wave oscillator.

Sawtooth (Ramp) Oscillator

Another common type of waveform generator is shown in Fig. 4.10. This oscillator produces a sawtooth or ramp type function at its output. It consists of relatively slow but linear rising sections followed by relatively fast falling sections, repeated at regular intervals. Negative polarity or a.c. type sawtooth outputs are equally feasible.

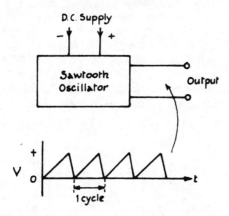

Fig. 4.10 Sawtooth (ramp) oscillator.

Sawtooth oscillators are commonly used for timebase applications in television receivers and cathode ray oscilloscopes where the frequency required may lie in the range from, say, 5 per minute to 1,000,000 per second.

Triangular Wave Oscillator

This type of oscillator produces an output with linear rising and falling sections of equal intervals, see Fig. 4.11. The frequency of

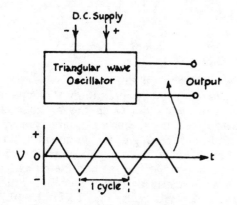

Fig. 4.11 Triangular wave oscillator.

oscillation may lie in the range of, say, 5 per minute to 1,000,000 per second depending upon the application which is more limited than for the other types of oscillator. One specialised use is in the production of pulse-width modulated pulses and is to be found in some television receivers.

AMPLIFIERS

Amplifiers are very widely used in electronics in a variety of applications. All amplifiers have the general property of amplifying, *i.e.* producing an output which is greater than the input. Amplifiers are usually conveniently arranged into three types:

(1) Voltage Amplifiers

The main function of this type is to amplify voltage, *i.e.* to provide an output voltage which is greater than the input voltage and is widely used.

(2) Current Amplifiers

The essential function of this second type which is less frequently used is to amplify current, *i.e.* to produce an output current that is greater than the input current.

(3) Power Amplifiers

The main requirement of this third type is to provide power amplification, *i.e.* produce an output power that is greater than the input power. Now the input power is the product of input voltage and input current whilst the output power is the product of output voltage and output current. Thus in a power amplifier there must be appreciable voltage gain, current gain or both.

A.C. and D.C. Amplifiers

Amplifiers may also be divided into two main classes: A.C. Amplifiers and D.C. Amplifiers. As it is of fundamental importance to distinguish between the two classes, they will be considered before dealing with the various types of amplifiers.

A d.c. amplifier is illustrated in Fig. 4.12 with a steady d.c. voltage applied to its input.

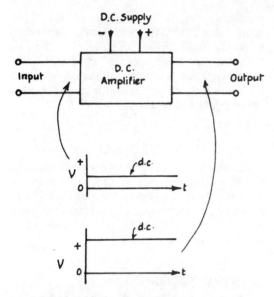

Fig. 4.12 D.C. amplifier (with steady d.c. input).

The output consists of a larger or magnified d.c. voltage as we are assuming that the amplifier produces voltage amplification. If the input were to be reduced to zero, then the output would also be reduced to zero.

With a fluctuating input voltage as in Fig. 4.13, the output voltage will be a replica of the input but of larger amplitude. This fluctuating voltage may be considered as a d.c. voltage component plus an a.c. voltage

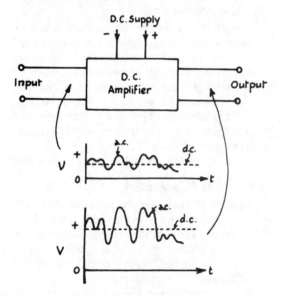

Fig. 4.13 D.C. amplifier (with d.c. and a.c. input).

component, *i.e.* an alternating voltage component fluctuating about the d.c. or mean value of the waveform as indicated. This is an important concept in electronics and is often used. The amplifier is therefore seen to be amplifying both the a.c. component and the d.c. component of the input. This is true of most d.c. amplifiers in that they will amplify both d.c. and a.c. signals.

An a.c. amplifier is illustrated in Fig. 4.14. The input consists of an a.c. signal (sine wave) fluctuating about a positive d.c. component. The output of the amplifier shows a replica but magnified version of the a.c. component of the input, but the d.c. component is not present. This is true of all a.c. amplifiers in that they will amplify only a.c. signals.

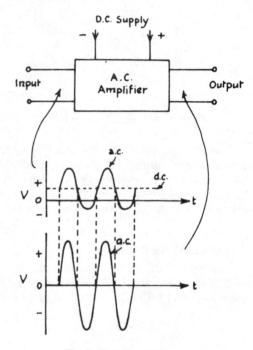

Fig. 4.14 A.C. amplifier.

A.F. Voltage Amplifier

One of the many applications for amplifiers is in audio work. Such amplifiers are called a.f. (audio frequency) since they are concerned with the processing of the audio spectrum of frequencies. For high quality music the audio frequency range may be considered as from 30Hz to 15kHz or higher, but a restricted range of frequencies, say, 100Hz to 10kHz may give reasonable results.

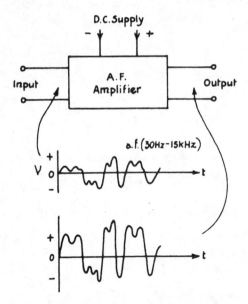

Fig. 4.15 A.F. voltage amplifier (A.C. type).

An example of an a.f. voltage amplifier is given in Fig. 4.15 showing a typical a.f. input waveform. During passages of high quality music the frequencies present in the input signal may lie in the range of, say, 30Hz to 15kHz. If the amplifier is well designed, the output signal will be a perfect replica of the input signal but of larger amplitude as shown.

We will now consider how the amplification or gain of a typical a.c. audio amplifier varies with frequency, see Fig. 4.16. Note that a logarithmic scale has been used for frequency owing to the wide range of frequencies in which we are interested. Over the larger part of the audio bandwidth the gain is **flat**

(constant) but then gradually drops-off towards the high and low frequency ends. Between points A and B the gain is said to be substantially flat and the frequency separation between these points gives the bandwidth of the amplifier. If, for example, in a high quality audio amplifier point A corresponds to 30Hz and point B to 20kHz, the bandwidth will be 20kHz − 30Hz = 9,970Hz. With an audio amplifier designed to handle telephone speech, A may be at 300Hz and B at 3000Hz giving a bandwidth of 3000Hz − 300Hz = 2700Hz.

The frequencies corresponding to points A and B is where the voltage gain has been reduced to 0·707 of its mid-band value. Taking 1kHz as the mid-band frequency (where a gain of 100 has been assumed), the gain at points A and B will be 70·7. In some practical amplifiers, the gain may not be so flat as shown and there may be some variation over the ideally flat portion.

Although an a.c. amplifier has been used in the above example, d.c. amplifiers are now very common in audio work. With a d.c. amplifier, the gain-frequency response will not show the gradual reduction towards low frequencies but will remain flat down to 0Hz (d.c.), see Fig. 4.17.

The actual voltage gain of the amplifier which is given by Output Signal Voltage/Input Signal Voltage depends upon the type of amplifier used. Voltage gains up to 1000 are generally easy to obtain, but become more difficult as the band of frequencies to be amplified is increased. The gain of a single stage amplifier may be limited by noise, the

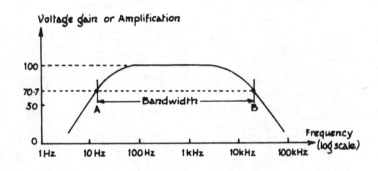

Fig. 4.16 Typical gain-frequency response for A.F. amplifier (A.C. type).

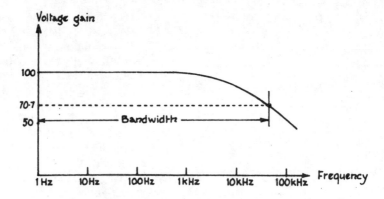

Fig. 4.17 Typical gain-frequency response for A.F. amplifier (D.C. type).

amount of distortion that can be tolerated (amplifying devices are not perfect in operation) and the magnitude of the d.c. supply. When a greater gain is required than can be achieved by a single amplifying stage, amplifiers may be connected in **cascade** (the output of one connected into the input of the next) to increase the overall gain, as illustrated in Fig. 4.18. The overall voltage gain is the product of the individual gains. For example, if Amplifier (1) has a voltage gain of 50 and

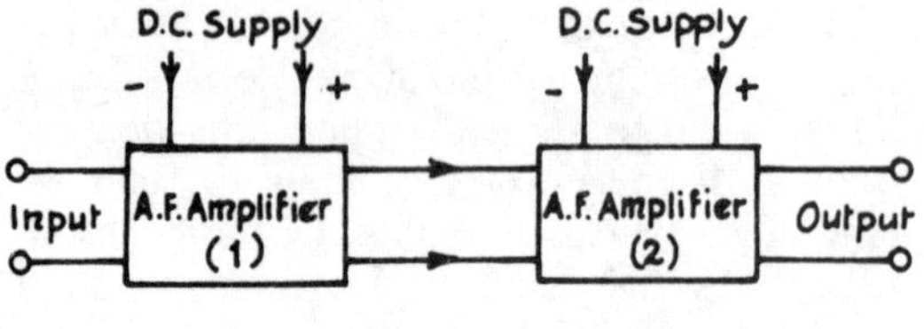

Amplifier (2) a voltage gain of 60, the overall voltage gain is $50 \times 60 = 3000$.

The voltage gain of an audio amplifier may be measured using a test signal source and a c.r.o., as illustrated in Fig. 4.19. The test oscillator is set to give a sine wave output at mid-band, say, 1kHz and connected to the input of Amplifier (1). Using the c.r.o., the peak-to-peak amplitude of the signal may be measured at the points indicated on the diagram. The voltage gain of Amplifier (1) is given by V_2/V_1, the voltage gain of Amplier (2) by V_3/V_2 and the overall voltage gain of the amplifier arrangement by V_3/V_1. The amplitude of the signal output of the test oscillator should be set so that the output of either amplifier is free from distortion, i.e. a pure sine wave. If the measurement is made at selected frequencies over the audio band, the gain-frequency response of the amplifiers may be obtained.

Fig. 4.18 Use of amplifiers in cascade to increase gain.

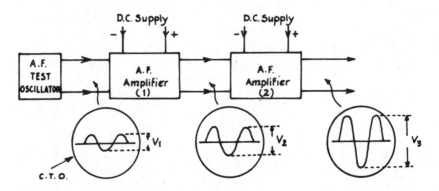

Fig. 4.19 Use of test oscillator and C.R.O. to measure voltage gain.

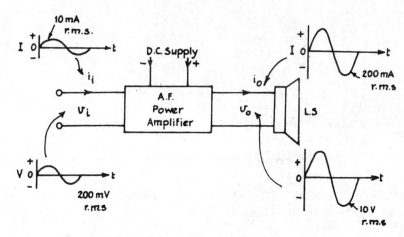

Fig. 4.20 A.F. power amplifier.

A.F. Power Amplifier

With a voltage amplifier the essential requirement is to produce voltage gain. However, in achieving the required voltage gain there may be appreciable power gain produced. For example, in a transistor voltage amplifier designed for a voltage gain of, say 100, the a.c. power supplied to the amplier from the signal source may be typically 0.1μW, whereas the a.c. power developed in the amplifier load at the output might be 10mW. In this case

the power gain $\dfrac{\text{output power}}{\text{input power}}$

would be $\dfrac{10 \times 10^{-3}}{0.1 \times 10^{-6}} = 10^5$

which is considerable. However, the actual power developed at the amplifier output is quite small and would be insufficient to fully drive a loudspeaker in an audio amplifier, for example.

Thus when appreciable power is required at the output of an amplifier, a power amplifier is used as illustrated in Fig. 4.20. A power amplifier must provide either appreciable voltage gain or current gain or a combination of both. If we assume that the signal voltage applied to the power amplifier is 200mV r.m.s. and that the input current is 10mA r.m.s., then the power input is

$$v_i \times i_i = 200 \times 10^{-3} \times 10 \times 10^{-3} = 2\text{mW}.$$

Now with voltage and current gains of 50 and 20 respectively, the output signal voltage and output signal currents become 10V r.m.s. and 200mA r.m.s. The power output is therefore $10 \times 200 \times 10^{-3} = 2$W. The power gain is

$$\frac{\text{output power}}{\text{input power}} = \frac{2}{2 \times 10^{-3}} = 1000.$$

It will be noted that the actual power gain in this case is less than the example given for the voltage amplifier. However, the power output is much greater and for this reason the amplifier is called a power amplifier, although in principle all amplifiers are esssentially power amplifiers.

Other examples where the use of a power amplifier may be required include driving a motor in a servo control system or an ultrasonic vibrator in a flaw detection system.

Voltage and power amplifiers are frequently combined together in many applications in electronics and one example for an audio amplifier is shown in Fig. 4.21. Here, one stage of voltage amplification and two stages of power amplification are cascaded to produce an audio amplifier that would be suitable for use in a record player or tape recorder (mono operation only).

As the input voltage may be quite small, say, 10mV, amplifier (1) is used to give a voltage gain of, say, 20 thus providing a signal input to amplifier (2) of 200mV. The signal power delivered to this stage may be of the order of 20μW. The driver stage is a medium power amplifier and its purpose is to provide

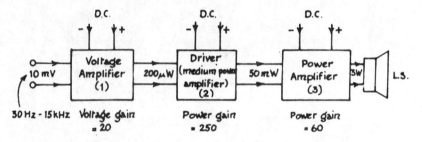

Fig. 4.21 Audio amplifier employing voltage and power amplifying stages.

sufficient drive power to the final power amplifier (3). The signal power output of the driver may be of the order of 50mW and this is raised to the desired output power (3W in this case) by amplifier (3) to operate the loudspeaker.

In a stereo audio amplifier the arrangement shown in Fig. 4.21 would have to be duplicated with one mono amplifier in each channel as shown in Fig. 4.22. The two channels have to be well isolated from one another from the signal point of view to avoid **cross-talk** between the channels which would otherwise spoil the stereo illusion.

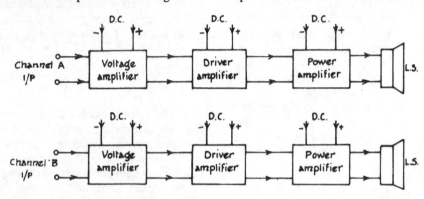

Fig. 4.22 Stereo audio amplifier.

Tuned Amplifier

A tuned or selective amplifier is one which has been designed to amplify a single frequency or a relatively narrow band of frequencies. Such an amplifier is illustrated in Fig. 4.23(a) with its gain-frequency response given in Fig. 4.23(b). At frequencies corresponding to the centre of the response and those in the immediate vicinity, the voltage gain of the amplifier is high but at all other frequencies the voltage gain falls to a low value (less than unity). The centre frequency of the response can be made any desired value over a large range, say, 1kHz to 20,000MHz depending

upon the application. This type of response is shown more clearly in expanded form in Fig. 4.24. For some purposes, it may be desirable to make the gain constant over a narrow band of frequencies and the amplifier may be given the response illustrated in Fig. 4.25.

The bandwidth of the amplifier is, as before, defined as the frequency separation between the points where the voltage gain has fallen to 0·707 of the maximum gain, or gain at the centre frequency. These points are shown as A and B in Figs. 4.24 and 4.25. These types of response are needed to amplify a carrier and

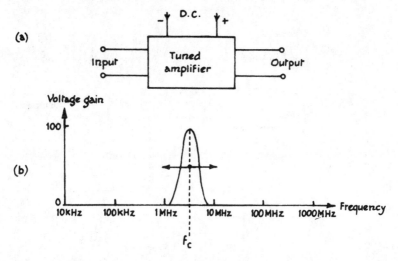

Fig. 4.23 A tuned (selective) amplifier and its response.

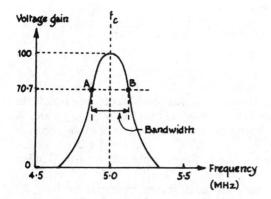

Fig. 4.24 Frequency response of tuned amplifier to expanded scale.

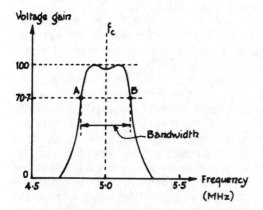

Fig. 4.25 Frequency response of tuned amplifier with approximately uniform response over a small band of frequencies.

its sidebands. It will be seen that tuned amplifiers discriminate against unwanted frequencies, *i.e.* they are **selective** in the frequencies that they amplify.

R.F. Amplifier

An r.f. amplifier is a tuned or selective amplifier. The designation r.f. (radio frequency) usually means that the amplifier is tuned to the **carrier frequency** of the system in which it is employed. For a.m. radio broadcasts the carrier may lie in the frequency range of 150kHz to 1600kHz, for f.m. radio broadcasts 88MHz to 108MHz and for television broadcasts 470MHz to 855MHz.

In receivers, the r.f. amplifier is the first stage in the amplifying chain and is thus concerned with amplification of modulated carriers. Whereas in transmitters an r.f. stage may be used to amplify modulated or unmodulated carriers. In transmitters both voltage and power r.f. amplifiers are employed but in receivers the main requirement is voltage amplification.

The carrier input to the r.f. stage in receivers may be amplitude modulated, frequency modulated or pulse modulated. An r.f. amplifier is illustrated in Fig. 4.26 fed with an amplitude modulated wave having a carrier frequency of 1MHz and an amplitude of, say, 100µV. Not only must the carrier frequency be amplified but also the sidebands. Thus the

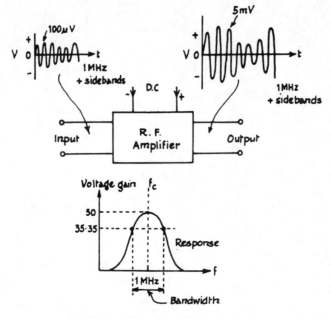

Fig. 4.26 R.F. amplifier and its response.

bandwidth of the amplifier must be sufficiently broad to embrace both upper and lower sidebands of the wanted signal and then the response should rapidly fall-off on either side so that unwanted signals are not amplified to any large extent. If a voltage gain of 50 at the carrier frequency of 1MHz is assumed, the bandwidth of the amplifier will be the frequency separation between the points where the voltage gain has fallen to 0.707×50, *i.e.* 35.35. For an a.m. radio broadcast these points should correspond to a bandwidth of about 9kHz, for an f.m. radio broadcast about 250kHz and for a television broadcast 8MHz.

The tuning of the amplifier is made variable so that the receiver can be tuned to different stations or channels and often the gain is automatically adjusted using automatic gain control (a.g.c.) to suit transmissions of differing signal strengths, to avoid overloading of the receiver when strong signals are received.

I.F. Amplifier

An i.f. amplifier is also a tuned amplifier but the frequency of the tuning is normally 'fixed'. It is exclusively used in superheterodyne receivers where the incoming carrier or r.f. signal is converted to a lower fixed frequency called the intermediate frequency (i.f.). An i.f. amplifier is essentially a voltage amplifier (although in transistor receivers the term power amplifier is more appropriate) and is responsible for producing most of the receiver gain. The actual frequency of the i.f. varies according to the type of receiver, *e.g.* 470kHz for an a.m. radio, 10.7MHz for an f.m. broadcast receiver and 39.5MHz (vision i.f.) and 33.5MHz (sound i.f.) for a television receiver. Except in an a.m. radio on the L.W., the i.f. is always lower than the incoming signal carrier frequency.

As with the r.f. amplifier, an i.f. amplifier must amplify the sidebands of the signal as well as the i.f. carrier. An example of an i.f. amplifier for use in an a.m. receiver is illustrated in Fig. 4.27. The amplifier is tuned to the i.f. of 470kHz where a voltage gain of 200 has been assumed. Again, the bandwidth is defined as the frequency separation between the points where the voltage gain has fallen to 0.707 of the centre frequency gain. In this case, the frequency separation is between points A and B where the gain has fallen to $0.707 \times 200 = 141.4$. This bandwidth should be adequate to amplify the i.f. carrier and its sidebands (9kHz for an a.m. receiver).

In receivers, two, three or four i.f. stages are

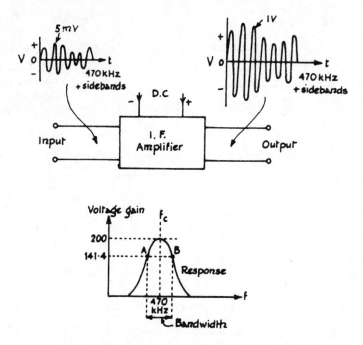

Fig. 4.27 I.F. amplifier (a.m. receiver).

normally used connected in cascade (one following the other) and the overall gain is the product of the individual stage gains. For example, with two identical stages in cascade each having a voltage gain of 200, the overall gain would be $200 \times 200 = 4 \times 10^4$. With three stages it would be $200 \times 200 \times 200 = 8 \times 10^6$. However there would be some bandwidth shrinkage and the overall bandwidth would be less than that of a single stage. This factor is taken into account by making the bandwidth of each stage slightly greater than required.

Video Amplifier

A video amplifier is used for amplifying baseband signals which are concerned with the transmision or reproduction of visual images whether they be for entertainment or information purposes. For 625 line television these baseband signals cover the frequency range of 0Hz to 5·5MHz. Thus, for example, a video amplifier dealing with this range of frequencies in a television camera or television receiver should have a 'flat' response over a wide frequency range. Since amplification

down to 0Hz is necessary, a d.c. amplifier is required.

The type of video amplifier employed in a television receiver is illustrated in Fig. 4.28. Here a single stage of amplification is generally used and essentially voltage amplification is required as the output is fed to the c.r.t. which is voltage operated. Depending upon the particular c.r.t. and its operating voltages, a voltage drive of 50–100V is usually necessary. Now as the video input voltage to the amplifier is of the order of 1–2V, a voltage gain of, say, 25 to 100 will be needed. In Fig. 4.28 a voltage gain of 50 has been assumed thus providing a 50V peak-to-peak output signal for a 1V peak-to-peak input signal.

In general all amplifiers may be **inverting** or **non-inverting**. In the previous amplifier diagrams non-inverting amplifiers have been shown. Here, an inverting has been used to provide a video signal that is negative-going which is of the required polarity to feed to the c.r.t. (when cathode modulation is used).

The bandwidth required in this case is 5·5MHz but in other applications, *e.g.* the video amplifiers found in some t.v. cameras,

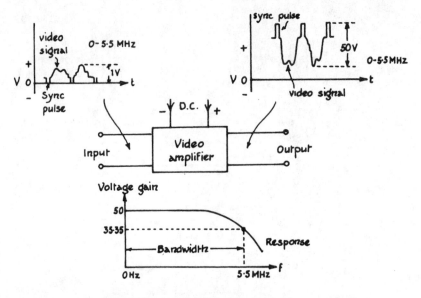

Fig. 4.28 Video amplifier (television receiver).

teletext receivers or computer data display monitors may have a bandwidth extending to 10MHz or better.

Buffer Amplifier

A buffer amplifier as its name implies is used

to help isolate one circuit from another, particularly from the effects of variable loading. One example is given in Fig. 4.29(a). Here the buffer amplifier is used to prevent changes in the loading of the variable attenuator from affecting the amplitude for frequency of the signal generated by the oscillator.

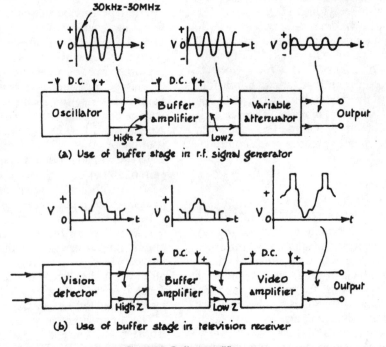

(a) Use of buffer stage in r.f. signal generator

(b) Use of buffer stage in television receiver

Fig. 4.29 Buffer amplifier.

The essential requirement of such a stage is that it has a high input impedance (high Z) and a low output impedence (low Z). The use of a high input impedance prevents undue loading of the oscillator by the buffer amplifier and the low output impedance prevents undue variations in the output of the buffer stage. In an r.f. signal generator application covering a wide range of frequencies, say, 30kHz to 30MHz, the buffer amplifier is required to produce a 'flat' response over the desired range of frequencies. The buffer stage found in transistorised equipment is usually a power amplifier of the type that does not produce any voltage gain, only current gain.

Another example is shown in Fig. 4.29(b) where a buffer amplifier is connected between the vision detector and video amplifier of a television receiver. Here the buffer stage prevents the low input impedance of the video amplifier from loading the detector, which would otherwise upset its operation. Again, in this application the buffer amplifier must have a 'flat' response over a wide frequency range (0Hz to 5·5MHz).

An alternative viewpoint of the operation of a buffer amplifier is to consider its action as a matching device, matching from a high impedance circuit to a low impedance one. Many wideband integrated circuits use buffer amplifiers in the output circuits to facilitate matching to discrete circuitry connected to the output pins of the i.c.

Differential Amplifier

A differential amplifier may be operated as a d.c. or a.c. amplifier and the basic idea of an a.c. type is illustrated in Fig. 4.30. The arrangement of the amplifier is such that the output is proportional to the difference between the two inputs A and B, *i.e.* Input A – Input B or Input B – Input A. There are a number of instances in electronics where it is necessary to be able to compare one signal with another and a differential amplifier may be used for this purpose. Sometimes the difference in amplitude is very small, and comparison by other means, *e.g.* by individual measurement with a voltmeter may not give sufficiently accurate results.

Consider the sinusoidal inputs of Fig. 4.30 where input A is 1·0V peak and input B is

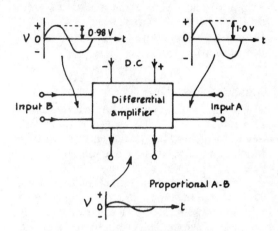

Fig. 4.30 Differential amplifier.

0·98V peak. The differential amplifier will produce an output voltage proportional to the difference of $1·0V - 0·98V = 0·02V$. Instead of a.c. inputs the amplifier may be used to compare two d.c. voltages with one another. Differential amplifiers are sometimes fitted to the Y input of a c.r.o. to enable waveform measurements to be made where the presence of earth connections would make measurements with an ordinary c.r.o. difficult.

A differential amplifier can be arranged to operate as a conventional a.c. or d.c. amplifier. When used as a d.c. amplifier it has the advantage that the amount of d.c. **drift** (changes in the steady d.c. output) due to temperature or supply variations can be made very small which is one of the difficulties of ordinary d.c. amplifiers. The output of the amplifier can be arranged to be balanced with respect to the supply line or unbalanced (one output line at a fixed potential). Many integrated circuit d.c. amplifiers employing several stages use differential amplifiers, especially in the first stage of amplification where the low d.c. drift characteristic is of particular value.

Differential amplifiers are essentially 'flat' amplifiers but the bandwidth depends upon the application, *e.g.* for a c.r.o. the flat response may extend from 0Hz to 10MHz.

MODULATORS

Modulators are used to either impress information onto a carrier in some way, *e.g.* in amplitude and frequency modulation systems or to prepare the information in a suitable form for transmission, *e.g.* in pulse modulation systems.

Amplitude Modulator

The basic idea of an amplitude modulator is illustrated in Fig. 4.31. In this diagram, the device which applies the information or modulating signal to the r.f. amplifier has been called the modulator, although sometimes the two blocks together are called the modulator. One input to the modulated r.f. amplifier is the r.f. carrier (generated by a separate sine wave oscillator) which is used to convey the information. The other input comes from the modulator which is fed with the information, *i.e.* speech, music, video or pulse signals. The modulator amplifies its input to a level to operate the modulated r.f. amplifier. At the output of the modulated r.f. amplifier is produced a modulated carrier wave having an amplitude that is proportional to the amplitude of the modulating signal.

The output which contains the carrier frequency and sidebands may be fed, after amplification, to an aerial system for transmission or an r.f. cable system for distribution.

Frequency Modulator

The idea of a frequency modulator is illustrated in Fig. 4.32. Here the modulating signal or information to be conveyed is fed to the modulator, the output of which is used to vary the frequency of an r.f. sine wave oscillator. At the output of the r.f. oscillator, a modulated carrier wave is produced having an instantaneous frequency that is proportional to the amplitude of the modulating signal. The variation in carrier frequency (the deviation) may, for example, be ±75kHz as with f.m. broadcast radio using a carrier frequency of 100MHz. Different devices may be used in the modulator but the effect is the same in that they alter the frequency of the oscillator in accordance with the amplitude of the modulation. Other methods of producing frequency modulation may be used but they will not be considered here.

After suitable amplification, the output may

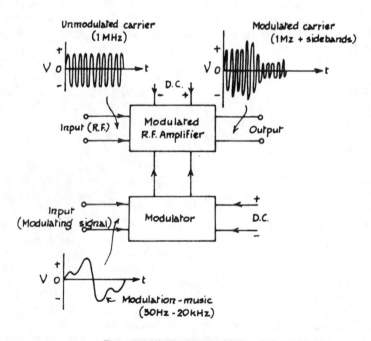

Fig. 4.31 Amplitude modulator.

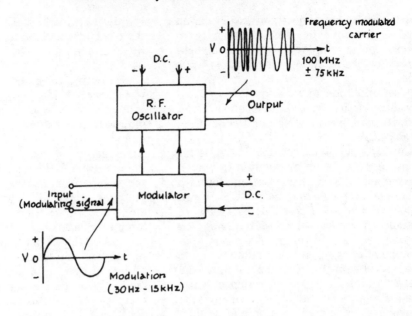

Fig. 4.32 Frequency modulator.

be fed to an aerial or r.f. cable system as for the amplitude modulator.

Pulse Modulator

There are various types of pulse modulators and two examples will be considered. One example is illustrated in Fig. 4.33 for producing pulse amplitude modulation (p.a.m.). The modulator comprises an electronic gate operated by a regular series of equal width pulses (the clock pulses). One may think of the gate as an electronic switch which is closed when a clock pulse is present thereby connecting the modulating signal source to the output and is open in the absence of a clock pulse thereby disconnecting the modulating signal from the output. As the clock pulses are only present for brief instances, **amplitude samples** are taken of the modulating signal which appear in the output of the gate as shown.

The number of samples taken (the **sampling rate**) is governed by the pulse repetition rate of the clock pulses which, in theory, must be at least twice the highest frequency present in the modulating signal. In practice the sampling rate is made more than twice the highest frequency present in the modulating signal, say, 8000 samples per second for a highest modulating frequency of 3400Hz.

The output from the gate thus comprises pulses of equal width and spacing having an amplitude which varies in accordance with the modulating signal (sine wave assumed). This p.a.m. signal may be fed to a cable system for direct transmission of the pulses over lines, fed to an a.m. or f.m. modulator to be impressed

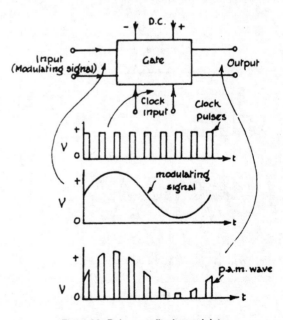

Fig. 4.33 Pulse amplitude modulator.

upon a carrier for radio transmission via an aerial or fed to a light emitting device to produce pulse amplitude modulated light signals for distribution using a fibre-optic cable.

Pulse amplitude modulation is only used occasionally in its own right. It is, however, an essential part in producing pulse code modulated signals.

Another example is given in Fig. 4.34 for producing pulse width modulation (p.w.m.). The modulator comprises a comparator (a differential amplifier may be used) with two inputs. One input is a triangular wave of constant frequency which determines the **sampling rate**, waveform (a). The other input is the modulating signal (assumed to be a sine wave), waveform (b). Now the output of the comparator is a voltage which is of positive or negative polarity depending upon whether the triangular wave is greater in amplitude than the modulating signal (output positive) or less in amplitude than the modulating signal

(output negative). Waveform (c) shows both the triangular and modulating signals, so that their amplitudes may be compared more easily.

The output of the comparator is shown in waveform (d). It will be noted that when the triangular wave is larger in amplitude than the modulating signal the output is positive, but quickly switches to negative polarity when the triangular wave becomes less in amplitude than the modulating signal. Thus as a result of the comparison in amplitudes, a series of pulses is produced at the output of constant amplitude but having a width that varies directly in accordance with the amplitude of the modulating signal. This p.w.m. signal may be fed to a cable system for direct transmission of the pulses over lines, fed to an a.m. or f.m. modulator to be impressed upon a carrier for radio transmission via an aerial or fed to a light emitting device to produce pulse width modulated light signals for distribution using a fibre-optic cable, as for the p.a.m. system.

DEMODULATORS

Demodulators are used to extract or recover the information or modulation from the modulated signal, *i.e.* they perform the reverse process of modulation.

A.M. Demodulator

The basic idea of an amplitude modulation (a.m.) demodulator is shown in Fig. 4.35. It is

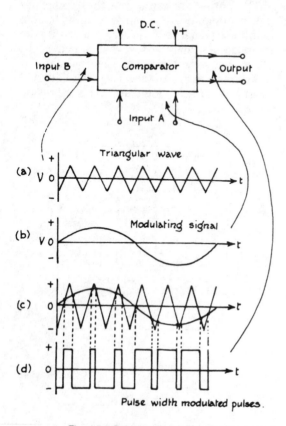

Fig. 4.34 Pulse width modulator.

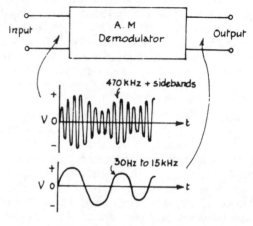

Fig. 4.35 A.M. demodulator.

used extensively in a.m. receivers for recovering the modulating signal. The input to the demodulator is an amplitude modulated wave. In an a.m. radio receiver it would be on an i.f. carrier of about 470kHz at an amplitude of, say, 100–200mV. The demodulator detects the amplitude variations and produces an output containing the modulating signal only, which is a replica of the modulating signal originally used to modulate the carrier. A d.c. supply may or may not be required depending upon the type of demodulator used.

F.M. Demodulator

An example of a frequency modulation (f.m.) demodulator is illustrated in Fig. 4.36. The input consists of an f.m. wave which for a broadcast f.m. received would be on an i.f. carrier of 10·7MHz with sidebands extending to 120kHz either side of the carrier at an amplitude of, say, 100mV. The output consists of the modulating signal only which, also, is a replica of the modulating signal originally used to modulate the carrier. This type of demodulator is used extensively in f.m. receivers. As for the a.m. demodulator, a d.c. supply may or may not be required depending upon the type of demodulator used.

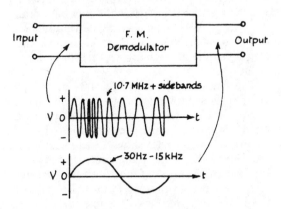

Fig. 4.36 F.M. demodulator.

Pulse Demodulator

A pulse demodulator is used to extract the information or modulating signal from the modulated pulses, p.a.m., p.w.m. or p.c.m. type signals. The basic idea of a demodulator for extracting the modulating signal from

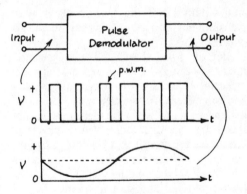

Fig. 4.37 Pulse demodulator.

pulse width modulated signals is illustrated in Fig. 4.37.

The input to the demodulator consists of pulses of constant amplitude but varying width which contain the information. By detecting the mean or average value of these pulses the modulation may be extracted (sine wave assumed). A low pass filter may be used for the demodulator to detect the mean value of the pulses.

If the pulses are modulated on a carrier, the signal must be fed first to an a.m. or f.m. demodulator depending upon the type of carrier modulation used, prior to being fed to the pulse demodulator.

Different circuit arrangements may be used in the pulse demodulator for the detection of p.a.m. and p.c.m. signals.

MIXER

A mixer is a device for translating a signal from one frequency band to a signal in another frequency band. The basic idea of a mixer is shown in Fig. 4.38. Applied to one input is a signal of frequency f_1 and to the other input a signal of frequency f_2 (both assumed to be

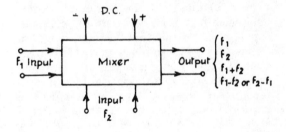

Fig. 4.38 Mixer.

sinusoidal). Let f_1 be the signal we wish to translate in frequency (this may be variable); and let f_2 be a fixed frequency which may be higher or lower than f_1. The output of the mixer contains the original input signal frequencies f_1 and f_2, the sum frequency $f_1 + f_2$ and the difference frequency $f_1 - f_2$ or $f_2 - f_1$ depending on which is the higher frequency. It is the sum and difference frequencies that we are interested in as these represent frequency translation of the input signal frequency f_1.

Consider the example when $f_1 = 5\text{MHz}$ and $f_2 = 100\text{MHz}$. The sum frequency is $(100 + 5)\text{MHz} = 105\text{MHz}$ and the difference frequency is $(100 - 5)\text{MHz} = 95\text{MHz}$. Thus available at the mixer output are signals at 95MHz and 105MHz. Either of these may be selected using a suitable filter, the output of which represents frequency translation of the 5MHz input signal f_1 to a higher frequency band (95MHz or 100MHz). This is sometimes called **up-conversion**.

Consider another example when $f_1 = 100\text{MHz}$ and $f_2 = 110\text{MHz}$. The sum frequency $= (110 + 110)\text{MHz} = 210\text{MHz}$ and the difference frequency $= (100 - 100)\text{MHz} = 10\text{MHz}$. If the difference frequency is selected, then this represents the translation of the 100MHz input signal frequency f_1 to a lower frequency band of 10MHz. This is often called **down-conversion**.

In general when a complex signal is applied to one of the inputs, each frequency component of the input signal produces corresponding sum and difference frequencies so that the complete signal is translated to a higher or lower frequency band.

The mixer principle is used in superheterodyne receivers, video cassette recorders and signal generators.

FILTERS

In communication and other electronic equipment it is often necessary to be able to suppress or **attenuate** a certain range of frequencies lying within a particular larger band of frequencies but to pass or transmit all other frequencies. An electrical filter is used for this purpose. A filter is an electrical network which is designed to severely attenuate certain frequencies but to pass other frequencies without loss. A filter will pass at least one band of frequencies (the **pass** band) and attenuate at least one band of frequencies (the **attenuation** band). There are four basic types of filter used in electronics and their symbols and characteristics are shown in Fig. 4.39.

The low pass filter of Fig. 4.39(a) will pass low frequency signals (ideally without loss) but severely attenuate high frequency signals above a certain frequency. Fig. 4.39(b) shows the response where the ratio of v_o/v_i is plotted against frequency. Over the range where $v_o/v_i = 1$, the output voltage v_o is equal to the input voltage v_i and here the filter is passing signal frequencies without loss. As practical filters do not suddenly change from **pass** to **attenuate** but do so less abruptly as shown, it is necessary to specify a frequency where (for practical purposes) the filter changes over from pass to attenuate. This frequency, called the **cutoff frequency** f_{co}, is taken to be the frequency where the output voltage has fallen to 0·707 of the input voltage. Thus above f_{co} the low pass filter is attenuating the input signal as the ratio v_o/v_i is less than 0·707.

The high pass filter of Fig. 4.39(c) will pass high frequency signals applied to the input of the filter but severely attenuate low frequency signals below a certain frequency. A response for a high pass filter is given in Fig. 4.39(d) which is a mirror image of the low pass filter response. The filter passes signal frequencies down to a frequency f_{co} and below this frequency the filter changes over from pass to attenuate.

The band pass filter of Fig. 4.39(e) is used where it is desirable to pass a particular band of frequencies within a larger frequency band but to suppress frequencies on either side of the band. Fig. 4.39(f) shows a response for a band pass filter. The pass band lies between the frequency limits of f_1 and f_2 where the ratio of v_o/v_i is equal to or greater than 0·707. Below f_1 and above f_2 where v_o/v_i is less than 0·707, the filter changes over from pass to attenuate.

Where the opposite type of characteristic to the band pass filter is required, a band stop filter is used, Fig. 4.39(g). This type of filter attenuates a particular band of frequencies within a larger band but passes frequencies on either side of this band. A response for a band stop filter is given in Fig. 4.39(h). The attenuation band lies between the frequency

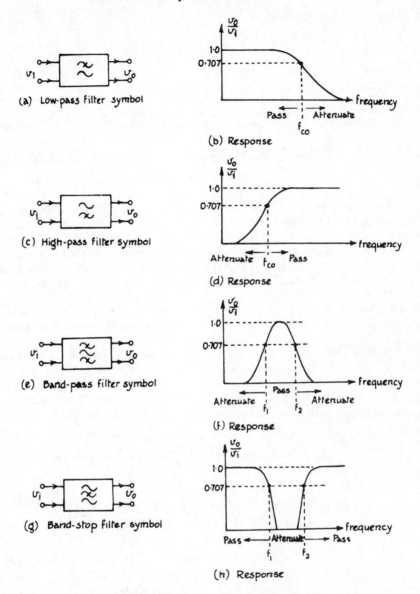

(a) Low-pass filter symbol

(b) Response

(c) High-pass filter symbol

(d) Response

(e) Band-pass filter symbol

(f) Response

(g) Band-stop filter symbol

(h) Response

Fig. 4.39 Four basic filter types used in electronics.

limits of f_1 and f_2 where the ratio of v_o/v_i is less than 0·707. Below f_1 and above f_2 the filter changes over from attenuate to pass.

Low Frequency Filter

Filters which are concerned with the filtering of frequencies at power frequencies are examples of low frequency (l.f.) filters. The smoothing filter used in a power supply following the rectifier as in Fig. 4.40 is an l.f.

filter. This filter is required to pass the d.c. (0Hz) from the rectifier to the output but attenuate the ripple frequency which is either 50Hz or 100Hz depending upon whether a halfwave or fullwave rectifier is used. The low pass filter used for this purpose would have a response similar to that shown in Fig. 4.39(b). The ripple voltage is not sinusoidal but consists of a fundamental frequency and harmonics. However, if the fundamental component (50Hz or 100Hz) is adequately

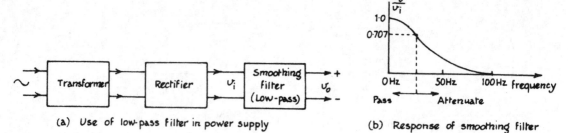

(a) Use of low-pass filter in power supply   (b) Response of smoothing filter

Fig. 4.40 Low frequency filter.

attenuated, the harmonics will be heavily attenuated as the filter becomes more efficient as the frequency is raised.

Note that although a low pass filter is used the comparitively low frequencies of 50Hz and 100Hz are attenuated. Thus the frequency range of the pass and attenuation bands depends upon the application.

Audio Frequency Filter

An audio frequency (a.f.) filter is one which is concerned with the filtering of frequencies in the a.f. range of approximately 20Hz to 20kHz. One example is the decoupling filter fitted into the d.c. supply line to an audio amplifier. This is used to remove spurious a.f. signals (and other frequencies) developed across the internal impedance of the d.c. supply. Without a decoupling filter these spurious signals may cause instability (oscillation) in the amplifier if fed back along the supply line. The idea of this type of filter is shown in Fig. 4.41. Any spurious signal (v_i) in the range of 20Hz to 20kHz is heavily attenuated by the filter. However, the filter must be capable of passing 0Hz (d.c.) thus a low pass filter with a cut-off frequency (f_{co}) of, say, 20Hz would be suitable.

Another example of an a.f. filter is the tone

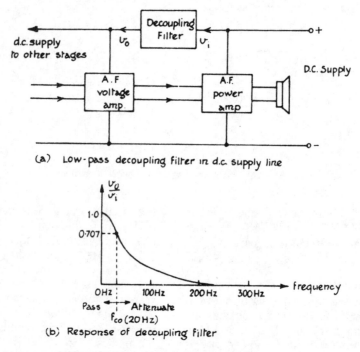

(a) Low-pass decoupling filter in d.c. supply line

(b) Response of decoupling filter

Fig. 4.41 Decoupling filter in A.F. amplifier.

(a) Tone control filter for providing 'top' cut and 'bass' cut

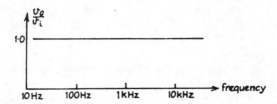

(b) Tone control set for level response 30Hz – 15 kHz

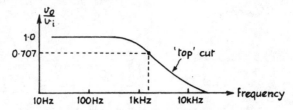

(c) Tone control set for 'top' cut (low-pass filter)

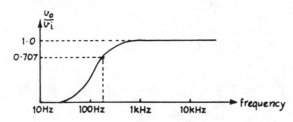

(d) Tone control set for 'bass' cut (high-pass filter)

Fig. 4.42 Tone control filter in A.F. amplifier.

control fitted in an audio amplifier, see Fig. 4.42. When the tone control is set for level response, v_o is equal to v_i and the response of the tone control circuit is as in Fig. 4.42(b), *i.e.* **flat** over the required audio range for the amplifier of, say, 30Hz to 15kHz. When the tone control is set for **top cut**, the higher audio frequencies become attenuated and the tone control circuit operates as a low pass filter, as shown in Fig. 4.42(c). Conversely, by setting the tone control for **bass cut**, the lower audio frequencies become attenuated. The tone control circuit then operates as a high pass filter as shown by the response in Fig. 4.42(d).

Sometimes it is necessary to restrict the low frequency performance of an audio amplifier to reduce the transmission of motor rumble from a record player or to attenuate the low frequencies from sources containing excessive bass. This may be accomplished by using a **rumble** filter which is a high pass filter with a cut-off frequency of about 35Hz. The filter passes the required audio range into the amplifier but severely attenuates frequencies below 35Hz.

I.F. Filter

Intermediate frequency (i.f.) filters are found in receivers and are used for either suppressing the intermediate frequency of the receiver or passing it.

The output of the detector in a super-

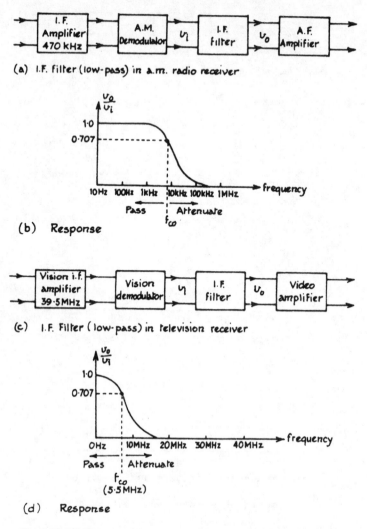

Fig. 4.43 I.F. filters used for suppressing the intermediate frequency.

heterodyne receiver contains not only the modulation frequencies but also the intermediate frequency and harmonics which are not required. A filter is used to suppress the i.f. and its harmonics but to pass the modulation frequencies. In an a.m. radio receiver, Fig. 4.43(a), the i.f. filter is required to pass the modulation frequencies of, say, 30Hz to 10kHz but to attenuate the i.f. of 470kHz and its harmonics. The i.f. and its harmonics must be prevented from entering the a.f. amplifier otherwise radiation may occur to earlier stages of the receiver causing instability. A low pass filter is thus required with a response similar to that of Fig. 4.43(b).

The i.f. filter used following the vision detector in a television receiver, Fig. 4.43(c), serves the same purpose as in a radio receiver. It must, however, possess a broader **pass band** to pass on the video frequencies of 0Hz to 5·5MHz to the video amplifier and provide rapid attenuation beyond the upper video frequency to suppress the i.f. of 39·5MHz and its harmonics. Thus a response similar to that shown in Fig. 4.43(d) will be needed.

I.F. amplifiers used in superheterodyne receivers are required to amplify the i.f. and its side frequencies which carry the information to be detected. To achieve this, each stage of i.f. amplification will comprise an amplifying

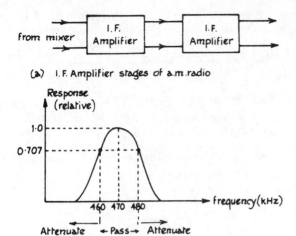

(a) I.F. Amplifier stages of a.m. radio

(b) Response of i.f. filter (band-pass) used in each i.f. stage

Fig. 4.44 I.F. filters used for passing the intermediate frequency and side frequencies in a radio receiver.

device and an i.f. filter. These i.f. filters are band-pass filters and an example is given in Fig. 4.44 where the i.f. stages of an a.m. radio are considered. The filter used in each i.f. amplifying stage of Fig. 4.44(a) will have a band-pass response similar to that in Fig. 4.44(b), assuming that the received side frequencies extend to 10kHz either side of the carrier. Thus, frequencies between 460kHz and 480kHz are passed and amplified by the amplifier but frequencies below 460kHz and above 480kHz are attenuated.

The i.f. filters used in the i.f. stages of any type of receiver are essentially band-pass filters but the pass band depends upon the range of modulation frequencies to be dealt with and any other special considerations.

In the i.f. stages of a television receiver, narrow band-stop filters are also used in the vision channel in addition to the normal band-pass filters which provide the selectivity. These additional filters are used to suppress unwanted intermediate frequencies that are produced by channels adjacent to the channel that the receiver is tuned to. The adjacent channel carrier frequencies give rise to intermediate frequencies which lie close to the normal band-pass of the i.f. amplifier. The use of band-stop filters suppresses these unwanted frequencies (called **adjacent channel sound i.f.** and **adjacent channel vision i.f.**) but allows the

passing of the normal i.f. and its side frequencies.

R.F. Filter

A radio frequency (r.f.) filter is concerned with the filtering of frequencies in the r.f. range of approximately 20kHz to 300,000MHz. This range of frequencies includes the intermediate frequencies of receivers discussed in the previous section, thus an i.f. filter could be designated an r.f. filter. However, in dealing with receivers, filters which are concerned with intermediate frequencies are i.f. filters whilst those associated with filtering frequencies which lie at the carrier frequency or close to it are called r.f. filters.

An example of an r.f. filter is shown in Fig. 4.45(a). This filter which may be found in the **pre-selector** stage of an a.m. radio is used to select the desired transmission but to reject all other transmissions. Thus a band-pass filter will be required with its centre frequency lying at the frequency of the selected transmission, say, 1MHz as shown in Fig. 4.45(b). The bandwidth of the filter must be sufficient to pass the carrier and its sidebands. In this application, the r.f. filter is tuneable so that

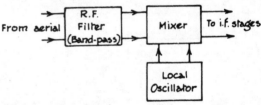

(a) R.F. filter (band-pass) in a.m. radio

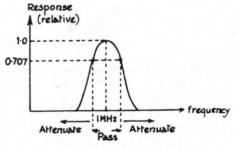

(b) Response of r.f. filter

Fig. 4.45 R.F. filter used for passing carrier and side frequencies in a radio receiver.

the filter may produce a band-pass action on the selected transmission.

Another example is the decoupling filter used in the d.c. supply line to the r.f. amplifier in a radio or television receiver. This filter serves the same purpose as the decoupling filter described for the a.f. amplifier. It is basically a low-pass filter and provides a large amount of attenuation at the carrier frequencies used in the receiver.

A further example is given in Fig. 4.46 where a filter is used to prevent the bias oscillator from feeding signals into the record amplifier of a tape recorder. This filter must pass the normal audio signals from the record amplifier to the recording head but prevent the bias oscillation of, say, 40kHz from reaching the record amplifier. A low-pass filter could be used for this purpose but a band-stop filter is more efficient at removing the bias frequency. Since the filter has to attenuate only a single frequency in this case, a narrow band-stop filter would be used.

An r.f. filter (low-pass) is often fitted in the mains supply to electronic equipment to prevent r.f. interference picked up in the mains from entering the equipment where the r.f. **spikes** could cause damage to semiconductor devices.

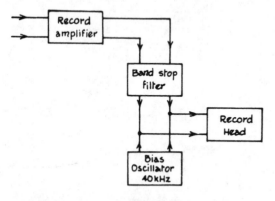

Fig. 4.46 Use of R.F. band stop filter in audio tape recorder.

WAVESHAPING

In electronics it is most useful to be able to alter the basic waveshape of complex waveforms such as rectangular, sawtooth and triangular type waveforms, and a waveshaping circuit may be used for this purpose. Differentiating and integrating circuits are commonly used waveshaping networks and they will now be considered.

Differentiator

A **differentiator** is a circuit which produces an output that is directly proportional to the slope or rate of change of the input waveform. The idea is illustrated in Fig. 4.47 where a square wave input is used.

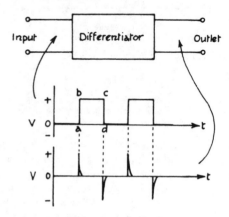

Fig. 4.47 Differentiation of a square wave.

On the rising edge of the input waveform between a and b, a positive-going spike is obtained but between b and c there is no output since the input voltage is constant. Later on when the input voltage falls between c and d, a negative-going spike is obtained. Thus an output is only obtained when the input voltage is changing level. The differentiator is a highpass filter, passing only the rapid changes to the output.

Another example is shown in Fig. 4.48 where a sawtooth input is used. During the rise in input voltage between a and b, an output voltage v_1 is obtained since the input is changing level. The magnitude of v_1 is, however, constant since the slope or rate of change of voltage during this period is constant. Between b and c where the input voltage is falling, an output voltage v_2 is obtained. This is of opposite polarity to v_1 since between b and c the input is of negative slope, whereas between a and b it is of positive slope. The magnitude of the output voltage is

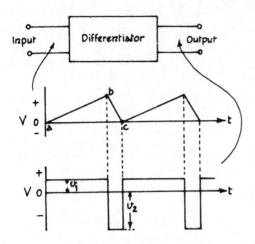

Fig. 4.48 *Differentiation of a sawtooth wave.*

now much greater since the rate of change of the input is greater. Thus by using a differentiator we are able to produce a rectangular waveform from a sawtooth one. By using different input waveforms, other output waveshapes are possible.

Integrator

An **integrating** circuit is one which produces an output that is directly proportional to the area under the input waveshape at every instant. One example is shown in Fig. 4.49 with a square wave input. During the positive section of the input waveform when it is increasing in area between a and b, the integrator output is rising and at a constant rate since the pulse area is increasing at a

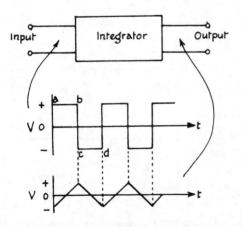

Fig. 4.49 *Integration of a square wave.*

constant rate. Later on during the negative section of the input waveform between c and d where the area is again increasing but in the opposite direction, the output of the integrator is falling (also at a constant rate since the pulse area is increasing at a constant rate). An integrator is a low-pass filter, passing only the low frequency components of the input waveform to the output.

Another example is shown in Fig. 4.50 fed with a sawtooth waveform. Here integration of the sawtooth wave produces a parabolic wave in the output. With any integrator, the input wave indicates the approximate slope or rate of change of the output wave.

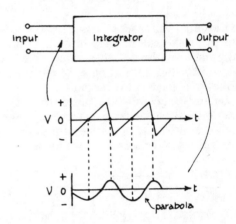

Fig. 4.50 *Integration of a sawtooth wave.*

Limiters or Clippers

Another common requirement in electronics is to be able to limit or clip the amplitude of a waveform at a particular voltage level. A limiter or clipper may be used for this purpose. As the action of these circuits may affect the shape of a waveform, they are included here under the general heading of **waveshaping**.

One example is given in Fig. 4.51 using a sine wave input. If the limiter is arranged to clip the input waveform when its amplitude exceeds the level x or when the amplitude falls below the level y, the output will be severely clipped on its peaks as shown producing an approximate square wave.

Another example is shown in Fig. 4.52 where a limiter is used to remove unwanted positive-going spikes of the input waveform, so that only the negative-going spikes remain

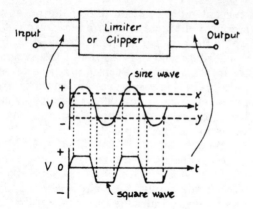

Fig. 4.51 *Limiting or clipping a sine wave to obtain a square wave.*

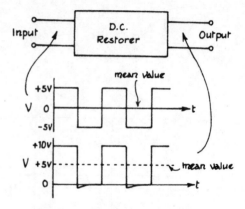

Fig. 4.53 *Positive D.C. restoration.*

in the output. In practice, some small residual positive spike will be present at the output. Alternatively, the negative-going spikes may be limited thus permitting only the positive spikes to appear in the output.

Limiters may also be used to remove interference pulses from a waveform or to limit the amplitude of a waveform to prevent overloading of an amplifier, for example.

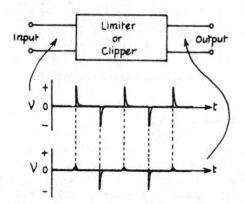

Fig. 4.52 *Use of limiter to remove positive spikes.*

RESTORERS

A restorer does not affect the shape of a waveform to any signicant extent. Its function is to either reinsert any d.c. component that may be lost during the passage of a waveform through a coupling circuit or to introduce any required d.c. into a waveform.

An example is given in Fig. 4.53 using a square wave input. It will be noticed that the

input is a pure a.c. type waveform, *i.e.* its mean value is zero. If it is desirable to ensure that the most negative part of this waveform does not fall below 0V, a positive d.c. restorer circuit may be used as illustrated. The peak-to-peak amplitude of the output waveform (10V) is still the same as the input waveform, but a positive d.c. component (+5V) has been introduced into the output.

Another example is given in Fig. 4.54 fed with a television video waveform at its input. Again, the input is a pure a.c. type waveform. In this case, a negative d.c. component is introduced into the output so that the sync. pulse tips do not exceed 0V. This is an example of negative d.c. restoration.

Using negative or positive d.c. restoration it

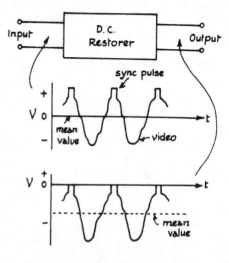

Fig. 4.54 *Negative D.C. restoration of television video waveform.*

is possible to restore either the positive or negative-going peak of a waveform to any required d.c. voltage level (positive or negative) within reasonable limits.

TRANSDUCERS

A **transducer** is a device which converts one kind of physical quantity or signal into a physical quantity of another kind. An electric light bulb conforms to this denition since it converts the electrical energy supplied to it into light energy, thus an electric light bulb is a transducer. Other examples are as follows.

D.C. Motor and D.C. Generator

A d.c. (or a.c.) motor is supplied with electrical energy which it converts into mechanical energy in order to drive its load, see Fig. 4.55(a). A d.c. (or a.c.) generator on the other hand, is supplied with mechanical energy causing it to turn, which it converts into electrical energy at its output, see Fig. 4.55(b).

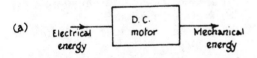

Fig. 4.55(a) Transducer. Electrical energy–mechanical energy.

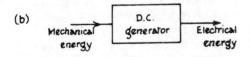

Fig. 4.55(b) Transducer. Mechanical energy–electrical energy.

Microphone and Loudspeaker

When a microphone is supplied with sound energy (variation in air pressure) it converts it into electrical energy (an electrical signal) at its output, see Fig. 4.56(a). The reverse process occurs in a loudspeaker which converts the electrical energy supplied to it into sound energy, Fig. 4.56(b).

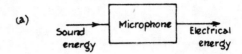

Fig. 4.56(a) Transducer. Sound energy–electrical energy.

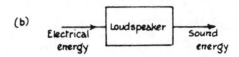

Fig. 4.56(b) Transducer. Electrical energy–sound energy.

Tape Recorder Record and Playback Heads

The record head in a magnetic tape recorder converts the electrical energy supplied to it, *i.e.* the signal to be recorded, into magnetic energy which is transferred to the magnetic tape, Fig. 4.57(a). When the tape recorder is in the playback mode, the playback head converts the magnetic energy stored on the tape into electrical energy (an electrical signal) which is the converse action of the record head, Fig. 4.57(b).

Fig. 4.57(a) Transducer. Electrical energy–magnetic energy.

Fig. 4.57(b) Transducer. Magnetic energy–electrical energy.

Transmitting and Receiving Aerials

A transmitting aerial converts the electrical energy (a.c. signal) supplied to it from the transmitter into an electromagnetic wave which radiates from the aerial, Fig. 4.58(a). A receiving aerial on the other hand, converts

(a)

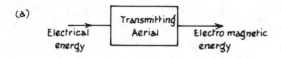

Fig. 4.58(a) Transducer. Electrical energy–electromagnetic energy.

(b)

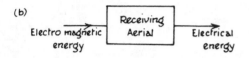

Fig. 4.58(b) Transducer. Electromagnetic energy–electrical energy.

the electromagnetic wave back into electrical energy which is fed to the receiver, Fig. 4.58(b).

Television Camera and Picture Tube

A television camera converts the light energy (electromagnetic energy) from the scene to be televised into electrical energy (video signal) at its output, Fig. 4.59(a). The reverse process takes place at the television picture tube which converts electrical energy (video signal) back into light energy at its output, Fig. 4.59(b).

(a)

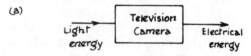

Fig. 4.59(a) Transducer. Light energy–electrical energy.

(b)

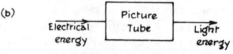

Fig. 4.59(b) Transducer. Electrical energy–light energy.

QUESTIONS ON CHAPTER FOUR

(1) A power supply is a device to:
  (a) Change d.c. to a.c.
  (b) Enable a battery to be used to supply electronic equipment
  (c) Change the a.c. supply to d.c.
  (d) Amplify a.c. power.

(2) An oscillator is a device which:
  (a) Produces an a.c. output from d.c. supply
  (b) Amplies a.c.
  (c) Amplies d.c.
  (d) Converts a sine wave into a square wave.

(3) The amplifier in a good quality record player would be designed to cover a frequency range of:
  (a) 300Hz–3kHz
  (b) 0Hz–1MHz
  (c) 30MHz–40MHz
  (d) 30Hz–15kHz.

(4) A video amplifier in a television receiver is concerned with handling frequencies in the range of:
  (a) 470MHz–890MHz
  (b) 30Hz–20kHz
  (c) 0Hz–100MHz
  (d) 0Hz–5·5MHz.

(5) A buffer amplifier is used to:
  (a) Isolate one circuit from another
  (b) Provide a mismatch
  (c) Provide a variable load for an oscillator
  (d) Act as an attenuator.

(6) A differential amplifier is normally used for:
  (a) Adding two signals together
  (b) Subtracting one signal from another
  (c) Blocking a particular input frequency
  (d) Generating sine waves.

(7) A high pass filter may be used to:
  (a) Pass a band of frequencies but to attenuate on either side
  (b) Attenuate low frequencies and pass high frequencies
  (c) Attenuate high frequencies and pass low frequencies
  (d) Pass all frequencies except the u.h.f. ones.

(8) A receiving aerial converts:
  (a) Air pressure into electrical energy
  (b) Electrical energy into mechanical energy
  (c) Sound energy into light energy
  (d) Electromagnetic energy into electrical energy.

(9) In principle all amplifiers are:
  (a) Inverting
  (b) Non-inverting
  (c) Power amplifiers
  (d) Current amplifiers
(10) The intermediate frequency in an f.m. radio receiver will be:
  (a) 10·7MHz
  (b) 470kHz
  (c) 39·5MHz
  (d) 33·5MHz.
(11) A selective amplifier will amplify:
  (a) Frequencies in the range 0Hz–5·5MHz
  (b) Frequencies in the range 30Hz–20kHz
  (c) Frequencies in the range 300Hz–3kHz
  (d) A narrow band of frequencies.
(12) An i.f. amplifier in a radio receiver is normally:
  (a) Of variable tuning
  (b) Fixed tuned
  (c) Tuned to the aerial signal frequency
  (d) Tuned to the frequency of the local oscillator.
(13) Which of the following would produce the output waveform shown in Fig. 4(a)

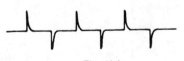

Fig. 4(a)

when a square wave was applied at the input:
  (a) An integrator
  (b) A low-pass filter
  (c) A differentiator
  (d) A d.c. restorer.
(14) The mean value of the waveform given in Fig. 4(b) is:

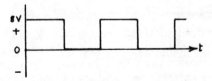

Fig. 4(b)

  (a) 0V
  (b) +0·36V
  (c) +4·0V
  (d) +8·0V
(15) The waveform shown in Fig. 4(c) is a:

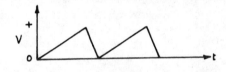

Fig. 4(c)

  (a) Sine wave
  (b) Sawtooth
  (c) Triangular wave
  (d) Parabolic wave.

(Answers on page 219.)

CHAPTER FIVE

LOGIC UNITS

Objectives

1 States typical logic voltage levels and understands the terms bit period, bit rate and data byte.
2 Considers serial and parallel data buses.
3 Identifies basic logic gates and forms truth tables.
4 Understands basic action of bistable oscillator and binary counter.

THE ELECTRONIC UNITS described in the previous chapter are mainly concerned with the processing of analogue type signals. This chapter is devoted to the characteristics of logic or digital units which are used in computers, data-processing systems, industrial control systems, teletext decoders, remote control systems and digital communication systems.

In spite of the complexity of a large scale digital system such as a digital computer there are only a few operations that have to be performed, but these are repeated very many times and at extremely high speeds. The four most common logic units or circuits used in such a system are known as the AND, OR, NOT and BISTABLE (or FLIP-FLOP).

Logic Levels

Logic units deal with digital signals which are electrical pulses having two distinct states **high voltage** and **low voltage** and are normally represented by binary 1 (high voltage) and binary 0 (low voltage). They are in fact **binary digital signals**, but since these signal levels are handled by logic circuits they are more usually called **logic 1** and **logic 0**. The logic levels pertaining to the two states are shown in Fig. 5.1. Logic 0 (low voltage or low state) is usually between 0V and 0·8V whilst logic 1 (high voltage or high state) lies somewhere between about 2·4V and 5·0V.

When the more positive of the two levels is used as logic 1, the systems is said to use **positive logic**. On the other hand, a **negative logic** system is one which makes the more positive of the two levels logic 0 and the more negative level, logic 1. Positive logic will be assumed throughout the remainder of the chapter. The precise voltage levels are not of any real significance although the voltage ranges are convenient for digital electronic circuits; the main point is that there must be sufficient voltage separation between the two states so that there is no confusion in recognising logic 0 from logic 1 by the logic circuits.

Bits and Bytes

A pulse train of logic 1s and 0s (data) is shown in Fig. 5.2. Each low or high state in the pulse train is called a **data bit** (or just **bit** for

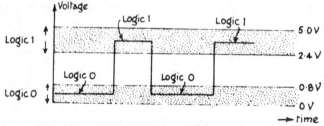

Fig. 5.1 Logic levels.

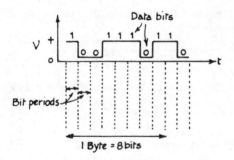

Fig. 5.2 Train of data bits.

short) and each bit is allocated a particular time interval, called a **bit period**. These bit periods are very short in duration, a fraction of a micro-second. The number of bits sent per second is called the **bit rate**. For coding purposes, bits are usually grouped and a group of 8 bits is called a **byte**.

With a digital system using eight bit bytes where each bit can be either a 1 or 0, a total of $2^8 = 256$ different codes are available. Some of the codes may be used for instruction in a computer and others may be used to represent alphabet characters or data. For example, the pattern of bits 00101011 may be used as the code for the instruction STOP in a computer programme, the code for the letter C or the code for the decimal number 43 depending upon the code used.

Data pulses can be sent in serial form, *i.e.* one following the other using a single line or conductor (**single data bus**) as in Fig. 5.3(a) or

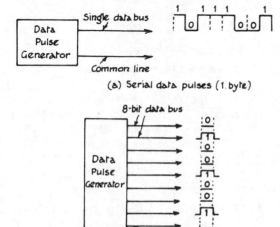

(a) Serial data pulses (1 byte)

(b) Parallel data pulses (1 byte)

Fig. 5.3 Serial and parallel data.

in parallel form using eight lines or conductors (**eight bit data bus**) as in Fig. 5.3(b).

LOGIC GATES

A logic gate is a circuit that operates on a number of input digital signals to perform a particular logical function. Logic gates are the building blocks from which many different kinds of digital systems can be constructed.

AND Gate

An AND gate has two or more inputs and a single output. The symbol for an AND gate is given in Fig. 5.4(a) where A and B are the inputs and F the output (any other letters may be used). Alternative logic circuit symbols are given in Appendix A. The output from an AND gate will assume the logic 1 state only if all the inputs are at the logic 1 state.

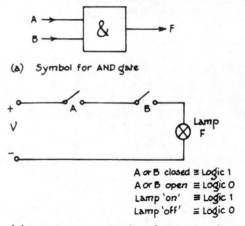

(a) Symbol for AND gate

A or B closed ≡ Logic 1
A or B open ≡ Logic 0
Lamp 'on' ≡ Logic 1
Lamp 'off' ≡ Logic 0

(b) Electrical representation of AND gate

Fig. 5.4 AND gate.

An electrical representation of an AND gate is shown in Fig. 5.4(b). The lamp will only light if switches A and B are both closed. Here, it is assumed that when the switches are open they are at logic 0 and when closed they are at logic 1. If the lamp is on the output (F) is at logic 1 but when the lamp is 'off' the output is at logic 0.

The operation may be summarised in a **truth table** which shows all the possible conditions of the switches or inputs and the resultant effect on the lamp or output, as in Fig. 5.5. As each

Inputs		Output
A	B	F
0	0	0
0	1	0
1	0	0
1	1	1

Fig. 5.5 Truth table for AND gate.

of the two inputs may be either at logic 1 or 0, there are $2^2 = 4$ possible combinations. It will be seen that a logic 1 (lamp 'on') is only obtained at the output for the condition A = 1 and B = 1, *i.e.* both switches closed.

A three input AND gate together with its truth table is shown in Fig. 5.6. With three inputs there will be $2^3 = 8$ possible combinations of the input logic conditions. Again, a logic 1 is obtained at the output only when all three inputs are at logic 1.

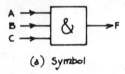

(a) Symbol

Inputs			Output
A	B	C	F
0	0	0	0
0	0	1	0
0	1	0	0
0	1	1	0
1	0	0	0
1	0	1	0
1	1	0	0
1	1	1	1

(b) Truth table

Fig. 5.6 Symbol and truth table for three input AND gate.

The idea of the AND gate may be further reinforced by considering logic waveforms applied to the inputs A and B of a two input AND gate, as illustrated in Fig. 5.7. It will be noted that a logic 1 pulse appears in the output only when waveforms A and B are simultaneously at logic 1.

OR Gate

An OR gate has two or more inputs and a single output. The symbol for a two input OR gate is given in Fig. 5.8(a). The output of an OR gate will assume the logic 1 state when either of its inputs are at logic 1.

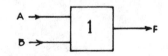

(a) Symbol for OR gate

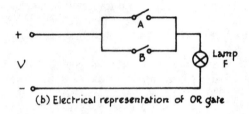

(b) Electrical representation of OR gate

Fig. 5.8 OR gate.

An electrical representation of an OR-gate is shown in Fig. 5.8(b). The lamp will light if either or both of the switches are closed (logic 1). A truth table showing the relation of the logic states between inputs and output is given in Fig. 5.9.

Inputs		Output
A	B	F
0	0	0
0	1	1
1	0	1
1	1	1

Fig. 5.9 Truth table for OR gate.

A three input OR gate together with its truth table is shown in Fig. 5.10. Note the order of setting down the logic states of the

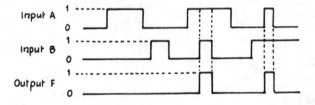

Fig. 5.7 Waveform diagram illustrating AND function.

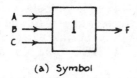

(a) Symbol

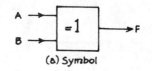

(a) Symbol

Inputs			Output
A	B	C	F
0	0	0	0
0	0	1	1
0	1	0	1
0	1	1	1
1	0	0	1
1	0	1	1
1	1	0	1
1	1	1	1

(b) Truth table

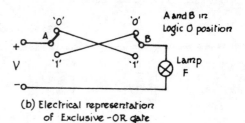

(b) Electrical representation of Exclusive-OR gate

Fig. 5.10 Symbol and truth table for three input OR gate.

inputs in the table, counting up in binary from 000 to 111 (assuming the input in the right-hand column is the least significant digit).

The action of the OR gate is further illustrated by the waveform diagram of Fig. 5.11 for a two input OR gate.

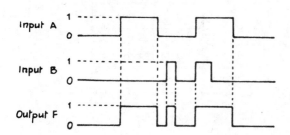

Fig. 5.11 Waveform diagram illustrating OR function.

This particular OR gate is sometimes called 'Inclusive-OR' since a logic 1 at the output includes the condition when all inputs are at the logic 1 state.

Exclusive-OR Gate

An exclusive-OR gate has two inputs and a single output. Its symbol is given in Fig. 5.12(a). The output from an exclusive-OR gate will assume the logic 1 state if one and only one input is at logic 1.

An electrical representation is given in Fig. 5.12(b). The lamp will be 'on' if either A

Inputs		Output
A	B	F
0	0	0
0	1	1
1	0	1
1	1	0

(c) Truth Table

Fig. 5.12 Exclusive-OR gate.

or B is set to logic 1, but will be 'off' when A and B are both at logic 1 (or at logic 0). This switch diagram arrangement may be used when it is desirable to, say, control a light in a room using switches placed in different locations.

The truth table is shown in Fig. 5.12(c) where it will be seen that logic 1 at the output **excludes** the condition A = B = 1.

NOT gate

A NOT gate has a single input and a single output. Its symbol is shown in Fig. 5.13(a). The output from a NOT gate will assume the logic 1 state only if its input is not at logic 1. The NOT gate is thus an inverter, producing at its output the opposite of the input. The small circle in the symbol at the output is the inversion or negation sign.

An electrical representation of a NOT gate is illustrated in Fig. 5.13(b). If the switch is open, *i.e.* A at logic 0, the relay is de-energised and the supply is fed to the motor causing it to turn. Thus the output F is at logic 1. When the switch is closed (A at logic 1), the relay is energised and the relay contacts open. The

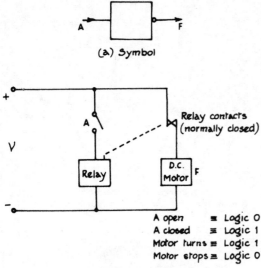

A
F
(a) Symbol
+
A
V
Relay contacts
(normally closed)
Relay
D.C.
Motor
F
-
A open ≡ Logic 0
A closed ≡ Logic 1
Motor turns ≡ Logic 1
Motor stops ≡ Logic 0
(b) Electrical representation of NOT gate

Fig. 5.13 NOT gate.

motor will stop and the output F will be at logic 0.

The truth table for the NOT gate is given in Fig. 5.14. When a logic waveform is applied at its input, see Fig. 5.15, it appears inverted at the gate output.

Input	Output
A	F
0	1
1	0

Fig. 5.14 Truth table for NOT gate.

1
Input
0
1
Output
0

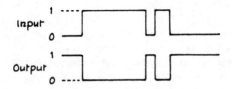

Fig. 5.15 Waveform diagram for NOT gate.

NAND Gate

The NAND gate performs the opposite of the AND logic function, thus its output is at logic 1 except for the case when all of its inputs are at logic 1. Its symbol is shown in Fig. 5.16(a) and may have two or more inputs. The NAND gate is equivalent to an AND gate followed by a NOT gate as shown in Fig. 5.16(b).

A truth table for a three input NAND gate is given in Fig. 5.16(c). If this is compared with that given for the three input AND gate in Fig. 5.6, it will be seen that the F output is inverted.

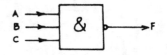

A
B
C
&
F
(a) Symbol for NAND gate
AND
NOT
A
B
C
&
F
(b) Equivalent of NAND gate

Inputs			Output
A	B	C	F
0	0	0	1
0	0	1	1
0	1	0	1
0	1	1	1
1	0	0	1
1	0	1	1
1	1	0	1
1	1	1	0

(c) Truth table

Fig. 5.16 NAND gate.

If all of the input terminals of a NAND gate are connected together it will act as a NOT gate, see Fig. 5.17.

&

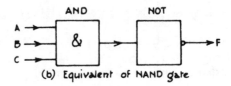

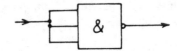

Fig. 5.17 Producing a NOT gate from a NAND gate.

NOR Gate

The NOR gate performs the opposite of the inclusive OR logic function, thus its output is at logic 0 when any of its inputs are at logic 1.

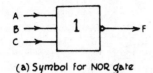

(a) Symbol for NOR gate

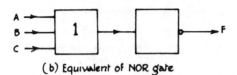

(b) Equivalent of NOR gate

Inputs			Output
A	B	C	F
0	0	0	1
0	0	1	0
0	1	0	0
0	1	1	0
1	0	0	0
1	0	1	0
1	1	0	0
1	1	1	0

(c) Truth table

Fig. 5.18 NOR gate.

Its symbol is given in Fig. 5.18(a) and may have two or more inputs. The NOR gate is equivalent to an OR gate followed by a NOT gate as illustrated in diagram (b).

A truth table for a three input NOR gate is given in Fig. 5.18(c). This should be compared with that given for the three input OR gate of Fig. 5.10 where it will be noticed that the F output is inverted.

If all of the input terminals of a NOR gate are connected together it, also, will act as a NOT gate, see Fig. 5.19.

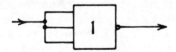

Fig. 5.19 Producing a NOT gate from a NOR gate.

Exclusive NOR Gate

An exclusive NOR gate or coincidence gate has two inputs and a single output. It performs the opposite logic function to the exclusive OR gate. Its symbol and truth table are given in Fig. 5.20. It will be noted from Fig. 5.20(b)

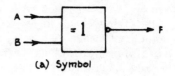

(a) Symbol

Input		Output
A	B	F
0	0	1
0	1	0
1	0	0
1	1	1

(b) Truth table

Fig. 5.20 Exclusive-NOR (coincidence) gate.

that a logic 1 is obtained at the output only when the inputs are of the same logic state, *i.e.* are coincident.

Gate Combinations

Logic gates are frequently used in combination with one another to produce complex digital logic systems and some simple examples will be considered.

(a) Control of Motor

Suppose that it is desirable to control a motor from two positions with the aid of switches B and C. Before the motor is allowed to run, however, it is important that a safety guard (covering the moving parts of the motor) is correctly positioned indicated by a third switch A, operated by the safety guard. The electrical switch diagram for the simple system may be arranged as shown in Fig. 5.21. The motor will start, *i.e.* F at logic 1 only if switch A is closed and either switches B or C, or both, are closed.

The logic gate arrangement to produce the equivalent action of the electrical switches is

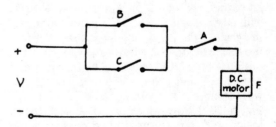

Fig. 5.21 Controlling a motor.

shown in Fig. 5.22 together with its truth table. As the table shows, a logic 1 is obtained at the output only when A is at logic 1 and either B or C or both are at logic 1. The output F may be used to allow the supply of power to the motor.

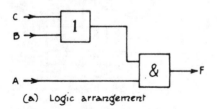

(a) Logic arrangement

Inputs			Output
A	B	C	F
0	0	0	0
0	0	1	0
0	1	0	0
0	1	1	0
1	0	0	0
1	0	1	1
1	1	0	1
1	1	1	1

(b) Truth table

Fig. 5.22 Logic system for Fig. 5.21.

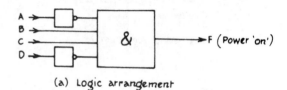

(a) Logic arrangement

	Inputs			Output
A	B	C	D	F
0	0	0	0	0
0	0	0	1	0
0	0	1	0	0
0	0	1	1	0
0	1	0	0	0
0	1	0	1	0
0	1	1	0	1
0	1	1	1	0
1	0	0	0	0
1	0	0	1	0
1	0	1	0	0
1	0	1	1	0
1	1	0	0	0
1	1	0	1	0
1	1	1	0	0
1	1	1	1	0

Correct code → (row A=0, B=1, C=1, D=0)

(b) Truth table

Fig. 5.23 Security code.

(b) Security Code

Suppose that for security reasons an item of electronic equipment is to be switched on only when the correct code is given. The code is implemented when the correct combination of four push buttons are operated in sequence. Let the four push buttons be A, B, C and D and power on be indicated by a logic 1 at the output F. If the required code is A = 0, B = 1, C = 1 and D = 0 where logic 1 means button pressed, the logic gate arrangement shown in Fig. 5.23(a) could be used to implement this logic task.

The AND gate will only produce a logic 1 at its output when all four inputs are at logic 1. This is the reason for the NOT gates connected in series with the A and D inputs. If these inputs are at logic 0 (buttons not pressed), the outputs of the NOT gates will be at logic 1 and providing B and C are at logic 1 and AND gate will operate. The truth table is given in Fig. 5.23(b) from which it will be seen that a logic 1 at F (power 'on') only occurs when the correct code is given.

As only four push buttons are used there are only $2^4 = 16$ possible combinations, which could be tried in sequence until the correct code was established. Thus the arrangement may be improved to give an alarm should the incorrect code be given.

One idea for the alarm is shown in Fig. 5.24. The alarm may be operated from the output of the NOT gate connected at the output of the four input AND gate. However, to ensure that the alarm does not operate continuously, the output of the NOT gate is connected to the alarm X via an AND gate. The other input of this AND gate is fed from the output of an OR gate which gives out a logic 1 if either inputs A or D are set at logic 1. A truth table is given in Fig. 5.25. It will be seen that the alarm does not operate if the buttons are not touched (all inputs at logic 0), the correct code is given or when either B or C are set at logic 1 with all other inputs at logic 0.

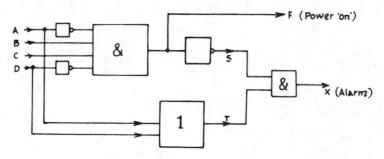

Fig. 5.24 *Modification of Fig. 5.23 to include an alarm.*

Inputs				Outputs		
A	B	C	D	S	T	X
0	0	0	0	1	0	0
0	0	0	1	1	1	1
0	0	1	0	1	0	0
0	0	1	1	1	1	1
0	1	0	0	1	0	0
0	1	0	1	1	1	1
0	1	1	0	0	0	0
0	1	1	1	1	1	1
1	0	0	0	1	1	1
1	0	0	1	1	1	1
1	0	1	0	1	1	1
1	0	1	1	1	1	1
1	1	0	0	1	1	1
1	1	0	1	1	1	1
1	1	1	0	1	1	1
1	1	1	1	1	1	1

Fig. 5.25 *Truth table for logic arrangement of Fig.5.24.*

(c) Binary Addition

Logic gates are used to perform addition and subtraction of binary numbers, as in a pocket electronic calculator. The addition of two binary numbers must comply with the rules

$$0 + 0 = 0$$
$$0 + 1 = 1$$
$$1 + 0 = 1$$
$$1 + 1 = 0 \text{ and carry } 1.$$

A logic gate arrangement for the addition of a pair of binary digits is given in Fig. 5.26(a). The exclusive-OR gate output will produce the sum digit (S) and the AND gate output will give the carry digit (C), if any. The truth table for the sum and carry digits is given in Fig. 5.26(b). The logic arrangement could be used to add the least significant digits of a pair of binary numbers. However, in general there

may be a **carry** digit from the previous column, see Fig. 5.27(a). The result of the addition of the first pair of digits of binary numbers A and B gives a sum of 0 and a carry 1 to the next column. The second pair gives a sum of 1 and no carry, the third pair a sum of 0 and a carry 1 to the next column and the fourth pair a sum of 0 and a carry 1 to the next column.

To deal with the 'carry-in' digit, the logic arrangement of Fig. 5.26(a) is duplicated as shown in Fig. 5.27(b) but with the addition of an OR gate. This logic circuit is known as a **full binary adder** and would be used to add digits from one column of a pair of binary numbers. Thus to add two binary numbers each having, say, eight digits, the arrangement in

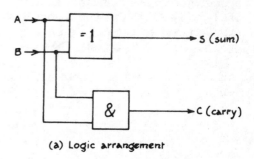

(a) Logic arrangement

Inputs		Outputs	
A	B	S	C
0	0	0	0
0	1	1	0
1	0	1	0
1	1	0	1

(b) Truth table

Fig. 5.26 *Addition of two binary digits.*

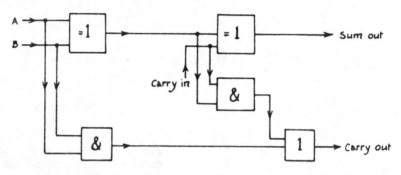

4th pair   1st pair

	0	1	0	1	← Binary number A
+	1	1	0	1	← Binary number B
1	0	0	1	0	

(a)   Need for 'carry-in' digit

(b)   Logic arrangement to deal with 'carry-in' digit

Fig. 5.27 Full binary adder.

Fig. 5.27(b) would need to be repeated eight times. However, since the same circuit arrangement is used for each pair of digits, manufacture of an electronic binary arithmetic unit is made easier.

(d) Standardisation

It is possible to produce all of the logic operations previously described by using just one type of gate. This **standardisation** enables manufacturers to concentrate on the mass production of similar circuits. The types most commonly manufactured are NAND and NOR gates.

NAND logic is illustrated in Fig. 5.28 where two input NAND gates are used. The AND function is shown in Fig. 5.28(a) and consists of a NAND gate followed by a NOT gate. Three NAND gates are required to produce the OR function, one connected as a NAND gate and the other two as NOT gates, see Fig. 5.28(b). If a further NOT gate is connected at the output of Fig. 5.28(b) the NOR function may be achieved.

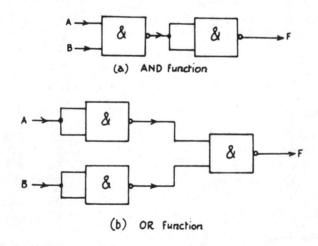

(a)   AND function

(b)   OR function

Fig. 5.28 Use of NAND gates to produce AND-function and OR-function.

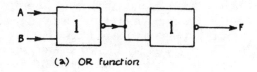

(a) OR function

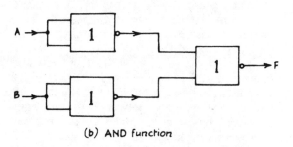

(b) AND function

Fig. 5.29 Use of NOR gates to produce AND-function and OR-function.

NOR logic is illustrated in Fig. 5.29 where two input NOR gates are used. The OR function is shown in Fig. 5.29(a) and consists of a NOR gate followed by a NOT gate. Three NOR gates are required to produce the AND function, one connected as a NOR gate and the other two as NOT gates, see Fig. 5.29(b). If a further NOT gate is connected at the output of Fig. 5.29(b), the NAND function may be achieved.

BISTABLE OSCILLATOR

A **bistable** oscillator consists of two devices, see Fig. 5.30, which are usually transistors but may be considered as switches since they operate as such. A d.c. supply is required to operate the bistable, and to cause it to change state the circuit has to be triggered with pulses. Either positive or negative-going pulses may be used.

As the name bistable implies, a bistable

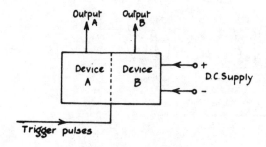

Fig. 5.30 Bistable oscillator.

oscillator has two stable states. One stable state is shown in Fig. 5.31(a) when the d.c. is applied but there are no trigger pulses present. Device A is 'on' and its output is of low voltage, whereas device B is 'off' and its output is of high voltage. Usually, the low output voltage is assumed to be 0V and the high output voltage equal to the value of the d.c. supply.

If trigger pulses are applied as in Fig. 5.31(b), the first trigger pulse to arrive (pulse 1) will cause the bistable to change its state. In the new state device A switches 'off' and device B switches 'on'. Accordingly, output A goes to a high voltage and output B to a low voltage. This is the second stable state. When the next trigger pulse arrives (pulse 2) the bistable changes state again as shown in Fig. 5.31(c). Device A comes 'on' and device B goes 'off'. Output A is then at low voltage and output B at high voltage. The circuit is now back in its starting state of Fig. 5.31(a) after the application of two trigger pulses.

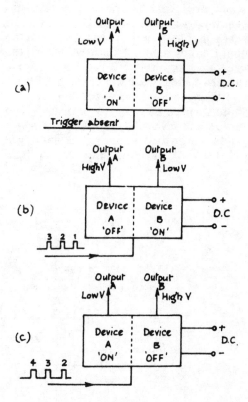

Fig. 5.31 Diagrams illustrating operation of bistable.

Each succeeding trigger pulse will cause the bistable to change its state causing outputs A and B to oscillate between the two voltage levels. When the last trigger pulse has been applied, the bistable will remain in the state corresponding to the last trigger pulse and will remain in that state until further trigger pulses are applied.

Bistable Counter

We will now consider how a string of bistables may be used as a binary counter. Suppose that a chain of four bistables are connected as in Fig. 5.32 with a lamp connected between the output of device A of each bistable and the supply line of +10V (this being the normal supply voltage to each bistable). When a device is 'off' we will assume that its output is +10V (high V) and when 'on' its output is 0V (low V). It will also be assumed that initially all the left hand devices are 'off' thus all the right hand devices will be 'on' as shown. Under these conditions, all of the lamps will be extinguished as there will be no voltage across them. The pulses to be counted (negative-going in this case) are supplied as trigger pulses to the input of bistable 1 with the output from its right hand device feeding the trigger input of bistable 2 and so on. Some form of switching circuit will be required to set the bistables to these initial conditions.

Pulse 1 will cause device A of bistable 1 to come 'on' and device B to go 'off'. Thus device A output will go to 0V and device B output will go to +10V. As a result lamp L1 will light.

When device B output changes from 0V to +10V, the output moves in a positive direction and this change in voltage is fed to bistable 2. It has no effect on bistable 2 however, since in this case negative-going trigger inputs are required to change over any bistable.

When pulse 2 arrives bistable 1 changes state causing L1 to be extinguished. This action causes device B output of bistable 1 to move in a negative direction (from +10V to 0V). The negative-going voltage step acts as a trigger pulse for bistable 2 which thus changes its state. As a result the lamp L2 lights. The change in voltage at device B output from bistable 2 has no effect on bistable 3 since the voltage moves in a positive direction.

On pulse 3, bistable 1 changes state once again causing L1 to light. Lamp L2 remains 'on' as the trigger-in to bistable 2 is in the wrong voltage direction. This action continues down the chain of bistables as shown in the table of Fig. 5.33 which gives the state of the lamps after the application of each pulse. The four bistables will count up to 15 and will return to the original state on the 16th pulse, *i.e.* all lamps extinguished. However, by adding further bistables the count can be increased almost indefinitely. The pulses to be counted may, for example, be produced by interrupting a light beam with manufactured articles passing on a conveyer belt, thus giving a count of the quantity of items produced.

It will be appreciated from the foregoing that the action of the bistable is ideally suited for counting in binary. However, reading the count in binary form is more difficult thus a

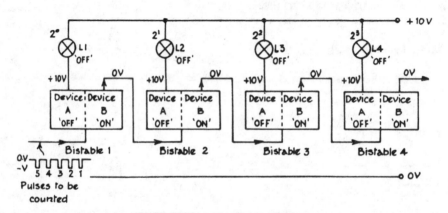

Fig. 5.32 Binary counter using bistables.

Trigger pulse No.	2^3 (8s) L4	2^2 (4s) L3	2^1 (2s) L2	2^0 (1s) L1 ← Binary digits ← Lamps
0	OFF	OFF	OFF	OFF
1	OFF	OFF	OFF	ON
2	OFF	OFF	ON	OFF
3	OFF	OFF	ON	ON
4	OFF	ON	OFF	OFF
5	OFF	ON	OFF	ON
6	OFF	ON	ON	OFF
7	OFF	ON	ON	ON
8	ON	OFF	OFF	OFF
9	ON	OFF	OFF	ON
10	ON	OFF	ON	OFF
11	ON	OFF	ON	ON
12	ON	ON	OFF	OFF
13	ON	ON	OFF	ON
14	ON	ON	ON	OFF
15	ON	ON	ON	ON
16	OFF	OFF	OFF	OFF

Fig. 5.33 Table showing state of lamps during count.

decimal count is more convenient. To achieve a decimal count, a binary-to-decimal converter (decoder) is required which will convert the binary count as indicated by the voltage state of device A of each bistable into decimal form. The 'readout' could then take the form of a seven-segment display (see Chapter Six) giving a normal decimal count.

Bistable Divider

Bistable oscillators are frequently used for **frequency division**. Consider the basic bistable block of Fig. 5.34 where in the absence of trigger pulses it is in the state shown with output A at +10V and output B at 0V. If

trigger pulses are now applied, the first trigger pulse will switch output A to 0V and output B to +10V. On the second trigger pulse output A will revert back to +10V and output B to 0V and so on with succeeding trigger pulses. The outputs at A and B will therefore switch between the two voltage levels as indicated by the waveforms as long as the trigger is applied.

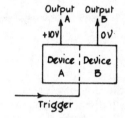

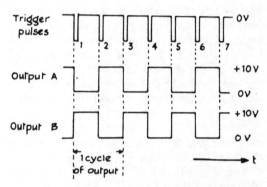

Fig. 5.34 Use of bistable as a divide by two stage.

It will be noted that for every complete cycle at the output, two trigger pulses are applied at the input, *i.e.* the bistable has divided by a factor of two.

If three bistables are connected in a chain as shown in Fig. 5.35 where the output of one

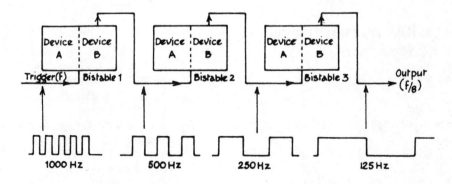

Fig. 5.35 Use of three bistables to give division of eight.

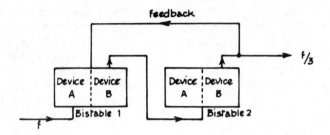

feedback

$f/3$

Bistable 1   Bistable 2

Fig. 5.36 Two bistables with feedback giving division of three.

bistable is used to trigger the following bistable, a division of eight will be obtained. Bistable 1 will divide the trigger input by two, bistable 2 will divide the output of bistable 1 by two and bistable 3 will divide the output of bistable 2 by two, giving an overall division of eight. In general a string of bistables produces a division of 2^n where n is the number of bistables, *i.e.* division in powers of 2.

If we wish to divide by an odd number, it can be accomplished with the aid of 'feedback'. The idea is shown in Fig. 5.36 where a feedback line is used between the output of bistable 2 and the input of bistable 1. Without feedback two bistables will produce a division of four, but with one overall feedback line the division is reduced from 2^2 to $2^2 - 1$, *i.e.* 3. In general, with one overall feedback line, the division is reduced from 2^n to $2^n - 1$ where n is the number of bistables.

Apart from wishing to obtain division by an odd number, we may desire to divide by an even number which is not an exact power of two, *e.g.* 10. Again this may be achieved by using an appropriate number of bistables with feedback loops.

QUESTIONS ON CHAPTER FIVE

(1) A byte normally has:
    (a) 6 bits
    (b) 8 bits
    (c) 2 bits
    (d) 7 bits.

(2) Which of the following uses positive logic:
    (a) Logic 0 = +1V, logic 1 = −1V
    (b) Logic 0 = −1V, logic 1 = −3·2V
    (c) Logic 1 = −5V, logic 0 = 0V
    (d) Logic 0 = 0V, logic 1 = +4·3V.

(3) A logic 1 output is obtained from an AND gate when:
    (a) All inputs are at logic 1
    (b) Any input is at logic 0
    (c) Any input is at logic 1
    (d) All inputs are at logic 0.

(4) Which of the following will result in a logic 1 at the output of a three input inclusive-OR gate:
    (a) 101
    (b) 000
    (c) 001
    (d) 111.

(5) Which of the following will result in a logic 0 at the output of a four input NAND gate:
    (a) 1101
    (b) 1111
    (c) 1001
    (d) 0000.

(6) The logic function of the gates shown in Fig. 5(a) is:

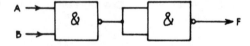

Fig. 5(a)

    (a) NAND function
    (b) AND function
    (c) NOR function
    (d) OR function.

(7) The result of adding three binary 1 digits always gives:
    (a) 0 carry 1
    (b) 1 carry 1
    (c) 2 carry 1
    (d) 3 carry 0.

(8) After the application of 14 pulses to a counter using 4 Bistables, the count will be:
    (a) 0011
    (b) 1110
    (c) 1111
    (d) 0111.

(9) The trigger input to the first stage of a five stage bistable divider has a frequency of 64kHz. The frequency of the output from the last bistable will be:
    (a) 2kHz
    (b) 12·8kHz
    (c) 16kHz
    (d) 320kHz.

(10) The logic function represented by the truth table of Fig. 5(b) is:

Inputs		Output
A	B	F
0	0	0
0	1	1
1	0	1
1	1	0

Fig. 5(b)

    (a) NAND function
    (b) Exclusive-OR function
    (c) NOR function
    (d) NOT function.

(Answers on page 219.)

CHAPTER SIX

DISPLAY UNITS

Objectives

1 States that a c.r.o. is an automatic graph drawer and describes operation of basic diagram for c.r.o.
2 Shows how a c.r.o. is used to plot voltage against time and measures amplitude and frequency of a waveform.
3 Understands the operating principle of analogue moving coil instrument and the basic ideas of digital measuring instrument.

IN ELECTRONICS IT is often necessary to be able to display information in some way and a **display unit** is used for this purpose. Common examples are cathode ray tubes used for displaying alphanumerical and graphical information with a computer, waveforms in a cathode ray oscilloscope and picture or text information in a television receiver. In addition, various meter instruments are commonly used for indicating the magnitude of voltage and currents encountered in electronic circuits.

THE OSCILLOSCOPE CATHODE RAY TUBE

A cathode ray oscilloscope (c.r.o.) is a device used mainly for displaying voltage or current waveforms. It is an automatic graph drawer, plotting voltage or current against time. It may be used to plot any electrical quantity against another but the description will be restricted to plotting a voltage against time.

In the cathode ray tube (c.r.t.) a beam of electrons is produced in the electron gun, see Fig. 6.1. This beam of very fast moving electrons bombards the phosphor screen. When the electrons strike the screen they cause it to glow thereby indicating the position of the beam. The beam may be deflected so that the spot of light takes up a position anywhere on the screen by using either an electric or magnetic field. In cathode ray oscilloscopes the deflection is always by means of an electric field. Magnetic deflection, however, is used in all cathode ray tubes for television and computer displays.

With electric field or electrostatic deflection, the deflection is carried out with two sets

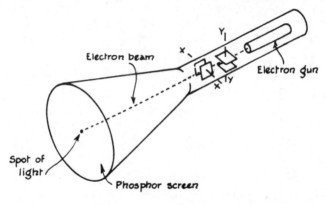

Fig. 6.1 Basic diagram of cathode ray tube.

of plates at right angles to each other as shown. The first pair deflect the beam in a vertical direction and are called the Y deflecting plates. The second pair deflect the beam horizontally and are known as the X deflecting plates. If an alternating voltage is applied to the Y plates, the beam and spot of light will move up and down in proportion to the voltage. If, at the same time, the beam can be made to move at a uniform rate horizontally it will draw out a graph of voltage against time. This process must be repeated rapidly several times per second to produce a steady display.

The X-Deflection

The X-deflection is produced by feeding to the X-plates a sawtooth waveform at a frequency that is equal to or a sub-multiple, *i.e.* ½, ⅓, ¼, *etc* of the frequency of the voltage fed to the Y-plates. The sawtooth waveform is obtained from an oscillator in the c.r.o. and is usually referred to as the **timebase** oscillator, see Fig. 6.2.

Between A and C of the sawtooth timebase waveform, the voltage changes at a constant rate which causes the spot of light to move at a constant rate from the left hand side of the screen to the right hand side. This period of the sawtooth is called the **scan**. When point C is reached, the voltage drops rapidly to its original value at D and the electron beam rapidly returns to the left hand side of the screen to await the next scan. The period from

C to D is called the **flyback**. The flyback trace is not normally visible as it is blanked out by a suitable blanking pulse applied to the electron gun. The next scan does not commence immediately at the end of the flyback period but after an interval D to E where the timebase waveform is at a steady voltage level. During this interval blanking is also applied to prevent the appearance of a bright spot of light at the left hand side of the screen.

The effect on the screen, and thus to an observer, of this repetitive timebase action is to produce a continuous movement of the spot of light from left to right across the screen. If the frequency of the timebase waveform is high enough, say, 25Hz, due to 'persistence of vision' the observer sees a steady trace of light as shown.

Displaying One Cycle of a Sine Wave

All modern oscilloscopes use an arrangement consisting of a trigger circuit and a timebase. The signal to be examined is applied to the Y-input of the c.r.o. and from this signal a trigger pulse is produced which is used to initiate the commencement of the timebase scan (this is called 'triggered timebase operation'). By adjusting a **trigger level** control on the c.r.o., the start of the timebase scan can be made coincident with any desired part of the waveform under examination. The idea is shown in Fig. 6.3 where the timebase (waveform (c)) is triggered so as to commence its

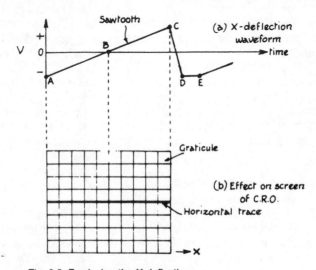

Fig. 6.2 Producing the X-deflection.

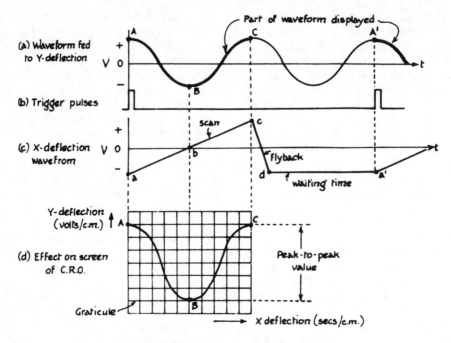

Fig. 6.3 Displaying one cycle of a sine wave.

scan at point A on the waveform fed to the Y-input, Fig. 6.3(a). During the scan period abc, the portion ABC of the Y-input signal will be traced out on the screen, see Fig. 6.3(d). As the trigger circuit produces each trigger pulse at the same part of the input waveform, see Fig. 6.3(b), the timebase will not commence its next scan until point A' is reached. In this way, the same part of the input waveform is traced out on the screen resulting in a steady display.

With triggered timebase operation, the repetition rate of the timebase is made a sub-multiple of the Y-input waveform by varying the duration of the period d to a'. This is the waiting period for the beam at the left hand side of the screen.

Effect of Decreasing Timebase Speed

The effect of reducing the timebase speed is shown in Fig. 6.4. Here the timebase speed is made one third of the frequency of the Y-input signal as opposed to one half for Fig. 6.3. During the timebase scan period abc, two cycles of the Y-input signal are displayed on

the screen of the c.r.o. Here the waiting time is set so that the next part of the Y-input signal to be displayed will commence at point A.

To facilitate measurement of voltage and time a **graticule** (see Figs. 6.3 and 6.4) is fitted to the screen of the c.r.o. This consists of a piece of transparent plastic, engraved or marked in cm squares. Additional markings are often provided to give smaller divisions, *e.g.* one-fifth of a cm. To make the engraving stand out, the engraving is illuminated from the edge by one or more bulbs. The Y-deflection is calibrated in volts/cm and is adjustable to suit the magnitude of the signal to be measured from, say, 50V/cm to about 5mV/cm. The X-deflection is calibrated in secs/cm and is normally adjustable from about 1sec/cm to 1μs/cm by the timebase speed control.

Measuring a Waveform

A c.r.o. enables the shape, amplitude and frequency of a waveform to be examined or measured. Two examples are considered in Fig. 6.5. Assume that in Fig. 6.5(a), the

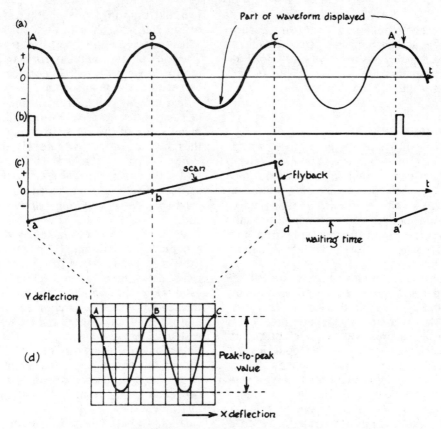

Fig. 6.4 *Effect of reducing timebase speed.*

Y-deflection is set to give a **deflection sensitivity** of 10V/cm and the X-deflection is adjusted to give a **deflection sensitivity** of 1ms/cm. Since the peak-to-peak value of the sine wave occupies four squares, its peak-to-peak value is $4 \times 10V = 40V$.

The frequency of the waveform may be determined by measuring the periodic time (time for one cycle) of the waveform. In this case, the time for one cycle corresponds to four squares, thus the periodic time = $4 \times 1ms = 4ms$. Therefore the frequency = 1/periodic time = $10^3/4Hz = 250Hz$.

The peak-to-peak amplitude of the square wave shown in Fig. 6.5(b) assuming a Y-deflection sensitivity of 100mV/cm will be 400mV. Its frequency will be, for an X-deflection sensitivity of 10μs/cm, $10^6/30Hz = 33.33kHz$.

A block diagram for a c.r.o. is given in **Standard Systems**, Chapter Seven.

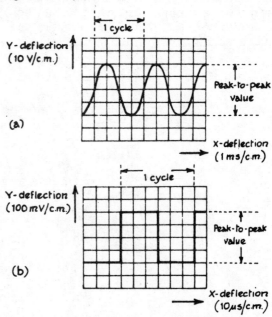

Fig. 6.5 *Measuring the amplitude and frequency of a waveform.*

METERS

The most common instruments for measuring voltages and currents in electronic circuits are the voltmeter and the ammeter. Both of these instruments are available with either analogue or digital type displays.

Analogue Instruments

Analogue instruments are those which usually incorporate a pointer that moves over a scale and can, within limits, assume any reading, *i.e.* they are capable of continuous indication of voltage or current magnitude. There are a number of instruments that fall into this category but the most important for electronic servicing is the moving coil meter, see Fig. 6.6.

The moving coil meter consists of a coil of fine copper wire mounted on an aluminium former and pivoted at either end so that it is free to turn in a strong magnetic field. The magnetic field is provided by a small powerful permanent magnet with shaped pole pieces. The magnetic circuit is completed by a cylinder of soft iron so that only a narrow gap is left in which the two sides of the coil swing. This results in an intense magnetic field of radial direction and uniform strength. When a direct current is passed through the coil it takes up a position depending upon the magnitude of the current. The current to be measured is supplied to the moving coil via

two control springs, one mounted at either end of the coil. Attached to the coil is a pointer which moves over the scale of the instrument. The moving coil meter is an example of the motor principle which is considered in the Science Background section.

In a moving coil instrument the movement of the pointer is directly proportional to the mean value of the current flowing in the coil thus the scale of the instrument is a linear one. When a current is applied, the force produced moves the coil against the action of the control springs. These springs return the pointer to zero when current no longer flows through the coil.

With this type of analogue display the accuracy of measurement depends not only on the design accuracy (*e.g.* 1% from one tenth of full scale to full scale on d.c.) but also on the estimation of the pointer position relative to the scale. To reduce reading errors, a knife-edge pointer may be used and the scale is fitted with a mirror. By aligning the pointer with its reflection in the mirror, the scale is always viewed at right angles. The current necessary to produce full scale reading or **full scale deflection** depends upon the design of the instrument, *e.g.* 20µA. To enable larger currents to be measured a 'shunt' resistor is placed in parallel with the moving coil. Although the moving coil instrument is essentially an ammeter, it may also be used to measure voltage by connecting a resistance

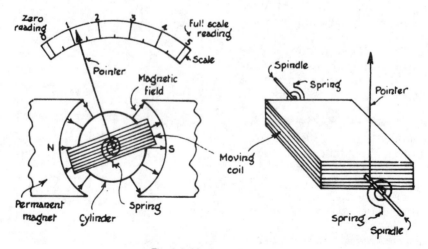

Fig. 6.6 Moving coil ammeter.

'multiplier' in series with the moving coil. To measure different ranges of voltage, different values of multiplier resistance are used. The instrument may be used as an ohmmeter for measuring circuit resistance with the aid of an internal battery. General symbols for the ammeter, voltmeter and ohmmeter are shown in Fig. 6.7. For electronic servicing work the functions of current, voltage and resistance measurement are combined in a 'universal' instrument such as the AVOMETER.

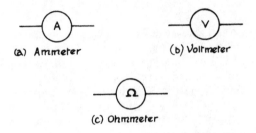

(a) Ammeter　　　(b) Voltmeter

(c) Ohmmeter

Fig. 6.7 General meter symbols.

The disadvantage of the basic moving coil instrument is that it will only operate directly on d.c. since it is a mean or average reading instrument. However, by using a rectifier unit (full wave) to convert a.c. into d.c., the instrument may also be used to measure alternating currents and voltages, see Fig. 6.8.

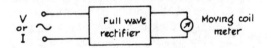

Fig. 6.8 Measuring A.C. with the moving coil instrument.

Although the instrument reads the **mean value** of the rectified a.c. it is normally calibrated to indicate the 'r.m.s. value'. The r.m.s. calibration only holds good when measuring sine waves. A.C. measurement facilities are incorporated into universal instruments which are accurate up to about 20kHz in a typical instrument. Beyond this frequency, stray capacitance produces a deterioration in performance.

Digital Instruments

Digital instruments produce readings of current, voltage or resistance in discrete steps. They give a **read-out** in direct form which is free from human reading error. These instruments have no moving parts and are usually smaller and cheaper than analogue counterparts.

In a digital instrument, the basic element of the digital read-out is the **seven segment display**, see Fig. 6.9(a). The seven segments (a–g) may be constructed using 28 light emitting diodes (l.e.ds) with four diodes to each segment as in Fig. 6.9(b). These diodes are caused to emit light (usually red or green) in groups of four when suitable voltages are applied to them.

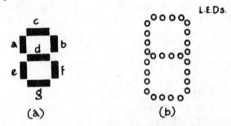

(a)　　　(b)

Fig. 6.9 LED seven segment display.

An alternative to the l.e.d. display is one which uses a **liquid crystal**. The basic idea of one form of liquid crystal display is shown in Fig. 6.10(a) which illustrates the construction of a seven segment element. Here a liquid crystal material is sandwiched between two

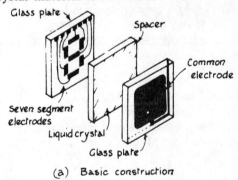

(a) Basic construction

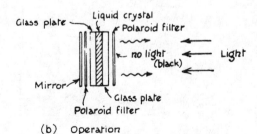

(b) Operation

Fig. 6.10 Liquid crystal seven segment display.

sheets of glass which have conductive coatings on their inside. One glass plate has the seven segment display etched on it and the other plate has a common electrode etched on it. These very thin conductive coatings (tin oxide) will allow the transmission of light through them.

To produce a particular display digit, a voltage is applied between the appropriate segments and the common electrode. This causes a change in the optical properties of the liquid crystal which appears as the display. The operation is illustrated in Fig. 6.10(b) with the addition of two polaroid filters disposed at right angles to one another and a mirror. Without any voltage applied between the electrodes, external light falling on the device is polarised by the first filter and is twisted through 90° by the liquid crystal so that it will pass through the second filter. After reflection by the mirror the light returns by the same path. In this state the cell is 'clear'. When a voltage is applied between any of the segments and the common electrode the optical properties of the liquid crystal changes in those areas. The liquid crystal then no longer produces the 90° twisting of the polarised light as it enters, thus the light will not pass through the second polaroid filter. Hence the parts of the display where the electric field is applied appears black.

The shape of the ten digits that can be produced with a seven segment readout is shown in Fig. 6.11.

Idea of Digital Voltmeter

In a digital voltmeter giving a read-out correct to four significant figures, there will be one seven segment device for each significant

Fig. 6.11 Form of numerals produced with seven segment read out.

figure and also a decimal point associated with each figure. To enable readings to be registered from ·0001 to 999·9, four seven segment devices and four decimal points would be required. The decimal point may be formed by a single light emitting diode in a l.e.d. display or by a small area electrode in a liquid crystal display.

The basic idea of one form of digital voltmeter is shown in Fig. 6.12 with associated waveforms given in Fig. 6.13. The voltage to be measured (d.c.) is fed to a comparator where it is compared with a rising ramp supplied from a ramp generator. The comparator generates a pulse output which is terminated as soon as the ramp voltage rises above the input voltage. The pulse output of the comparator is then fed to a two input AND gate as one of the inputs. The other input comes from a clock oscillator which supplies 10kHz pulses. During the period of the gating pulse therefore, 10kHz pulses will appear at the output of the AND gate. These pulses are then fed to a counter where they are counted, the count being proportional to the magnitude of the voltage to be measured.

The output of the counter (in binary form) is

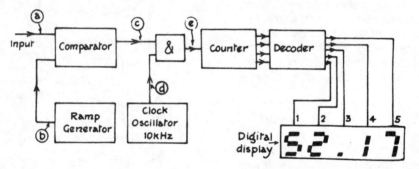

Fig. 6.12 Basic idea of digital voltmeter.

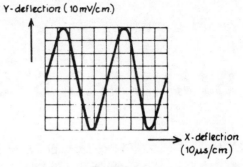

Fig. 6(a)

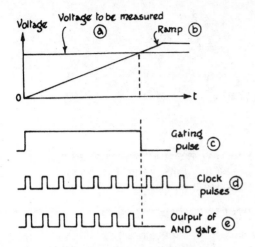

Fig. 6.13 Waveform associated with Fig.6.11.

then decoded using seven segment decoders which provide outputs to operate the seven segment display digits. For simplicity only four output lines have been shown (1, 2, 4 and 5) to operate the four digits, whereas in practice there will be seven lines for each seven segment device (1 line for each segment). The decoder must also give out a signal to operate the decimal point (this could be changed when operating the voltage range switch). A reset switch will be required to reset the counter and ramp generator. This is normally operated automatically as the instrument usually provides a new reading every ten seconds. To prevent the display from changing during counting, a latch is required to hold the final count.

QUESTIONS ON CHAPTER SIX

(1) Which of the following are used to produce horizontal deflection in a c.r.o.:
(a) X-plates
(b) Y-plates
(c) Z-plates
(d) Deflector coils.

(2) The X-deflection waveform in a c.r.o. is normally a:
(a) Sine wave
(b) Sawtooth
(c) Square wave
(d) Parabolic.

(3) The peak value of the waveform shown in Fig. 6(a) is:
(a) 7·07mV
(b) 10mV
(c) 40mV
(d) 80mV.

(4) The frequency of the waveform shown in Fig. 6(a) is:
(a) 10kHz
(b) 20kHz
(c) 50kHz
(d) 50MHz.

(5) A moving coil instrument normally has:
(a) A digital display
(b) A liquid crystal display
(c) A logarithmic scale
(d) A linear scale.

(6) Which of the following is necessary to enable a.c. to be read with a basic moving coil instrument:
(a) Centre reading scale
(b) Low-pass filter
(c) Reversing switch
(d) Rectifier.

(7) One type of seven segment display is normally constructed using:
(a) 4 LEDs
(b) 28 LEDs
(c) 7 LEDs
(d) 2 LEDs.

(8) In a liquid crystal display a voltage is applied between the electrodes to:
(a) Alter its optical properties
(b) Switch-off the display
(c) Produce red light
(d) Produce green light.

(Answers on page 219.)

CHAPTER SEVEN

STANDARD SYSTEMS

Objectives
1 Shows how basic electronic units may be connected together to form standard systems.
2 Name the blocks and state the function of the individual units within the system.
3 Identifies the voltage or waveforms present at various points within the system.

IT WILL BE shown in this chapter how the electronic units previously described can be connected to build-up complete electronic systems. A knowledge of the function, application and signals associated with each system given is an important requirement of your course.

1. POWER SUPPLY

A block diagram of a stabilised power supply together with waveforms to illustrate the magnitude of voltage at the output of each unit is given in Fig. 7.1. The power supply is assumed to provide a stabilised d.c. output voltage of 15V which should be suitable for supplying different types of electronic equipment utilising solid state electronics.

The mains supply of 240V r.m.s. is fed to block (A) where it is stepped-down by a transformer. Now the peak value of the main

supply is approximately 340V, thus if a step-down ratio of 17:1 is used the output of the transformer unit will be 20V peak. This is fed to block (B) which rectifies the a.c. input using a full wave rectifier to provide 100Hz half-sine waves at its output of approximately 20V peak (there may be some small voltage drop in the rectifier unit but this will be ignored). To obtain a smooth d.c. the output of block (B) is fed to a smoothing filter in block (C). The d.c. output of this block will be about 20V, *i.e.* approximately equal to the peak value of the output from the rectifier unit. Although the output from the filter is quite smooth there may be fluctuations due to variations in the current demanded by the equipment to be fed, or variations in the mains supply voltage. These fluctuations are dealt with by the **stabiliser** or **regulator** of block (D) to give a constant d.c. output. There will be some voltage drop in the stabiliser, say, 5V

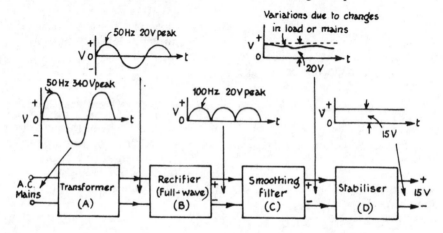

Fig. 7.1 *Block diagram of stabilised low voltage supply.*

thus a stabilised d.c. output of 15V will be obtained.

The principle of operation is exactly the same when the required d.c. output from block (D) is, say, 450V. In these circumstances, a step-up transformer would be used in block (A) and the voltage levels at the output of each block would increase.

Some form of protection is required in a power supply unit in case a fault develops in the power unit itself or the equipment being fed from it, causing excessive current to flow. The simplest from of protection is the fuse which is often used in elementary type power supplies. The correct size and type of fuse must be fitted. When a voltage regulator is used to provide a stabilised supply there is usually additional protection, since fuses are not very satisfactory with transistors which are likely to be damaged before the fuse clears the circuit. Sometimes electronic trip circuits are employed which switch-off the output voltage if an overload occurs. These have now been superseded by some form of current limit or constant current circuit. On drawing too great a current from the stabiliser the output voltage drops, so preventing the current from increasing.

Considerable care should be exercised when working on power supply units; the presence of mains supply and other possibly higher potentials are a dangerous hazard, see Chapter Eight.

2. A.M. TRANSMITTER

A block diagram of a simple a.m. transmitter is given in Fig. 7.2 together with waveforms to illustrate the operation.

The first requirement is a power supply (E) which provides a smooth d.c. output voltage to the various blocks of the transmitter. In practice there may be more than one power supply to supply different voltages to various parts of the transmitter. If valves are used in the transmitter, then these will require a heater supply which may be obtained from the power supply unit. In portable transmitters, batteries may be used to replace the mains fed power supply unit.

The r.f. oscillator of block (C) generates the **carrier** which is a sine wave of constant amplitude at the required carrier frequency, say, 1MHz. The unmodulated carrier from block (C) is fed to block (B) where it is amplitude modulated by the audio signal from

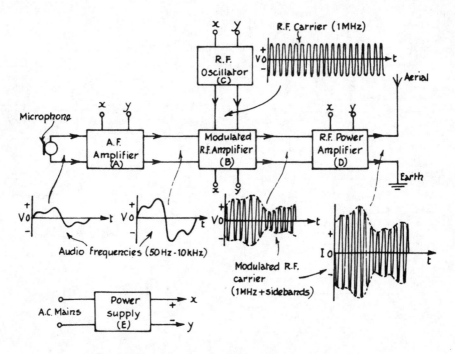

Fig. 7.2 Block diagram of simple A.M. sound transmitter.

block (A). A flat amplifier is used for block (A) providing voltage amplification of the small signal voltage delivered by the microphone. The response of this amplifier will be flat over the audio frequency signal range which has been assumed from 50Hz to 10kHz.

Block (B) is a tuned r.f. amplifier (sometimes referred to as the 'modulator') with its centre frequency tuned to the carrier (1MHz). It must have sufficient bandwidth to pass on to block (D) the side frequencies produced by the modulation process. Since the power output of the modulator may not be adequate, an r.f. power amplifier, block (D), is used to develop the required signal power to feed the aerial system. Block (D) is also a tuned r.f. amplifier and must amplify the carrier and side frequency components which are present in the modulated carrier waveform.

Essentially, in a television transmitter where the vision signals are amplitude modulated on to a carrier, the microphone will be replaced by the television camera and block (A) will be a video amplifier having a flat response from 0Hz to 5·5MHz. The frequency of the carrier input to block (B) will be much higher (in the u.h.f. band) and the bandwidths

of blocks (B) and (D) would have to be greater to accommodate the larger number of side frequencies produced by the modulator when receiving a video signal input.

3. A.M. RECEIVER

A block diagram of a superheterodyne receiver ('superhet' for short) suitable for the reception of a.m. signals, such as those from the a.m. transmitter of the previous section, is given in Fig. 7.3.

The basic idea of a superhet receiver is to change the frequency of the signal being received into a lower fixed frequency called the intermediate frequency (i.f.). As the frequency of the i.f. is lower than the signal received, it is easier to carry out amplification and response shaping. The receiver is designed so that the frequency of the i.f. is the same irrespective of the frequency of the received signal. This makes it easier to tune to different broadcast stations as the amplification and response shaping for selectivity can be carried out at the fixed intermediate frequency.

In a superhet receiver the process of

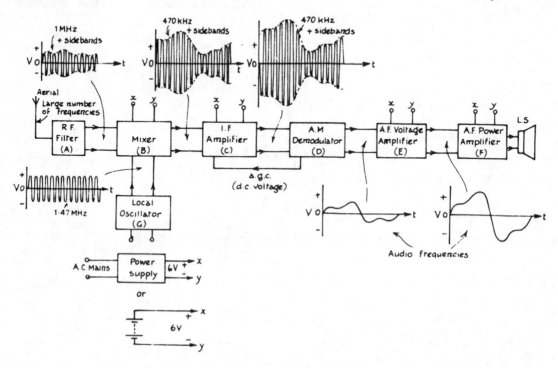

Fig. 7.3 Block diagram of A.M. superheterodyne receiver.

changing the frequency is known as the **heterodyne** method and is carried out by the mixer block (B) and the local oscillator block (G). These two blocks are commonly referred to as the **frequency changer** stage. The basic principle of the mixer was considered in Chapter Four. It will be remembered that if two frequencies are mixed together, two new frequencies are obtained, one being the sum of the two frequencies and the other the difference between the two frequencies. Assume that the incoming carrier frequency is f_1 and that of the local oscillator is f_2. When these are mixed in the mixer stage we obtain at its output $f_1 + f_2$ and $f_1 - f_2$. It is the difference frequency $f_1 - f_2$ which is used as the intermediate frequency of the receiver. If the local oscillator frequency is higher than the signal being received which is usually the case, the difference frequency will be $f_2 - f_1$, but this does not alter the basic principle.

Returning now to the block diagram the signal voltage induced into the aerial (usually a ferrite rode aerial) is fed to block (A) called the r.f. filter or pre-selector stage. The purpose of this stage is to select or pick out the wanted signal from the large number of signals that are induced into the aerial. This stage must therefore possess **selectivity** and a **band-pass** filter would be used for this purpose. The tuning of the r.f. filter must be variable so that different stations may be tuned in. The output of the r.f. filter is then fed to the mixer (B) which also receives another input from the local oscillator (G), a constant amplitude sine wave oscillation. In the mixer, the two inputs are mixed together and the difference frequency selected at the output of the mixer is fed to block (C). Assuming a carrier frequency of 1MHz and a local oscillator frequency setting of 1·47MHz, the difference frequency will be $1·47 - 1·0\text{MHz} = 470\text{kHz}$. This will not be the only difference frequency produced as the side frequencies of the received signal will mix with the local oscillator frequency to create side frequencies centred around the intermediate frequency, *i.e.* the complete received signal is frequency translated to a new band of frequencies centred on the i.f. In block (C) the i.f. and its sidebands are amplified using a selective amplifier with its centre frequency lying at 470kHz. Most of the amplification of the

receiver is provided by the i.f. amplifier which is also responsible for most of the selectivity of the receiver.

The amplified output of block (C) is then fed to the a.m. demodulator of block (D). Here the audio frequencies are extracted from the amplitude modulated i.f. After voltage amplification in block (E) the audio signals are applied to the power amplifier in block (F) which drives the loudspeaker. Blocks (E) and (F) are 'flat' amplifiers with a bandwidth adequate for the required audio range. The a.f. power delivered to the loudspeaker will be in the range of 250mW to, say, 2W depending upon the type of receiver.

In order to change from one station to another both the tuning of the r.f. filter and the local oscillator must be varied such that the i.f. remains the same. In a.m. sound broadcast receivers the frequency of the i.f. is normally in the range of 450kHz to 470kHz. The actual frequency is not critical but it must remain constant with tuning and the waveband in use.

The r.f. filter is necessary because there are two incoming signal frequencies that will produce the intermediate frequency; this is more easily seen by taking typical figures. Suppose that the receiver i.f. is 470kHz and that the oscillator is set to 1500kHz. One incoming signal frequency that will produce the i.f. is $(1500 - 470)\text{kHz} = 1030\text{kHz}$, *i.e.* 1030kHz mixed with 1500kHz will produce a difference frequency of 470kHz. This is the signal frequency that is normally required and the r.f. filter would be tuned to this frequency. Another signal frequency that will produce the i.f. is $(1500 + 470)\text{kHz} = 1970\text{kHz}$, *i.e.* 1500kHz and 1970kHz mixed together will produce the i.f. of 470kHz. This is the unwanted frequency (sometimes called the **image** frequency) and the r.f. filter must be selective enough to cut out any station on this frequency. The frequency difference between the wanted and unwanted stations is twice the i.f. hence the selectivity of the r.f. filter does not need to be very great.

Since the design of the amplifiers used in the receiver, *e.g.* in blocks (B), (C), (E) and (F) is such that the output signal is proportional to the input signal, large changes in volume may occur when tuning from one station to another due to the differing signal voltage amplitudes induced into the aerial. A local station transmitter will produce a larger voltage in the receiving aerial than a distant station transmitter. Thus, as the receiver is tuned from a distant station to a local one the volume would increase which may cause overloading of the receiver and distortion in the output.

To overcome the effects of varying volume a system called **automatic gain control** (a.g.c.) is used in modern receivers. Ideally this works by keeping the average value of the i.f. carrier fed to the demodulator constant and independent of the magnitude of the signal induced in the aerial. Essentially the a.g.c. circuit which may be part of the demodulator (as in Fig. 7.3) or separate from it measures the average value of the i.f. carrier and produces a d.c. voltage proportional to the average value. This d.c. voltage (called the a.g.c. voltage) is fed to one or more of the i.f. stages to automatically vary the gain or amplification of those stages. Thus when a large signal is received at the demodulator a large a.g.c. voltage is developed which reduces the gain of the i.f. amplifier. This in turn reduces the signal voltage delivered to the demodulator. A state of equilibrium is reached where the signal voltage fed to the demodulator is slightly greater than with a weak signal but the variations are considerably reduced. On the other hand when tuning from a local station to a more distant one, the amplitude of the i.f. signal reaching the demodulator is reduced. This results in a smaller a.g.c. voltage being

developed which causes the gain of the i.f. amplifier to increase thereby allowing a larger signal voltage to arrive at the demodulator and thus tending to maintain a fairly constant volume. The amount by which the signal variations can be reduced depends upon the a.g.c. arrangement but it can be made very effective. Some kind of a.g.c. system is used in all a.m. receivers.

The d.c. supply voltages required by the various stages may be derived from a mains power supply unit or from batteries as shown.

4. F.M. TRANSMITTER

A block diagram of a simple f.m. transmitter intended for sound transmission is given in Fig. 7.4.

The output from the microphone is amplified in the audio frequency amplifier A which is a 'flat' amplifier covering the audio frequency range of, say, 30Hz to 15kHz. In block B the amplified audio signal from A is used to frequency modulate a radio frequency carrier which is generated by the oscillator (LC type) of block B. The output from this stage is thus an r.f. carrier of constant amplitude but whose frequency varies in accordance with the amplitude of the audio signal. For f.m. sound radio transmission, a carrier of about 100MHz is used with a frequency variation (deviation) of ±75kHz. The signal is then fed to the r.f. power

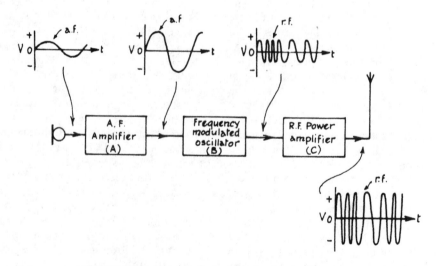

Fig. 7.4 Block diagram of simple audio F.M. transmitter.

amplifier of block C which raises the power of the modulated carrier to a suitable level before being fed to the transmitting aerial. The r.f. power amplifier is a tuned amplifier but it must have sufficient bandwidth to amplify both the carrier and its sidebands. D.C. supplies will be required to each stage and these may be obtained from a mains power supply or from batteries.

In practice a more involved arrangement is necessary. As it is most important that the centre frequency of the modulated carrier is very stable, it is usual to control the centre frequency using an **automatic frequency control loop** stabilised by the output of a crystal oscillator. Also since the crystal oscillator works at low frequency it may be necessary to include several **frequency multiplier** stages between blocks B and C when the frequency of the radiated carrier is high, *e.g.* 600MHz as with television f.m. sound.

5. F.M. RECEIVER

An f.m. receiver for use with f.m. broadcast transmissions is given in block diagram form in Fig. 7.5. This uses the **superhet** principle and is thus similar in operation to the a.m. receiver. The main differences lie in the type of demodulator used and the carrier and intermediate frequencies. To demodulate f.m. signals an f.m. demodulator must be used, block (D). The incoming aerial signal will have a frequency lying in the range of 87·5MHz to 100MHz which is the band reserved for v.h.f. f.m. broadcasts. A higher intermediate frequency is used in an f.m. receiver of this type due to the much higher transmission frequencies employed and 10·7MHz is the usual i.f. for such receivers.

With an f.m. receiver an r.f. amplifier is invariably used (block (A)) to amplify the selected station to improve the signal-to-noise ratio. At frequencies up to about 5MHz, the

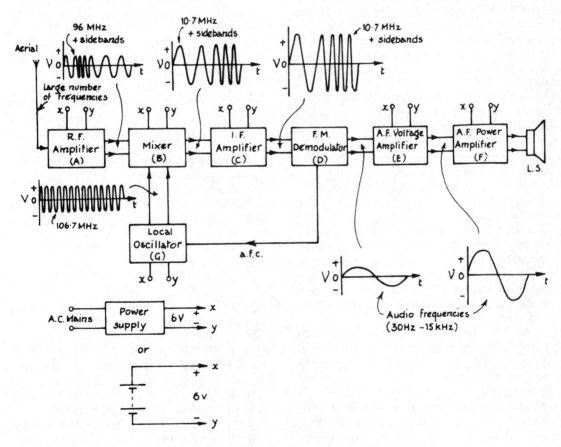

Fig. 7.5 Block diagram of F.M. superheterodyne receiver.

noise induced into the aerial is larger in amplitude than the noise generated by the receiver. Thus in a LW/MW receiver an r.f. amplifier would amplify the aerial noise together with the signal producing little if any improvement in signal-to-noise ratio. At higher frequencies the aerial noise decreases and the noise generated by the mixer stage becomes more predominant. Thus in a receiver designed for use at high frequencies as with an f.m. sound receiver, the use of an r.f. amplifier will improve the signal-to-noise ratio. Apart from this advantage, the r.f. stage also assists in isolating the oscillator from the aerial which prevents radiation from the oscillator via the aerial. Block (A) is a selective amplifier and must have sufficient bandwidth to amplify the carrier and its sidebands. In some receivers the input circuit of the r.f. amplifier is tuned to a fixed frequency but the bandwidth is made broad to cover all of the f.m. broadcast stations. In better quality receivers the input and output tuning of the r.f. stage is made variable. This provides better selectivity which assists in removing the effects of the unwanted **image** frequency discussed in the a.m. receiver section.

The local oscillator (G) develops a continuous sine wave oscillation of constant amplitude at a frequency which is usually higher than the incoming signal frequency by an amount equal to the required i.f. The mixer (B) operates in the same way as for the a.m. receiver by mixing the signal and oscillator inputs to produce the required difference frequency of 10·7MHz which is the i.f. of the receiver. The output of the mixer is fed to the i.f. amplifier (C) which is a selective amplifier tuned to 10·7MHz. Its bandwidth, however, is greater than in an a.m. receiver to deal with the larger number of side frequencies present in the f.m. signal; a bandwidth of 200–250kHz is fairly typical.

The f.m. demodulator extracts the audio signal information from the f.m. i.f. carrier input and its design is such that it is immune to amplitude variations of the i.f. carrier. If the demodulator is of the type which is not immune to amplitude variations, an amplitude limiter is placed before the demodulator which prevents any variation in output with amplitude of the carrier. Because an f.m. receiver is made insensitive to amplitude variations, a.g.c. is not normally required.

If a receiver is not correctly tuned the output signal will be distorted. With an a.m. receiver this is because the sidebands are not being received at their correct amplitude due to partial removal by the selective amplifiers of the receiver. In an f.m. receiver it is due to the demodulator not working on the correct part of its characteristic. To ensure correct tuning, **automatic frequency control** (a.f.c.) is sometimes used, particularly in f.m. and television receivers. The basic idea is to keep the i.f. produced by the mixer stage at a constant frequency regardless of any small mistuning by the user or frequency drift in the local oscillator, thereby ensuring that the demodulator operates on the correct part of its characteristic. A circuit is required which will sense changes in the i.f. and the demodulator may be used for this purpose. Any change in the i.f. produces a d.c. voltage output from the demodulator. This voltage is fed to the oscillator via a suitable circuit where it is used to correct the oscillator frequency so that the i.f. produced by the mixer is of the correct frequency or very nearly so. Sometimes a switch is fitted so that the a.f.c. may be switched out of circuit. The receiver is then tuned in approximately by the user with the a.f.c. 'off'. If the a.f.c. is switched 'on' the a.f.c. system will tune the receiver accurately and compensate for any subsequent drift in the local oscillator frequency.

The d.c. supply necessary to operate the various stages of the receiver may be obtained from a mains fed power unit or alternatively from a battery source as illustrated.

6. AUDIO TAPE RECORDER

In an audio tape recorder the signal is recorded on to a special magnetically coated tape in the form of a variation of magnetism. This magnetic tape is used as a means of permanently storing the signal thereby allowing the signal to be replayed whenever desired, over and over again. A basic arrangement for an audio tape recorder is illustrated in Fig. 7.6 shown in the **record** mode.

The audio signal to be recorded which may originate from a radio receiver, record player or microphone is fed to block (A) where it is

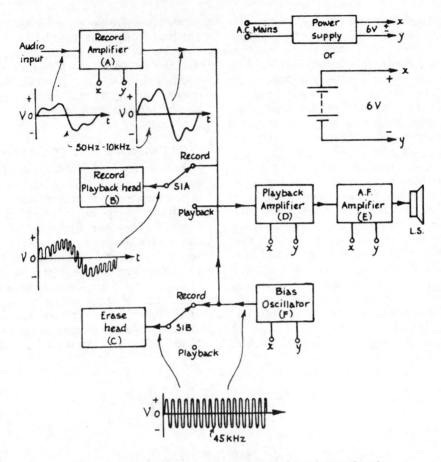

Fig. 7.6 Block schematic of audio tape recorder shown in record mode.

amplified. This amplifier is essentially a 'flat' amplifier with a bandwidth covering the audio signal frequency range required of, say, 50Hz to 10kHz. The essentially flat response is however modified or **equalised** to produce a rising gain towards the higher audio frequencies to compensate for high frequency losses which occur in the recording process. From block (A) the signal is fed to the record head (B). Here the electrical audio signal is converted into a magnetic field which varies in intensity and frequency in sympathy with the electrical signal fed to the head. As the tape moves past the head at a constant speed, the varying magnetic field produced by the head permanently magnetises the magnetic coating of the tape. If only the record signal were fed to the head, then on replay the output signal would be very distorted. To avoid the distortion the tape has to be **biassed** in a special

way. This is achieved by additionally feeding the record head with a constant amplitude sine wave having a frequency lying somewhere in the range of 40kHz to 100kHz. This signal is obtained from the bias oscillator (F) which, say, generates a sine wave of 45kHz as shown. The actual signal fed to the record head consists of the high frequency bias with the record signal superimposed on it, *i.e.* the two signals are added together. Before a new recording is made on the tape any previous recordings have to be erased. This is the purpose of the erase head (C) which is so positioned that the tape passes the erase head before coming in contact with the record head. A high frequency sine wave is used to erase previous recordings and this is supplied by the same oscillator that is used to generate the bias signal for the record head.

In the **playback** mode the recorded tape is

moved past the replay head at the same constant speed that was used on recording. A separate replay head may be used but commonly a combined record/replay head is employed as shown. As the magnetic field pattern of the tape passes the replay head an electrical signal is induced into the head. This is the reverse process of recording and the electrical audio signal obtained is fed via the record/playback switch S1A to the playback amplifier (D). Here the signal is amplified using essentially a 'flat' amplifier which has a modified response to produce a rising gain towards the lower audio frequencies and sometimes the higher audio frequencies to compensate or **equalise** for defects in the replay process. The output of (D) is fed to a power amplifier (E) having a 'flat' response which is used to drive the loudspeaker. During replay the erase head must be disconnected from the bias oscillator and this is accomplished by S1B.

A suitable d.c. supply is required for the various stages of the recorder and this may be obtained from a mains fed power supply or alternatively from a battery source. Supplies will also be required to operate the motor which pulls the tape past the heads and operate the supply and take-up reels during normal and fast wind operation.

7. CATHODE RAY OSCILLOSCOPE

A basic block diagram of a cathode ray oscilloscope is given in Fig. 7.7. As the signal to be examined (a.c. or d.c.) may be of small amplitude, a Y amplifier, block (B), is required. This is a 'flat' amplifier having a uniform response up to, say, 5MHz, 10MHz or higher. It is usually a d.c. amplifier so that the d.c. component of the signal may be measured. So that the c.r.o. may be used with a wide range of input voltages, say, 1mV to 400V applied to the Y terminal, a variable attenuator block A is used. An attenuator is a device that will reduce the signal fed to the Y

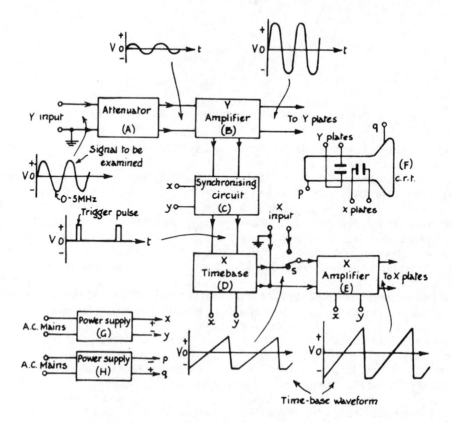

Fig. 7.7 Basic block diagram of cathode ray oscilloscope.

amplifier and operates like a volume control or potential divider. The attenuator and Y amplifier are calibrated so that the actual amplitude of the waveform or voltage to be examined can be determined from its size on the screen. The attenuator is calibrated in volts per cm, usually from 2mV/cm to 50V/cm. Amplifier B output is fed to the Y plates of the c.r.t. to produce vertical deflection of the electron beam.

The X timebase block (D) generates a variable frequency sawtooth voltage and is normally calibrated in time/cm, usually from 1μs/cm to 100ms/cm so that the periodic time or any relevant period of a waveform may be determined. The output of the timebase is amplified by the X amplifier block (E) and then applied to the X plates of the c.r.t. to provide horizontal deflection of the electron beam. Facility is usually provided for the X deflection voltage to be applied from an external source and this is applied to the X input terminals. Changeover from external X input to internal timebase operation is via the switch S. In order that the signal to be examined is locked to the timebase so that a steady display is obtained, a synchronising circuit (C) is used. This is fed with a sample of the signal from the Y amplifier and generates a suitable trigger pulse to synchronise the X timebase.

A mains fed power supply (G) is required to provide a d.c. supply voltage to the blocks as shown. Additionally another power supply (H) is needed to provide a high voltage d.c. supply of 1000V to 1500V to operate the c.r.t.

8. DIGITAL CLOCK

The basic idea of a digital clock is shown in schematic form in Fig. 7.8. The accuracy of the time read-out in a digital clock is achieved by using a crystal oscillator (A) which has inherent frequency stability. Typically the oscillator will operate at a frequency of about 32kHz. The oscillator output (sine wave) is fed to a divider stage (B) where the input is divided by 250 to produce pulses at 128 per second at its output. This is further divided in (C) by a factor of 128 to produce pulses at one per second which will serve as the **seconds** display. Further dividers (D) and (E) each dividing by a factor of 60 produce pulses at one per minute and one per hour for the **minutes** and **hours** displays. Bistable oscillators may be used in blocks (B) to (E) to produce the required frequency division.

Each of the decoder blocks (F), (G) and (H) serves two main functions. One function is to decode the pulse input to operate the display units which may be formed from seven segment display units using either liquid crystal or l.e.ds. The other function is to count the pulses fed to each decoder so that each display may be reset on reaching the maximum count. With a 24 hour clock, the seconds display will run from 0–59 seconds, the minutes display from 0–59 minutes and the

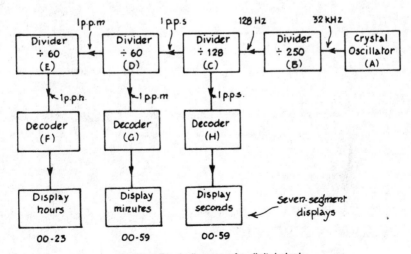

Fig. 7.8 Block diagram of a digital clock.

hours display from 0–23 hours, thus each must be reset to zero on reaching the maximum count. Two seven segment displays will be needed for each display. The various electronic units used in the clock will be manufactured in integrated circuit form except for the crystal which is a discrete component.

Each block will require a low voltage d.c. supply which may be obtained from a mains fed power supply or a battery source.

9. SPEED CONTROL SYSTEM

There are many instances in industry where the speed of a motor which is used to drive a load of some sort (*e.g.* conveyor belt, milling machine, drilling machine *etc*) needs to be regulated to a high degree of accuracy. This is often the requirement of automatic production lines where an accurately adjusted motor speed is needed in spite of changes in supply voltage, load and temperature. Some form of electronic regulating circuit is invariably used in these circumstances and the basic idea of one form of electronic speed control system is illustrated in Fig. 7.9.

Here a d.c. motor (D) is used to drive a load, the speed of which needs to be accurately maintained close to various nominal speeds set by the **set speed control** of block (A). We will assume that the motor is to be accurately maintained at nominal speeds of 1000 r.p.m., 1500 r.p.m. and 2000 r.p.m. The set speed control could thus take the form of a three-position switch and in each position of the switch, a constant but different d.c. voltage is supplied to block (B). In order that there is some means of sensing the motor

speed and hence the load, a small d.c. generator (tacho-generator) is used and is driven by the motor. This generator produces a d.c. output voltage that is proportional to the speed of the motor and is fed as the second input to block (B). In block (B) the d.c. output of the generator is compared with the d.c. voltage from the set speed control using a differential amplifier. The resulting amplified **difference** or **error voltage** is then used to drive the motor at the desired speed after amplification in block (C). As considerable power may be required to drive the motor a power amplifier is needed and this is essentially a 'flat' amplifier. The amount of power that is supplied to the motor and hence its speed will increase with an increase in the amplified difference voltage from block (B).

At the instant the system is switched on the motor will be stopped and there will be no output from the generator. Thus the only input to the differential amplifier is from block (A). In consequence there will be a large amplified difference voltage output from (B) which after power amplification in (C) will cause the motor to start turning and for its speed to pick up. There will now be a d.c. output from (E) resulting in the amplified difference voltage from (B) reducing in magnitude. In consequence less power (but more than it requires to maintain the correct speed) is fed to the motor causing its speed to continue to increase. However, as the motor speed increases so does the output voltage from the generator. This reduces the 'error' voltage from (B) and less power is supplied to the motor. As the motor speed continues to rise towards the desired nominal value, the

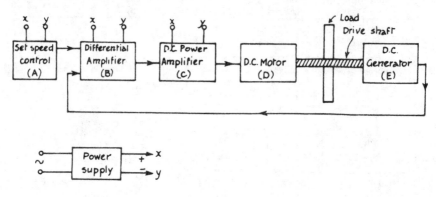

Fig. 7.9 Speed control system.

'error' voltage from (B) continues to fall and after a short settling down period the voltage difference between the two inputs of (B) falls to a small but finite value. This small difference voltage is necessary to drive the motor at the desired speed via the power amplifier.

Should the load on the motor increase thus causing the motor speed to reduce, the output from (E) will fall and a larger 'error' voltage will be generated. This will cause more power to be supplied to the motor and so the motor speed will increase to compensate for the increase in load. The converse action takes place if the load decreases.

If the set speed control is altered by, say, increasing the 'reference' voltage fed to (B) to give an increase in motor speed, the 'error' voltage produced after the 'settling down' period will be larger than that at a lower speed. This increase in 'error' voltage is necessary to drive the motor at the higher selected speed. At any of the selected speeds there will be a small speed error but in a well designed system it can be kept small, *e.g.* 0·25% or better.

10. PHASELOCKED LOOP

There are occasions in electronics and communications where it is necessary to synchronise an oscillator with an external signal so that the frequency and phase of the oscillator output waveform is the same as that of the external signal source and a phase locked loop may be used for this purpose. Common examples of frequency and phase locking include the synchronisation of a clock oscillator in a computer system with an external synchronising source, synchronisation of a **reference** oscillator in a colour television received decoder with a transmitted **colour burst** and the synchronisation of the rotating vision heads in a video cassette recorder with an external reference source.

The basic idea of the phase locked loop principle is illustrated in Fig. 7.10. The oscillator to be synchronised in frequency and phase is that of block (D). This will be assumed to be a sine wave type oscillator generating an output waveform of frequency f_o. The design of the oscillator is such that its frequency may be altered by applying a d.c. voltage at its input, hence the name 'voltage controlled oscillator' (v.c.o.). The oscillator output is fed as one input to the phase discriminator of block (A) via a buffer amplifier (E). A buffer amplifier is required to reduce the effects of variable loading on the v.c.o. by the phase discriminator and circuits supplied from the output terminal to prevent changes in amplitude and frequency of the v.c.o. output.

The other input to block (A) is the **reference signal** whose frequency and phase is that which we wish the v.c.o. to assume. Let this signal be a sine wave of frequency f_s. In block (A) the reference signal f_s is compared in frequency and phase with the v.c.o. signal f_o. If there is a frequency or phase difference between the two inputs, the phase discriminator generates a correcting signal voltage V_e. This **error signal** is fed via a filter (B) and a d.c. amplifier (C) to the v.c.o. where it is used to correct the frequency and phase of the v.c.o. The filter is a low-pass filter with values used so that only d.c. and low frequencies are passed on to the d.c. amplifier. The bandwidth of the filter determines the frequency range over which the free-running v.c.o. can vary and still acquire frequency lock with the reference input (the **capture range**). The d.c. amplifier amplifies the d.c. error voltage from the filter to a suitable level to control the v.c.o. The polarity of the d.c. error voltage input to block (C) may be either positive or negative depending upon whether f_o is initially higher or lower in frequency than f_s.

With no reference input to block (A) but

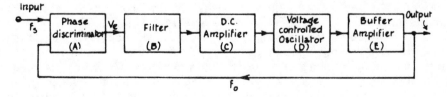

Fig. 7.10 Phase locked loop.

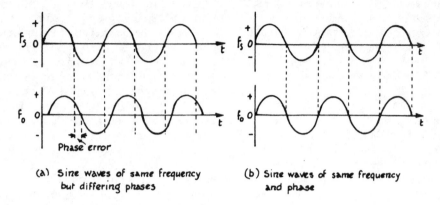

(a) Sine waves of same frequency but differing phases

(b) Sine waves of same frequency and phase

Fig. 7.11 Phase error.

with d.c. power applied, the v.c.o. will commence to oscillate but there will be no output from block (A). In these circumstances there will be no error signal fed to the d.c. amplifier and the v.c.o. will oscillate at its **free-running frequency**. Assume that the free-running frequency is lower than the frequency of the reference input which is now applied. As a result, block (A) generates a correcting signal of, say, positive polarity which after passing through blocks (B) and (C) corrects the frequency of the v.c.o. to make it the same as the reference input. At this time there may be a phase difference between f_s and f_o, see Fig. 7.11(a). The phase difference between f_s and f_o will cause block (A) to generate a small correcting signal to make the phase of the v.c.o. the same or nearly that of the reference input, see Fig. 7.11(b). In practice there will always be a small phase error in order to generate a correcting voltage to shift the phase of the v.c.o. towards that of the reference input. If initially the frequency of the v.c.o. is higher than that of the reference input, block (A) will generate a correcting signal of negative polarity which will correct the frequency and phase of the v.c.o. in the manner just described.

Once the v.c.o. has acquired frequency and phase locking with the reference signal input, any tendency for the v.c.o. to change either its frequency or phase due to temperature or supply voltage variations will be counteracted by the phase locked loop.

11. COMPUTER SYSTEM

A block diagram showing the essential ideas behind a general computer system is given in Fig. 7.12.

At the heart of the system is the **microprocessor** of block (C). A microprocessor consists of a large number of logic gates and a few shift registers manufactured on a single integrated circuit chip and acts as a kind of **universal digital circuit**. It serves as the Central Processing Unit (C.P.U.) of the computer system and executes arithmetical problems, logic comparison, data transfer and control operations that are presented to it as a sequence of instructions, step by step. The set of instructions or **program** is usually stored in a memory (D) which is external to the microprocessor. The program instructions may be permanently stored in the memory (usually referred to as **firmware**) or may be written into the memory from tape or disk (**software** programs). A number of program instructions need to be permanently stored in the memory so that at switch-on the computer will start to 'look' for software program input when this applies. Such instructions which are needed first by the computer are referred to as **housekeeping** routines.

In practice block (D) contains two different types of memory. One type, called a **Read Only Memory** (R.O.M.), is used to permanently store the housekeeping routines and the main program (if this is fixed) to which the computer will respond. The contents of the

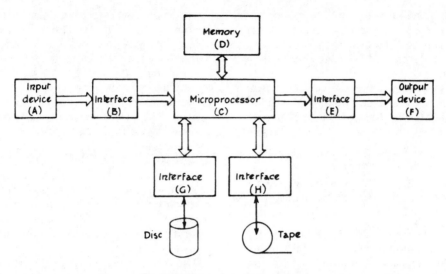

Fig. 7.12 *General computer system.*

R.O.M. are not lost when the computer is switched off. The other type, called a **Read and Write Memory** (R.A.M.), may be used to store software programs and to act as a temporary store for data handled by the microprocessor. At switch-off the contents of the R.A.M. are lost.

A programmed computer system may be used to provide control over industrial or domestic processes. The inputs to the microprocessor may then come from transducers used to measure physical quantities such as temperature, pressure, vibration and velocity. The output of the microprocessor in such a system may be used to control external devices such as pumps, motors, relays, alarms, heaters *etc.* Thus block (A) of Fig. 7.12 may be a transducer measuring, say, temperature and block (F) a motor whose speed is controlled by the microprocessor output. Alternatively the computer system may be used for Data Processing where the data is entered externally via a keyboard (**input device**) and the data after processing is displayed on a Visual Display Unit (**output device**), listed on a printer (**output device**) or stored on magnetic tape or disk (**output devices**).

In order for the microprocessor to communicate with input and output devices of the outside world, **interface circuits** of blocks (B), (E), (F), (G) and (H) are used. One function of an interface circuit is to provide correct matching between input/output devices and the microprocessor which deals with relatively small currents and voltages. For example, an output device such as a motor may require a high power to operate it whereas the microprocessor provides only a small output power, thus power amplification is required in the interface. In addition it should be noted that a microprocessor requires a digital signal input and produces digital signals at its output. Thus if the input device is a transducer producing an analogue voltage at its output, Analogue-to-Digital conversion is required by the input interface (B). On the other hand if the output device requires an analogue voltage to operate it, such as a motor or pen recorder, Digital-to-Analogue conversion is required by the output interface (E). Where analogue-to-digital conversion or digital-to-analogue conversion is used in a computer system it is normally controlled by the microprocessor in response to the program instructions.

12. COLOUR TELEVISION RECEIVER

A colour television picture is produced by mixing three basic coloured lights, called **primary** colours, in various proportions. There are two methods of mixing colours: mixing coloured lights (the additive system); or mixing coloured pigments such as paints, inks and dyes (the subtractive system). The additive system is used in colour television and the subtractive system in photography, printing and painting. The principles involved are different; only the additive system will be explained.

The three primary colours used in television are red, green and blue. Mixing of primary coloured lights (*e.g.* from the three projectors with coloured filters) gives the following colours:

RED   + GREEN = YELLOW
GREEN + BLUE = CYAN (a greenish-blue)
RED   + BLUE = MAGENTA (purplish)
RED   + GREEN
          + BLUE = WHITE

Varying the amount of the colours in the mixtures produces a whole range of colours. Theoretically it is not possible to produce all colours by this means but for practical purposes sufficient colours can be obtained.

Before describing the operation of a colour t.v. receiver, some details will be given first of the method used to encode the colour television signal.

Encoding the Colour Signal

Colour television was introduced in this country during 1967 using the PAL (Phase Alternation Line) system of transmission. We cannot consider this system in detail at this stage of your course and only a basic outline will be given. In designing the system consideration had to be given to owners of monochrome receivers so that they could continue to receive a normal monochrome picture, a feature referred to as **compatibility**. Also, it was essential that a colour t.v. receiver should be able to display a good monochrome picture as not all of the programmes would originate in colour (the occasional news item and some feature films are transmitted in monochrome). These requirements are incorporated into the PAL colour television system and a basic idea of a colour television transmitter is given in Fig. 7.13.

The first essential part of the process is to break down the coloured light falling on the camera lens into red, green and blue components of light. This is carried out in the colour camera of block (A) which produces at its output electrical signal voltages E_R, E_G and E_B having amplitudes proportional to the amount of red, green and blue light in the scene. The breaking down of the coloured light from the scene into its basic components is achieved through the use of special mirrors in the camera (called **dichroic** mirrors). These mirrors split the coloured light so that it falls

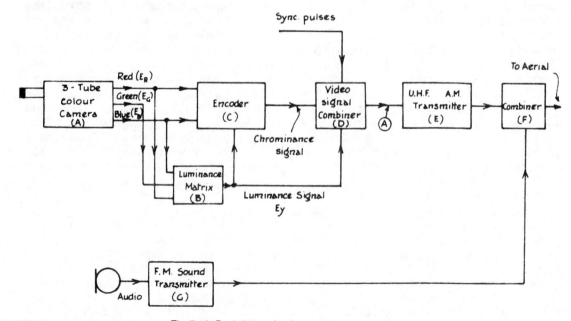

Fig. 7.13 Basic idea of colour television transmitter.

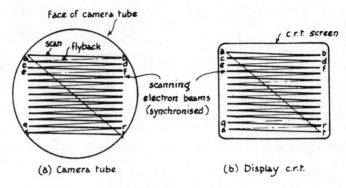

Fig. 7.14 Simple scanning.

onto the face of three camera tubes. All of the camera tubes are **scanned** in synchronism using internal electron beams.

The basic idea of simple scanning is shown in Fig. 7.14(a). Inside each of the three camera tubes an electron beam traces out a series of sloping lines across the face of the tube. As the electron beam is moving across the tube face, a force is exerted on the beam causing a downward movement (this is responsible for the downward slope of the lines). The beam commences scanning at the left hand side and traces out a line a–b. At the end of this **line scan** the beam rapidly returns to the left hand side (flyback) to commence the next line scan c–d. This process is repeated down the tube face until point *t* is reached when the beam rapidly returns to point *a* to repeat the procedure over and over again. In this way, the electron beam reads the amount of light falling at every point on the camera tube face. The movement of the beam from the top to the bottom constitutes what is known as the **field scan**. Exactly the same procedure occurs with the electron beams inside a colour display tube, see Fig. 7.14(b).

It has been mentioned that a signal is required by the monochrome receiver to enable the display of a monochrome picture and that the colour receiver is also required to display monochrome pictures occasionally. This need may be satisfied by transmitting a **luminance signal** (E_Y) which contains information relating to the brightness variations in the scene. When using a three tube colour camera the luminance signal is produced by adding together suitable proportions of the E_R, E_B and E_G outputs of the camera. The adding or **matrixing** is carried out in block (B).

If the scene is in black and white, the luminance signal is the only signal that is transmitted, apart from the normal line and field sync. pulses.

When the scene is in colour, additional information has to be transmitted which we will call the **colouring signal**. Now the E_R, E_B and E_G signal contain colour information but they are not transmitted directly for reasons that cannot be considered here. Instead, a colouring signal is produced which is composed of two components called **colour difference signals** and these are $E_R - E_Y$ and $E_B - E_Y$. These signals are simply the subtraction of electrical voltages and have nothing to do with coloured light. The colour differences are produced in Block (C) and the E_Y voltage is subtracted from the E_R and E_B voltages.

As extra bandwidth could not be given to transmit the colouring signal, it had to be fitted into the normal monochrome bandwidth of 0–5·5MHz and in such a way that it would not interfere with the normal luminance signal. This is achieved by amplitude modulating the colour difference signals on a specially chosen sub-carrier of 4·43MHz. To transmit the two colour difference signals on a single sub-carrier a special type of modulation, called **quadrature modulation** is used. Special amplitude modulation is also used called **suppressed carrier** which produces two sidebands but no carrier. All of these special processes are carried out in the **encoder** block (C). Thus out of block (C) we get the colouring signal which is usually called the **chrominance signal**. This is then fed to block (D) where it is added to the luminance signal and the line and field sync. pulses. The sync. pulses are necessary to synchronise the scanning electron beams

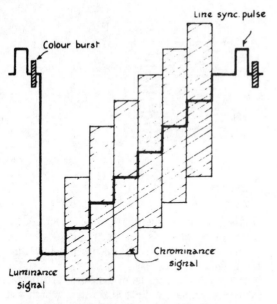

Fig. 7.15 Waveform at A of Fig.7.13.

inside the colour camera with the beams inside the colour display tube fitted in the receiver. The combined waveform at point A during the transmission of **colour bars** is shown in Fig. 7.15. This waveform additionally shows a **colour burst** signal which is produced in the encoder and is used for special synchronising purposes in the colour receiver decoder. The composite video signal from block (D) is then fed to the u.h.f. transmitter of block (E) where the video signal amplitude modulates the u.h.f. carrier (470MHz–582MHz or 614MHz–854MHz) for transmission via the aerial system.

Frequency modulation is used for the television sound signal and this is carried out in block (G). Here an f.m. sound carrier is produced lying in the u.h.f. band and close to the a.m. vision signal. Each t.v. channel occupies a bandwidth of 8MHz in the u.h.f. band. The vision and sound u.h.f. carrier signals are combined in block (F) before being fed to the common aerial system.

Colour Television Receiver

A basic block diagram of a colour t.v. receiver is given in Fig. 7.16. The u.h.f. signals picked up in the aerial are fed to block (1) where the desired u.h.f. channel is selected.

We must remember that during a colour programme the u.h.f. vision carrier is amplitude modulated with the combined luminance, chrominance and sync. signals which are present as **sidebands** on the vision carrier. Also, the sound u.h.f. carrier (spaced by 6MHz from the vision carrier) is frequency modulated by the audio signals and this information is present as sidebands on the sound carrier. All of these components are amplified in the selective u.h.f. amplifier and then passed on to the mixer stage (2). Here the u.h.f. sound and vision carriers and their sidebands are mixed with the output of the local oscillator (3) to change the frequency of the signal components down to lower intermediate frequencies, following normal superheterodyne receiver principles. The output of the mixer thus contains vision and sound i.f. carriers (nominally 39·5MHz and 33·5MHz) and sidebands. These components are amplified in the selective amplifier (4). To ensure that the receiver remains on tune with temperature variations, any frequency drift in block (3) is corrected by an automatic frequency control (a.f.c.) circuit of block (5). This is done by feeding the vision i.f. carrier to the a.f.c. circuit which produces a correcting signal voltage if the vision i.f. carrier is incorrect. The correcting signal is then used to alter the frequency of the oscillator (3) which in turn adjusts the frequency of the vision i.f. output of the mixer to make it correct. Without this feature the colour may be lost when the tuning drifts.

After i.f. amplification the vision signals are demodulated in block (6). It should be noted that although the luminance signal is detected in block (6), the chrominance or **colouring signal** is still in its **encoded** form. The luminance, chrominance and sync. signals are then fed to block (10) which amplifies the luminance and sync. signals only. The chrominance signal is extracted from the luminance and sync. signals in block (10) using a selective circuit and then fed to block (16) where it is amplified using a selective amplifier. The output of block (16) is fed to the colour decoder of block (17) together with the luminance signal from block (10). We cannot go into the details of the decoder block at this stage as many operations are carried out on the signals in the decoder which are outside

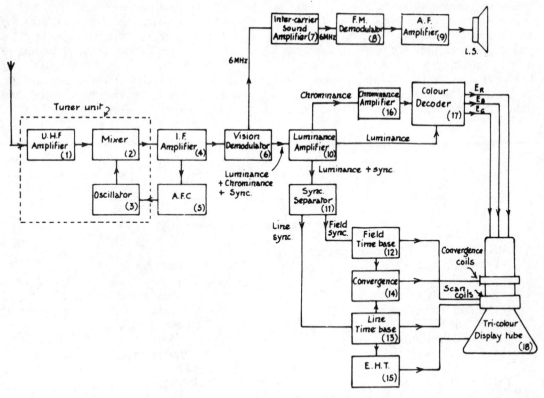

Fig. 7.16 Simple colour receiver.

the scope of an elementary introduction to colour t.v. However, the end result of the operations performed on the signals in the decoder is that E_R, E_B and E_G signals are available at its output during a colour transmission. It will be noted that these are the same signals that appeared at the output of the colour camera in Fig. 7.13 and are the signals required to drive the colour c.r.t. During a monochrome transmission the output of the decoder is the luminance signal (E_Y) on all three drive lines, since chrominance is not transmitted during a monochrome broadcast.

The tri-colour display c.r.t. of (18) uses three electron guns producing electron beams which are allowed to fall on different screen phosphors which emit light in the primary colours of red, green and blue. By turning the three guns 'on' and 'off' by varying amounts with the signals from the decoder, the colour can be varied on any part of the screen. For example, to produce yellow the red and green guns would be turned 'on' and the blue gun switched 'off'. To produce white all three guns

have to be turned 'on'. The screen phosphor may be in the form of triangular groups of small dots (delta gun tube) or in the form of vertical stripes (in-line tube). The way in which the c.r.t. operates cannot be considered in any detail in this book.

Returning now to consider the other output from block (10). This is fed to the sync. separator (11) where the sync. pulses are separated from the luminance signal. Suitable pulses are fed from block (11) to synchronise the field and line timebases of blocks (12) and (13). The line and field timebases supply sawtooth currents at 15625Hz and 50Hz respectively to the scan coils which deflect the three electron beams of the c.r.t. simultaneously over the face of the screen. To keep the three coloured rasters of the colour tube in register or **converged**, suitably shaped currents have to be fed into the convergence coils mounted on the tube neck. These currents are supplied by the convergence unit (14) which is fed with timing waveforms from the line and field timebases. In receivers fitted with modern in-line display tubes, block (14) and the convergence coils are not required. The line timebase also feeds high voltage pulses to block (15) where they are often doubled or trebled in magnitude and then smoothed to produce an e.h.t. voltage of about 18–24kV to operate the colour tube.

The other output of block (6) contains a 6MHz f.m. **inter-carrier sound i.f.** which is created in the vision detector by beating the vision and sound i.f. carriers together. This signal is amplified in block (7) using a selective amplifier and then fed to an f.m. demodulator (8). The demodulated audio signals are amplified in the audio amplifier (9) and then passed to the loudspeaker.

QUESTIONS ON CHAPTER SEVEN

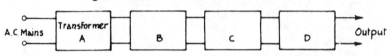

Fig. 7(a) Block diagram of modern power supply.

(1) Block B of Fig. 7(a) is most probably:
(a) An amplifier
(b) A stabiliser
(c) An oscillator
(d) A rectifier.
(2) Block C of Fig. 7(a) is most probably:
(a) A low pass filter
(b) A stabiliser
(c) A rectifier
(d) A fusible resistor.
(3) The output of block B in Fig. 7(a) will be:
(a) A sine wave voltage
(b) A smooth d.c. voltage
(c) A pulsating d.c. voltage
(d) A square wave.
(4) Block A of Fig. 7(b) is:
(a) A band pass filter
(b) A mixer
(c) A band stop filter
(d) An a.g.c. circuit.
(5) Block C of Fig. 7(b) is:
(a) A mixer
(b) An i.f. amplifier
(c) An r.f. filter
(d) An a.f. amplifier.
(6) The output from block D of Fig. 7(b) will be:

(a) A varying amplitude sine wave of constant frequency
(b) A square wave of variable frequency
(c) A modulated carrier wave
(d) A constant amplitude sine wave of variable frequency.
(7) The frequency of the bias oscillator in an audio tape recorder is probably:
(a) 5kHz
(b) 1·5MHz
(c) 575Hz
(d) 45kHz.
(8) Block C of Fig. 7(c) is most likely:
(a) A voltage controlled oscillator
(b) A d.c. amplifier
(c) An a.c. amplifier
(d) A full wave rectifier.
(9) A short time after the application of f_s the output of block D in Fig. 7(c) will be:
(a) A d.c. voltage
(b) A signal of frequency equal to f_s
(c) A signal of frequency greater than f_s
(d) A signal of frequency less than f_s.
(10) A typical application for the system of Fig. 7(c) would be:
(a) To provide a 180° phase shift in a signal
(b) To provide a 270° phase shift in a signal

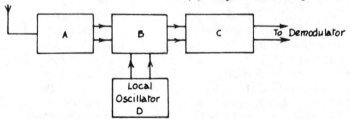

Fig. 7(b) Section of A.M. superheterodyne receiver.

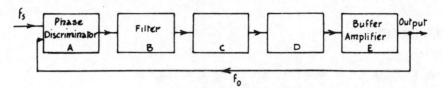

Fig. 7(c) Phase locked loop.

(c) To lock the amplitude of a remote oscillator to the d.c. level obtained from a potentiometer
(d) To lock the oscillations of an oscillator to a reference source.

(11) The three primary colours used in colour television are:
(a) Red, yellow and blue
(b) Green, red and blue
(c) Magenta, cyan and yellow
(d) White, black and red.

(12) When the colours yellow and blue are additively mixed, the resultant is:
(a) Cyan
(b) Green
(c) Magenta
(d) White.

(13) The frequency of the line time base in a colour television receiver is:
(a) 10kHz
(b) 15·625kHz
(c) 50Hz
(d) 625kHz.

(14) The vision i.f. of a colour television receiver is typically:
(a) 39·5MHz
(b) 10·7MHz
(c) 465kHz
(d) 470MHz.

(15) In a general computer system, software is the name given to:
(a) The print out of data on paper
(b) The electronic components of the computer
(c) The data signal lines
(d) The sequence of instructions recorded on tape or disk.

(16) Programming instructions that are permanently stored in the memory of a computer are usually called:
(a) Hardware
(b) Firmware
(c) Software
(d) Permware.

(17) Functions of the microprocessor in a computer systems include:
(a) Execution of arithmetical problems and logic comparison
(b) Storage of programming instructions and interfacing
(c) Memorising housekeeping routines and interfacing
(d) Printing out data on paper.

(18) Block B of Fig. 7(d) is:
(a) A d.c. generator
(b) A differential amplifier
(c) A power amplifier
(d) A phase discriminator.

(19) If the load in Fig. 7(d) is increased, it will cause:
(a) A larger a.c. voltage output from block B
(b) A smaller d.c. voltage input voltage to block C
(c) An increase in the d.c. voltage form block A
(d) A smaller d.c. voltage output from block E.

(20) Block C of Fig. 7(d) is a:
(a) D.C. power amplifier
(b) Differential amplifier
(c) Tuned amplifier
(d) Low pass filter.

(Answers on page 219.)

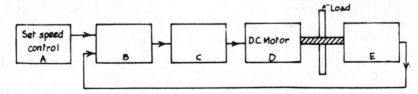

Fig. 7(d) Speed control system.

CHAPTER EIGHT

HEALTH AND SAFETY

Objectives
1 Describe the law relating to health and safety at work and states duties of employees and employers.
2 Describe precautions against and procedures to follow in the event of an electric shock.
3 Understands reasons for use of earthed lead with equipment and describes safe practices to follow in workshop and domestic environments.
4 States the importance of seeking qualified assistance and extent of first aid to be rendered in the event of burns, cuts, electric shock, or exposure to toxic fumes and irritant materials.
5 Describe methods of fire prevention and dealing with fires.

ALL SENSIBLE PEOPLE take an interest in their health and safety. We naturally expect those who provide us with manufactured articles, food, public transport, medical attention, *etc*, to exercise care and so safeguard our health and safety.

When we first start working this personal interest may be enhanced, especially in industrial environments where we are likely to meet with situations that might be hazardous. It soon becomes apparent that, apart from personal safety, our own actions at work may put at risk the health and safety of workmates, customers and the general public.

There has been a growing interest in health and safety following the Health and Safety at Work Act of 1974 which makes additional provision for:

(a) Improving the health, safety and welfare of people at work.
(b) Protecting the general public against risks to health and safety arising out of the actions of 'people at work', *e.g.* through manufactured goods or services.
(c) Controlling the storage and use of highly flammable, explosive or dangerous substances and preventing such substances being unlawfully acquired or used.
(d) Controlling the emission into the atmosphere of harmful or offensive substances from works premises.

'People at work', includes employers and employees and both have obligations under the Act.

Duties of Employers to Their Employees
So far as it is reasonably practical the duty of every employer is to minimise risks to health and safety of his employees by:

(a) Providing and maintaining plant and systems of work that are safe.
(b) Arranging that raw materials and goods are stored, handled and transported without risk.
(c) Providing a place of work (*e.g.* a building) and maintaining it in a safe condition. There must be a safe means of access and exit.
(d) Providing information on health and safety, together with training and supervision as necessary.
(e) By means of a written notice bringing to the attention of all employees the health and safety policy and the arrangements for carrying it out.
(f) Providing and maintaining a working environment that is safe and free from risk and providing adequate facilities in respect of first aid equipment, toilets and rest rooms *etc*.

Duties of Employees at Work
While at work it is the duty of every employee:

(a) To take reasonable care of his own health and safety.
(b) To generally take reasonable care so that the health and safety of workmates,

customers and others who may be affected by his/her actions or omissions are not put at risk.

(c) To co-operate with the employer in carrying out any health or safety regulations that may be imposed on the employer by the authorities.

(d) Not to interfere with or misuse anything provided by the employer in the interests of safety, health or welfare (*e.g.* remove safety guards, misuse fire extinguishers *etc*).

Obligations to Customers and General Public

The employer also has obligations to his customers and to the general public. As a manufacturer, products must be so designed and constructed as to be reasonably safe and without risk when used properly. During manufacturing processes it must be ensured that no harmful or offensive substances (poisonous gases or 'smells') are emitted into the atmosphere. Any installation that is made must be as safe as possible. Articles, such as ladders, carried by vehicles must be properly secured.

Under the Act the employer's duties are far reaching and in protecting the health and safety of the general public the co-operation of the employee is essential.

Consider the following situation and note what omissions or mistakes were made by the employer and employee.

A young apprentice television engineer reports to his employer at the town workshop on his first day of work at 9.00a.m. sharp. He is instructed to accompany one of the engineers to assist in the installation of a new television receiver. The employer tells the engineer 'You must be at 22 Willowfield Drive not later than 9.30 this morning otherwise the customer will be out'.

The engineer and apprentice quickly load the van and set off at 9.10. Knowing that Willowfield Drive is some four miles away, the engineer puts his foot down and speeds at about 60 m.p.h. to their destination. At 9.25 they arrive at the customers house and are relieved to find him still at home. They quickly take the receiver into the house and on starting to connect the receiver to the mains supply the engineer discovers that he has forgotten to bring a mains plug. He makes a temporary job by pushing the leads into the mains socket, switches on and adjusts the receiver controls to obtain a good picture. The apprentice looks on, very impressed by the engineer's skill and speed in making the installation in record time.

The engineer apologises to the customer for not bringing a mains plug and says 'I'll bring one tomorrow and finish the job'.

Pleased with their efficient service to the customer, the engineer and apprentice drive leisurely back to the workshop.

The engineer made the following mistakes:

(a) He exceeded the town speed limit thereby putting other drivers and the general public at risk.

(b) He forgot to take a mains plug (excusable) but made an unsafe installation (inexcusable). His 'action at work' put the customer and his family at risk from electric shock and fire by an unsafe connection to the mains supply.

(c) He did not make physical checks on the receiver to ensure that screws, screening cans, *etc* had not worked loose after the journey from the workshop.

(d) He set a very bad example to the apprentice.

The employer made the following mistakes:

(a) He failed to inform the young apprentice of his company's health and safety policy before the apprentice started work.

(b) Owing to his insistence on meeting time deadlines (through bad planning) he encouraged the engineer to drive fast.

(c) He probably did not have a safety policy for the engineer to follow regarding temporary repairs in customers' homes.

ELECTRICAL SAFETY

When dealing with electronic equipment it must be realised that electricity can be dangerous if precautions are not taken. **Electricity cannot be seen, heard or smelt, it is very rapid in action and its effects may be fatal.**

Injury may be caused in a number of ways:

(1) Shock

An electric shock is caused by an electric current flowing through the body. The degree of shock depends upon the current flowing (which depends on the voltage) and the electrical resistance of the body, a factor which varies in different persons and is much reduced if the skin is wet. The severity of the shock depends on which part of the body the current flows; in the vicinity of the heart it is most serious.

Shocks are possible from voltages as low as 15V and 20–25V may cause pain. Shocks are not usually fatal below about 120V a.c. but death can be caused by voltages as low as 70V. The normal mains supply of 240V a.c. and currents of 25–30mA or more are the most common cause of serious and fatal shocks. A current passing through the body causes contraction of the muscles. This may result in the person being unable to let go of the equipment. Quite minor shocks can lead to accidents such as causing a person to fall from a ladder, to drop equipment, *etc*.

The voltage supplies encountered in electronic equipment in general, range from voltages as low as 10V to as high as 25kV or more, thus great care should be exercised. The designation of voltages of different ranges are as follows:

Low Tension (L.T.) .... Below 250V
Medium Tension (M.T.) 250–650V
High Tension (H.T.) 650–3000V
Extra High Tension (E.H.T.)　Above 3000V

(2) Burns

A heavy current passing through the body may cause serious burns especially at the point of contact.

(3) Fire and Explosion

Electric sparks starting a fire or causing an explosion can endanger life and property. Batteries on charge emit hydrogen and oxygen (a very explosive mixture) and hence a spark or short circuit can cause a serious explosion. Sparks and short circuits should be guarded against, and good ventilation maintained to prevent the accumulation of gases.

Action to be taken in the event of an Electric Shock

If the victim is still in contact with the electric circuit, SWITCH OFF THE SUPPLY; if this is not possible pull the victim away

USING AN INSULATING MATERIAL. Ideally, rubber gloves should be used but dry cloth and wood are good substitutes such as a jacket, a scarf or a brush with a wooden handle.

If the victim has suffered serious shock apply articial respiration as soon as possible. You should learn artificial respiration but if you have not then get help quickly. Speed is vitally important particularly during the first few minutes; permanent damage to the brain results if it is deprived of oxygen for more than four minutes.

Artificial respiration should be given as follows:

(a) Lay victim on back and remove any obstructions from mouth and throat.
(b) Put one hand under neck and the other on the patient's forehead and tilt the head right back, raising the chin up. This prevents the tongue blocking the air passage in the throat.
(c) Seal the patients nostrils by pinching with the fingers or by resting your cheek against the nostrils.
(d) Breath in deeply, seal your lips around the patients mouth and blow into his lungs until they are filled, watching the chest rise.
(e) Remove your mouth and watch the chest of the patient fall, at the same time taking another deep breath.
(f) Repeat the process.

If necessary, artificial respiration should be maintained unceasingly for at least an hour.

Of course, if you are able to get help of more experienced persons or a doctor you should do so but not if it will appreciably delay starting artificial respiration.

Plugs and Flexible Conductors

The modern plug and socket for use on 240V a.c. mains supply has three flat pins and is of 13A rating. Older plugs and sockets have three round pins and are in 2A, 5A and 15A ratings. With three pin plugs and sockets, one pin is for the live (L) conductor, another is for the neutral (N) conductor and the third is for the earth (E) lead, see Fig. 8.1.

The British Standard colour code (1970) for use with three-core flexible conductors is:

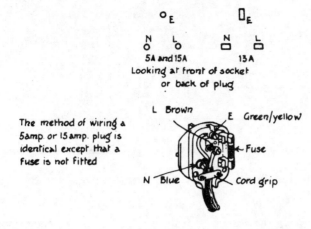

The method of wiring a
5amp. or 15 amp. plug is
identical except that a
fuse is not fitted

L Brown   E Green/yellow

← Fuse

N Blue   Cord grip

Fig. 8.1 Three pin plugs and sockets.

Earth   GREEN/YELLOW
Live   BROWN
Neutral   BLUE

Prior to 1970, the old British Standard colour code was:

Earth   GREEN or GREEN/YELLOW
Live   RED
Neutral   BLACK

Some countries may use other combinations of colours thus it is prudent before connecting equipment of foreign origin to check which conductors relate to particular colours. Many European countries use the same colour coding as the 1970 British Standard.

Reason for use of Earth Lead

With three pin sockets, the odd socket is for the earth lead and the reason for its use will now be explained. Generally, it is essential to earth all external metal work associated with electrical/electronic equipment. This is because if a fault develops inside the apparatus to produce a low resistance path between the live conductor and the casing, the case of the equipment becomes live at full mains voltage to earth (since the neutral is connected to earth at the substation as explained in Chapter One). Thus a person touching the casing will complete an electric circuit through them as shown in Fig. 8.2, thereby receiving a shock that might be fatal. As the current that flows through the person in this situation may only be several milliamps (sufficient for a fatality) the mains supply fuse will not normally blow.

If, however, the case of the equipment is connected to earth by a wire (which eventually gets back to the earth at the sub-station) a fault as shown in Fig. 8.3 will cause current to flow, but at no time will the case of the equipment be above earth potential. Thus a person touching the case is protected from an electric shock due to the use of the earth connection. If the fault is of low resistance, an excessive current

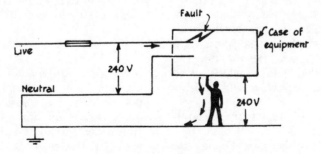

Fig. 8.2 Effect when case of equipment becomes live.

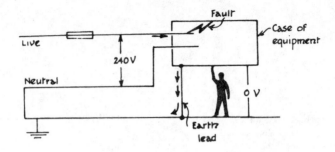

Fig. 8.3 Effect of earthing case of equipment.

will flow and blow the fuse in the live conductor thereby disconnecting the supply from the apparatus.

All portable electrical equipment should have a three-core cable, with the earth lead connected to the earth pin of the plug and to the casing of the apparatus. The only exception to this is with equipment called **double insulated** which is normally fitted with a two-core flex. Here two separate insulations are used between the mains supply conductors and the outer case of the device and so it is permissible to dispense with an earth lead. Some electrical drills are of this type (see later) but it is very important that other electric drills are properly earthed. For this reason, portable electrical equipment should not be run off two-pin sockets or lampholders.

Switches and Fuses

Any switches must be placed in the live lead (or a double-pole switch may be used which breaks both live and neutral leads). When fitting such switches it is **extremely important** that they are in the **live lead**, as otherwise the equipment is still live when switched off.

To prevent the passage of excessive current in a circuit, fuses (or in some cases circuit breakers) are used which must be **connected in the live conductor**. If fuses were not fitted and excessive current could be taken which would **overheat components or cables and possibly start a fire**.

Fuses feeding distribution circuits in rooms are commonly rated 5A, 15A or 30A. It is important that fuses of the correct rating are used and in no circumstances should larger fuses be fitted than that for which the circuit is

designed. If a fuse blows, the reason should be determined and the fault removed before replacing the fuse and switching on again.

The 13A plug is fitted with a fuse and when purchased has a 13A one fitted. If the plug is being fitted to equipment not requiring a 13A fuse then smaller fuses should be fitted. Fuses for 13A plugs are available in the following sizes: 2A, 3A, 5A, 7A, 10A and 13A, but only 3A and 13A are British Standard preferred. In general, one may assume a current of 4 amperes per 1 kilowatt rating; but where the starting current is higher than normal (*e.g.* a motor) a larger fuse will be needed to prevent it blowing when switching on. Some examples are:

1kW electric fire	5A (13A)
3kW electric fire	13A
Electric iron	5A (13A)
Electric kettle	1kW ... 5A (13A)
	2·5kW ... 13A
Radio	2 or 3A (3A)
Televison	2 or 3A (3A)
Reading lamp	2 or 3A (3A)
Vacuum cleaner	5A (13A)

The figures in brackets apply only if 3A and 13A fuses are to be used, *i.e.* British Standard.

SAFETY IN THE WORKSHOP

Most modern audio and industrial electronic equipment is isolated from the mains by a double wound transformer, hence the **frame** or **chassis** is not directly connected to the supply and should be earthed using the earth lead of a three-core flex. Exceptions to this are **double insulated** test equipment which do not require an earth; some cathode ray oscillo-

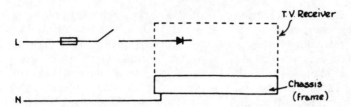

Fig. 8.4 Neutral of mains supply connected to chassis in some T.V. receivers.

scopes are double insulated. If a fuse or single-pole switch is fitted, it should be in the **live conductor**.

Many television receivers and some older radio receivers are, however, directly connected to the mains. For safety, the chassis should be connected to the **neutral** lead of the supply, see Fig. 8.4.

If the live and neutral leads are accidentally reversed, the receiver will work but the **chassis will be live** which is **very dangerous**. In a number of modern television receivers the **chassis is at half the mains supply potential regardless of which way round the live and neutral leads are connected**, thus **extreme caution** should be observed when working on such receivers.

There are a number of methods of checking whether the chassis is not live, among these being:

(a) A neon tester **which should not glow** when touched to the chassis. It is prudent to check that the tester is in good order by testing it on a live connection.

(b) An a.c. voltmeter connected between chassis and a known earth point, *e.g.* the earth pin of the plug. The voltmeter should be set on a suitable range, *e.g.* 250V a.c. and should not give an appreciable reading (remember that fatal shocks can occur on voltages as low as 70V).

(c) A 240V test lamp connected between chassis and a known earth point. **The lamp should not light**. Again, as a precaution, check the lamp immediately after making the test (by connecting across a 240V supply) in case the lamp has become open circuit.

Use of Isolating Transformer

Because of the potential danger of a live chassis with a television receiver and the presence of live conductors in other equipment which carry voltages of 120V or 240V with respect to earth, they should be supplied via an **isolating transformer** when work is to be carried out on them. Such a transformer is shown in Fig. 8.5 and is indicated as 'Isolation Transformer 1' and is used to supply the

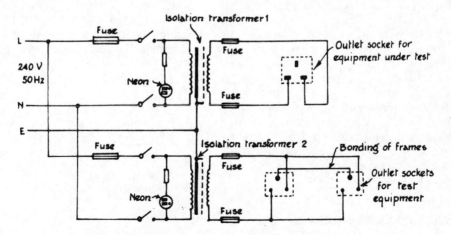

Fig. 8.5 The use of isolating transformers in workshop.

equipment under test, *i.e.* the television receiver or other electronic equipment.

In a workshop where test equipment, *e.g.* signal generators, oscilloscopes, *etc* which are to be connected to the equipment under test, the presence of an earthed frame on the test equipment presents a shock hazard to the engineer. Thus in the interests of safety, the test equipment may be supplied from a separate isolation transformer, labelled 'Isolation Transformer 2' in Fig. 8.5. The test equipment frames are not earthed but are bonded together to prevent potential differences existing between frames. Such measures together with the use of an earth-free area in the workshop considerably reduce the risk of shock to an individual due to contact between the live connection of the mains supply and earth. It must be stressed, however, that the use of an isolating transformer does not eliminate the risk of shock. For example there may be high d.c. potentials between exposed components of the equipment under test and chassis. Also across the secondary of the isolating transformer there will be 240V a.c. as the isolation transformer employs a 1:1 ratio between primary and secondary. Thus caution should be exercised at all times.

To prevent the equipment under test being plugged into the sockets intended for test equipment, it is a good idea to use a different type of plug and socket for the equipment under test as shown in Fig. 8.5.

When working on high voltages, it is prudent to use only one hand; the safest place for the other being in your pocket. If a shock is received it is then across your hand or between fingers, which is not usually serious. Do not hold the chassis or the frame of test equipment with one hand whilst probing live conductors with the other; any shock received is now between hands and is much more serious because the current passes near the heart. Always work on a rubber mat, never on a concrete floor (a good conductor to earth). Floor covering in a workshop should be made of an insulating material and benches constructed of insulating material, *e.g.* wood with wooden, formica or lino tops.

Handling Cathode Ray Tubes

In television, visual display units and oscilloscopes, high voltages are used to supply the cathode ray tube – up to 25kV in colour television receivers. Although the high voltage may sound dangerous, it may not be so since the current that can flow is often limited. Nevertheless, very unpleasant shocks may be received and there is no guarantee that they will not be serious so great care should be exercised.

When apparatus is run at high voltages (say above 10kV) X-rays are produced and this is particularly the case with colour television receivers. The amount of X-ray radiation under normal operating conditions is small of course and not dangerous. However considerable radiation comes from the e.h.t. rectifier and stabiliser (if valve). To protect the viewer these are enclosed in metal screening boxes which cut down the radiation to an acceptable level. The receiver should not be operated with the screening boxes removed; if they must be removed keep the operating time to a minimum.

When changing a cathode ray tube, protective goggles should be used. There is always a risk that the tube may implode if it is fractured by a chance blow, dropped on the floor or incorrectly mounted (which can set up excessive stresses on the neck).

When a t.v. receiver has been switched off, the capacitance of the c.r.t. may retain a charge for at least several hours. This charge exists between the e.h.t. connector and the external conductive coating, see Fig. 8.6. Thus before handling c.r.t. or any part of the e.h.t. circuit, this capacitance should be discharged. A suitable discharge device may be constructed from a length of e.h.t. lead with an insulated e.h.t. plug at one end and a crocodile clip at the other end. The crocodile

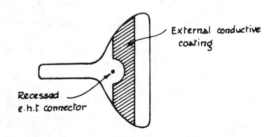

Fig. 8.6 Television cathode ray tube.

clip should be connected first to the external conductive coating or part of the frame connected to the coating. The e.h.t. plug is then fitted into the e.h.t. connector on the tube thereby shorting out the tube capacitance. When possible, the lead should be left in place all the time during handling as the capacitance tends to recover some charge (from the glass) when not shorted.

Tools and Equipment

Tools that are worn, misused or badly maintained cause accidents. In the interests of safety and good workmanship the following rules should be observed:

(a) **Use only good tools.**
(b) **Use in the correct way for the correct purpose.**
(c) **Keep tools clean and inspect them regularly for defects.**

Screwdrivers – Always use a screwdriver of the correct size. When screwing do not hold the workpiece in the hand. For electrical type work, use only screwdrivers which have good quality insulated handles (not wood). Ensure that handles are not cracked or split. A rounded screwdriver end is more likely to slip than one with a flat end. Never hit a screwdriver with a hammer as the handle or the blade might shatter.

Files – Only files fitted with handles should be used; a slip might cause the tang of the file to injure the hand. Do not use a file as a lever because it is brittle and liable to snap.

Hammers – Chipped or badly rounded hammers should not be used. The hammer head should be securely attached to its shaft which must be kept in a sound condition (*i.e.* not split). Oil and grease should not be allowd to get on the hammer.

Pliers and Sidecutters – When used for electrical type work pliers and sidecutters should have well insulated handles. Do not use pliers as spanners because the serrated jaws will round the nut being tightened and the pliers may be damaged. Stainless steel or spring wire should not be cut with pliers or

sidecutters as these materials are harder than the cutters and the cutting edge will be damaged.

Spanners – Open-ended spanners that are splayed or box spanners that are split should not be used. Use a spanner of the correct size as one that is loose fitting will damage the nut and strain the spanner. Never pack a spanner with shims or washers *etc* to make it fit. Whenever possible pull the spanner towards you and avoid using a spanner which is too long as it may strip the nut.

Power Tools – Some portable electric drills in common use have a **metal body which must be earthed**. Two arrangements for feeding earthed drills are shown in Fig. 8.7. In Fig. 8.7(a) the drill motor is fed directly from the mains supply. Since the metal body of the drill is at earth potential the user is protected from shock in the event of an internal fault developing. For this reason it is absolutely essential that the **earth and live leads are not crossed over** when wiring the mains plug. Attention is again drawn to the correct way of wiring a three-pin plug shown in Fig. 8.1.

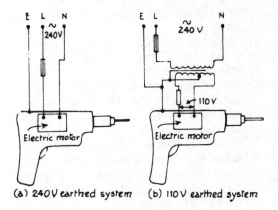

Fig. 8.7 Two systems for earthed drills.

An alternative arrangement for feeding the supply to an electric drill is given in Fig. 8.7(b). Here a step-down transformer is used to provide 110V for the drill motor. Since a centre-tapped transformer is employed, earthed at the centre-tap, the maximum voltage that could exist between a person's body and earth is only 55V. This is only likely to occur if the earth connection to the body of the drill became disconnected.

Another method of protecting the user is by double insulation. Portable electric drills of this type use only two wires (live and neutral), the need for an earth wire being eliminated by using two distinctly insulating systems. One system isolates the current carrying components of the drill from each other and any external metal parts. The second system isolates the motor frame from the body and transmission using insulating materials of such dielectric strengths that a current will not pass through them in the event of a fault developing in the tool or the wiring to it. This system is subjected to a 4000V test (16 times the normal 240V supply).

Here are some important rules to be followed in the use of portable electric tools:

(a) Before use check that the voltage rating is the same as the power supply. Also check that the fuse is of the correct rating.
(b) Before use check that the power plug is in good condition and that the cable is firmly held by the cleat. Check that the cable is free from damage particularly close to the plug and tool where fractures in the wiring often occur.
(c) Make sure that the power supply is switched OFF before plugging the tool into the supply socket.
(d) Ensure that the cable is clear of the working head before switching on.
(e) Regularly inspect and test the continuity of the earth connection to the tool. Tighten or renew bad connections.
(f) Make sure that the trailing lead will not cause yourself or anyone else to trip over it. In such an event the tool may be wrenched from your hand and might cause an accident.
(g) Check your person for loose clothing, long hair, bandages on the hand *etc* which could get entangled with any moving part of the tool.
(h) Stow the tool carefully after use. See that the tool does not become entangled with other tools as you might pull off the earth wire when removing it.
(i) Wear protective goggles when flying particles or dust is involved.

Soldering and Desoldering

Soldering irons should be of the 24V type, supplied from an isolating transformer and not use an earth. Most accidents with soldering irons are caused by burns. Mostly the burns are quite minor but they could be serious. Since soldering and desoldering form an essential part of the daily routine of an electronics technician the following should be noted:

(a) Regularly inspect the soldering iron for physical defects, especially the leads which if bared could cause an electric shock.
(b) If the soldering iron is fed directly from the mains, check that it is correctly earthed.
(c) Always keep the soldering iron on its rest when not in use. Ensure that the tip is protected as this reduces the risk of burns and fire.
(d) Never flick an iron to remove excess solder. Doing so may cause a burn or the solder may fall into live equipment causing a short.
(e) It is very dangerous to hook a soldering iron on to a piece of equipment.
(f) Use eye protectors.
(g) Keep the bit clean.
(h) Remove excess solder from the iron by carefully wiping it on a cleaning pad.
(i) During desoldering remove excess solder with a desoldering gun which sucks off the solder.
(j) Wearing a smock will give protection if solder droplets fall into your lap.
(k) Fumes from melting lead (used in solder) are toxic, so avoid breathing them in.

Equipment

Test equipment needs looking after as well, and the following general points should be noted:

(a) Check that the supply voltage is correct for the equipment.
(b) Check that the power leads are not frayed or damaged and that the mains plug is correctly wired.
(c) Use only the correct rating of fuse for the equipment.
(d) Periodically check the continuity of the

earth connection of equipment that uses an earthed frame. When equipment is used in systems employing an isolating transformer, it may be intentional to leave the earth wire disconnected.

(e) Do not place articles on top of test equipment as they may drop inside ventilation holes or block them.

(f) Do not lean on test equipment.

(g) Keep test equipment clean.

(h) Ensure that any test prod used for checking voltages inside equipment is in good order.

(i) Carefully read instructions supplied with test equipment.

SAFETY IN DOMESTIC ENVIRONMENTS

Service engineers who are called upon to service equipment in a domestic environment perform tasks ranging from minor adjustments to complex fault finding depending on the companys policy on domestic service.

In the interests of personal or customer safety the following general points should be observed:

(a) The polarity of the mains socket outlet and the polarity of the equipment under test should be checked. If the polarity of the mains socket outlet is incorrect, a reversible plug is in use or flexible leads or extensions are unsafe (*i.e.* flexes taped together), **the householder should be informed and equipment left disconnected** until such hazards have been corrected.

(b) If earthed test equipment is to be used to service the equipment, the **equipment under test** should be fed via **an isolating transformer** or battery operated test equipment used. Work should be carried out in an **earth-free area**, *i.e.* on a non-conducting floor and well clear of earthed fittings and pipes; this may entail the use of suitable extension leads.

(c) Before components are repaired or replaced, the equipment under test should be disconnected from the supply and soldering carried out using a low voltage soldering iron fed from a voltage isolating transformer.

(d) **Accompanied** working is desirable in a domestic situation. If a service engineer obtains a key to obtain entry to a house when the householder is absent, it is recommended that the **engineer is accompanied** or the **equipment removed to the workshop for repair**.

(e) When working on receivers where the **chassis is at half the mains supply potential** it is safest to use an **isolating transformer** and work in an **earth-free area**.

Remember that electricity can be very dangerous and possibly lethal. Therefore treat it with respect and **do not take chances – the first may be your last!**

GENERAL SAFETY

(1) Lifting and Carrying

Many accidents happen from lifting and handling articles. Heavy articles which are dropped endanger fingers, hands, toes and feet. Lifting too heavy a load may injure the back or cause a rupture or hernia.

Lifting an object off the floor by bending over it and then straightening up, with the legs kept straight, places too much strain on the back. The correct way is from the squatting position, making the legs and thighs do the work. With legs apart and evenly balanced, place one foot slightly in front of the other, bend the knees, grasp the object and holding it close to the body push yourself up.

Do not carry a load in front of the body so that your vision is obscured. You must be able to see where you are going to avoid any obstacles that might be in the way.

(2) First Aid

To be able to render first aid to an injured person before medical advice can be obtained is of inestimable value. However it is best that medical aid be summoned as quickly as possible. In serious cases, such as bad burns, one should ring for an ambulance by dialling 999.

Cuts – In the case of slight external bleeding from a cut the following points should be noted:

(1) If blood oozes from all parts of the wound do not be alarmed as bleeding usually

stops of its own accord and can be controlled by applying local pressure.

(2) Firmly press together the sides of the wound and if available apply a sterile dressing over it.

(3) Unless a fracture is suspected, elevate the area that is bleeding and apply support in that position.

(4) If the wound is dirty, gently wash it with running water. Take care not to disturb blood clots.

(5) Apply new dressings on top of old ones and maintain pressure with dressing, pad and bandage.

Should the wound be large with severe bleeding, the same general principles apply. If the wound is deep the sterile dressing should be pressed into it and then covered with a pad of soft material above the level and beyond the edges of the wound. Bind firmly with a bandage to keep the pad in position. If neither dressing nor bandage is available, firmly press the sides of the wound together to prevent loss of blood.

Burns – These can be extremely painful. The skin may be reddened, blistered or even destroyed. A big danger is shock and the risk of it quickly increases with the loss of body fluid from the affected area.

The assistance to be offered to a casualty is:

(1) Allow slow running cold water to flow over the burn or immerse in cool water.

(2) Promptly remove constrictive articles from the casualty such as rings, bracelets, belts, *etc* before swelling occurs.

(3) Cover the burn with a dressing or freshly laundered linen.

(4) Do not remove burnt clothing and do not break blisters or apply ointments.

(5) Give small cold drinks at frequent intervals to a badly burned but conscious person.

Cases of severe burns should be taken to hospital as quickly as possible.

If a colleagues clothing catches fire, quench the flames and cool the affected area with water or other non-inflammable fluid. If this is not possible lay him flat and smother the flames.

A burn from a corrosive chemical, such as sulphuric acid or caustic soda, should be flooded thoroughly and continuously with running water. As soon as possible remove any contaminated clothing. If a chemical has entered the eye, hold the head under a slow-running tap of cool water and gently flood the eye.

Toxic Fumes and Smoke – Inhaling poisonous fumes or smoke can be serious if taken in sufficient quantity. Poisonous fumes include carbon monoxide (a normal product of combustion); carbon tetrachloride, trichloroethylene (used in degreasing); hydrogen sulphide and cyanide fumes (given off by polyurethane foam when on fire). Some fumes have distinctive odours and are sometimes recognisable by their characteristic colours; others are odourless and colourless. Do not deliberately sniff an unknown substance to identify it.

Sufferers from the effects of toxic fumes or smoke should be taken into the fresh air immediately. If unconscious, give articial respiration as outlined on page 116 and summon assistance.

Irritant Materials – Mention should be made of 'industrial dermatitis' which is an inflammation of the skin caused by some industrial materials acting as irritants. It usually starts with an irritation of the skin accompanied by redness; sometimes there is swelling and blisters may appear. The hands and the arms are usually affected but if the irritant is in the form of a fine dust or fumes, the eyes, face and neck may be affected. Substances that can cause industrial dermatitis include mineral oils, paraffin, turpentine, petroleum products, tar, pitch, light, heat, X-rays and many chemical compounds.

The dermatitis is easier to prevent than cure and common preventative measures include the use of barrier creams, washing of hands and arms after contact with an irritant and wearing protective clothing.

Medical advice should be sought for treatment.

(3) Accident Reporting

All accidents at work – no matter how trivial – should be recorded in an **accident book**. This contains particulars of the injured person, details of the accident, nature and extent of the injury, *etc*. The accident book serves as a record that the accident happened at work and has been reported, information that subsequently may have legal implications. It may also be instrumental in having new regulations introduced with the object of avoiding similar accidents in the future.

(4) Fire Safety

A combination of combustible fuel, heat and **oxygen** is needed to start a fire. Obvious combustible fuels are wood, paper, petrol, oil, *etc*. Examples of heat sources that can set off a fire are electric currents, burning cigarette ends, mechanical friction, naked flames, *etc*. Oxygen, of course, is in the air.

Fire can spread very fast through a building. A fire starting at floor level can travel by flame spread, heat conduction or heat radiation across space to reach other combustible materials. Smoke and hot gases rise in a column to the ceiling, mushroom out and if they meet a shaft or open staircase will obtain a fresh supply of oxygen and so intensify the fire. The flow of hot gases to the ceiling may start a secondary fire by radiation or by hot particles falling on the floor. The ceiling is liable to collapse under the intense heat which may result in other parts of the building collapsing.

Fire Extinguishers and Their Uses

The action of a fire extinguisher is to remove one of the three elements of fuel, heat and oxygen from the other two which will make the fire go out. The principal methods of extinguishing a fire are:

STARVING (removing the fuel)
SMOTHERING (removing the oxygen)
COOLING (removing the heat)

Fire risks are classified into three main groups so that the most suitable extinguishing agent may be selected:

Class 'A' Fires

These are fires where the combustible material is **wood**, **paper** or **textiles** and all articles made from them or composed predominantly of them. **Water** is the most

effective agent and operates by cooling the fuel below the temperature of combustion.

There are two types of portable water extinguishers (RED body).

(1) The soda acid type in which a small quantity of sulphuric acid reacts with a weak solution of sodium bicarbonate. This generates carbon dioxide which builds up sufficient pressure to expel the water.
(2) The gas pressure type in which compressed gas (usually carbon dioxide) is used to expel the water.

The jet should be directed at the base of the fire.

Class 'B' Fires

These are fires where the combustible material is an inflammable liquid such as **oil**, **fat**, **petrol**, **paint** or **lacquer**.

There are three main types of suitable fire extinguishers for use with this type of fire:

(1) Foam (PALE CREAM body) in which chemical foam is expelled from the extinguisher by carbon dioxide gas.
(2) Dry powder (BLUE body) is expelled from the extinguisher by carbon dioxide gas.
(3) Carbon dioxide gas (BLACK body) is released from the extinguisher under pressure.

These agents have a smothering effect. **The jet should be directed on to the fire**.

Fires in small flat containers can be smothered by an asbestos blanket. When putting the blanket on to the fire, hold it so that the hands and face are protected. One should not be too hasty in removing the blanket.

Class 'C' Fires

This is where live electrical wiring and equipment is involved. It is not strictly a separate class but includes risks where there is a danger of electric shock.

The fire extinguishing agents used must be non-conductors of electricity. Three types may be used:

(1) Dry powder (BLUE body)
(2) Carbon dioxide (BLACK body)
(3) Vaporising liquid such as B.C.F. (GREEN body)

As there are various ways of operating portable extinguishers it is important that the makers instructions printed on the body are followed. It would be prudent to familiarise oneself with the type of extinguishers on the premises so that one can act immediately in an emergency.

On discovering a fire and one is alone

First call the Fire Brigade and then attempt to contain the fire.

If others are present on the premises

(1) **First call for assistance**
(2) **Call the Fire Brigade**
(3) **Sound the alarm**
(4) **Attempt to contain the fire.**

QUESTIONS ON CHAPTER EIGHT

(1) Your friend is suffering from severe electric shock having grasped a live conductor. The first thing you should do is:
   (a) Telephone for a doctor
   (b) Switch off the supply
   (c) Start articial respiration
   (d) Give him a cigarette.
(2) Accidents in a workshop may be reduced by:
   (a) Working in a careful and tidy manner
   (b) Ensuring that all workers are effectively earthed
   (c) Using three wire cables
   (d) Keeping the workers happy.
(3) Under the Health and Safety at Work Act of 1974, the responsibility for health and safety rest with:
   (a) The government only
   (b) The employer only
   (c) The employee only
   (d) Employer and employee in part.
(4) If the fuse blows in some equipment the first thing you should do is:
   (a) Check the mains voltage
   (b) Replace it with one of higher rating
   (c) Find the reason for the fuse blowing
   (d) Short it out with a thick piece of wire.

(5) The earth connection to the frame of an item of test equipment is used to:
   (a) Prevent internal faults from developing
   (b) Reduce the risk of electric shock
   (c) Limit the current flowing
   (d) Provide a magnetic screen.
(6) A three-core flex has wires coloured blue, brown and green/yellow. When connecting to a three pin plug you should connect:
   (a) The brown lead to the neutral terminal
   (b) The green/yellow lead to the earth terminal
   (c) The blue lead to the live terminal
   (d) The blue lead to the earth terminal.
(7) Accidents at work should be entered in the Accident Book:
   (a) Only if the accident is serious
   (b) Only if a doctor has been called
   (c) Only if someone has been negligent
   (d) On all occasions.
(8) The correct initial posture to adopt when lifting a heavy article off the floor is:
   (a) Back bent in an arc
   (b) Bent knees and a straight back
   (c) Kneeling position
   (d) Ready for a quick snatch.
(9) The **first** thing to do on discovering a colleague with a severe cut on his hand is to:
   (a) Ring 999
   (b) Immerse his hand in hot water
   (c) Try to stop the bleeding by pressing the wound together
   (d) Give him a cold drink.
(10) On discovering a workmate with a small burn on his arm, the **first** thing to do is:
   (a) Allow slow running cold water to flow over the burn
   (b) Break the blister and cover with a dressing
   (c) Apply a small amount of burn ointment and cover with a dressing
   (d) Give him a hot drink.
(11) Toxic fumes are:
   (a) Non-alcoholic
   (b) Non-poisonous
   (c) Invigorating
   (d) Poisonous.

(12) The conditions necessary for combustion are:
   (a) Water, petrol and air
   (b) Oil, heat and a match
   (c) Light, heat and fuel
   (d) Fuel, heat and oxygen.

(13) Which of the following is **not** suitable for dealing with a flammable liquid fire:
   (a) Carbon dioxide
   (b) Water
   (c) Foam
   (d) Dry powder.

(14) The body of a portable carbon dioxide fire extinguisher is normally painted:
   (a) Pink
   (b) White
   (c) Blue
   (d) Black.

(15) A class B fire is one where the substance on fire is:
   (a) Wood
   (b) Petrol
   (c) Electrical wiring
   (d) Textiles.

(16) Upon discovering that the mains outlet socket in a customer house is of the wrong polarity you should:
   (a) Inform the customer and recommend the use of an isolation transformer
   (b) Inform the customer and disconnect any equipment from the socket
   (c) Swap over the live and neutral leads in the mains plug
   (d) Say nothing for fear of upsetting the customer.

(17) An isolating transformer is used in a workshop primarily to:
   (a) Eliminate the risk of shock
   (b) Reduce the risk of shock
   (c) Eliminate mains interference
   (d) Stabilise the mains supply.

(18) A television receiver operated from a 13A outlet should have a plug fitted with a fuse rated at:
   (a) 3A
   (b) 7A
   (c) 10A
   (d) 13A.

(Answers on page 219.)

CHAPTER NINE

ELECTRICAL CIRCUITS, RESISTANCE AND UNITS

Objectives

1 Lists effects of a current and states properties of conductors and insulators.
2 States factors affecting resistance and solves problems involving resistance and resistivity.
3 States effects of temperature on resistance of conductors and insulators.
4 States the relationship of SI electrical units to each other. Calculates I, V, R and P in simple circuits.
5 Considers effect of power dissipation on component size.

ELECTRIC CURRENT

Simple Atomic Structure

ATOMS ARE THE smallest structures from which chemical elements such as oxygen, mercury, sulphur or copper are formed. All atoms consist of a central **nucleus** containing **protons having positive charge** and, with one exception, **neutrons having zero charge** around which orbit at high speed **electrons of negative charge**. The number of protons in the nucleus is known as the atomic number of the atom. In an electrically neutral atom the number of electrons is equal to the number of protons.

The simplest structure is that of the hydrogen atom, see Fig. 9.1(a). This consists of a central nucleus containing one proton around which orbits a single electron. The electron is kept in its orbit by a force of attraction existing between the equal but opposite electric charges of the electron and proton. The metal aluminium has an atomic number of 13, thus each aluminium atom consists of a nucleus containing 13 protons

around which orbit 13 electrons, see Fig. 9.1(b). The atom is electrically neutral since the negative charge of the electrons is exactly balanced by the opposite positive charge of the protons. The electrons are now arranged in 'shells', or energy levels, with the electrons(2) in the inner shell having the least energy and which are tightly bound to the atom. Electrons of higher energy occupy shells further away from the central nucleus. Electrons in the outer shell have the highest energy and are more easily detached from the atom and are known as the **valency electrons**. It is the valency electrons that take part in electrical conduction and chemical reaction.

An atom will part with one or more of its valency electrons if it receives sufficient energy from its surroundings. In a metal conductor such as copper, silver or aluminium the majority of the atoms will be short of at least one electon at normal room temperature since the thermal energy will be sufficient for electrons to breakaway. The idea is shown in Fig. 9.1(c), where an electron having escaped its parent atom becomes a **free** electron. On

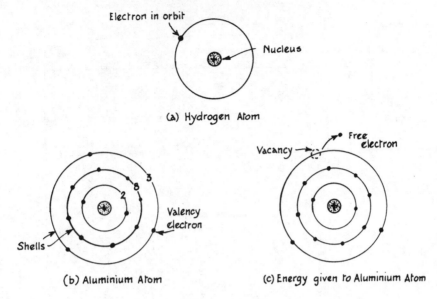

Fig. 9.1 Simple models of atoms.

leaving its atom the electron leaves behind a **vacancy** which causes the atom to acquire a net positive charge and is referred to as a **positive ion**. An atom that gains an electron is called a **negative ion**.

Even in a very short length of a metal conductor there are a very large number of electrons, for instance in a cubic centimetre of copper there are about 10^{23} free electrons. These free electrons are continually being released by thermal energy from the outside. An electron released in this manner has to travel only a very short distance before it encounters a neighbouring atom and the chances are that it will soon be recaptured by a neighbouring vacancy which provides an attractive force with the electron. Thus the image of a seemingly uninteresting length of copper wire is transformed into one of intense activity where there is a random but continuous motion of escape and recapture of free electrons.

Current Flow

When an **electrical force** is applied to a metal conductor a movement of free electrons carrying negative charge will occur in a particular direction. A method of providing the **electromotive force (e.m.f.)** is to apply a positive charge to one end of the conductor and a negative charge to the other end. This is shown in Fig. 9.2, where only a few free electrons are considered.

Due to a force of attraction, free electrons will drift to the left towards the positive terminal of the e.m.f. source. Drifting electrons will probably be, however, soon captured by neighbouring vacancies as shown, *i.e.* their **active life** is short lived. Free electrons close to the positive terminal will enter it, and at the same time electrons from the negative terminal will enter the conductor to fill vacancies left behind by electrons that have drifted to the left. The diagram is simply a 'snap' of a continuous process, whereby vacancies that have become filled with drifting electrons once again release them due to the thermal energy coming from outside.

Thus within the conductor there is a **motion of electrons** from right-to-left which constitutes **an electric current**. However, in the days long before the structure of atoms was known it was believed that an electric current was due to the motion of positive particles which would move towards the negative terminal and this idea is still used as a convention for current direction. Thus **conventional current (I)** is in the opposite direction to electron movement. There must be a **complete circuit** for current to

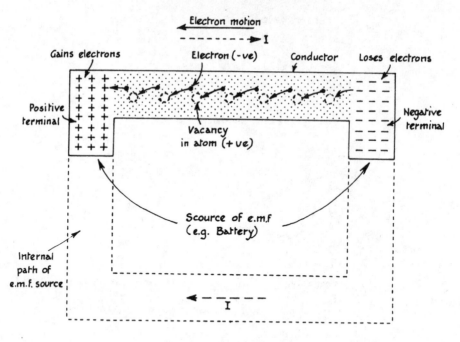

Fig. 9.2 Idea of current flow.

flow and this is provided by the internal path of the e.m.f. source as shown.

A question that may be posed is 'how fast do the electrons in a conductor move?'. The surprising answer is 'incredibly slow, relatively at a snail's pace'. It has been calculated that the maximum speed is about 0·2 cm/s. However, this does not apply to the speed at which the **start of movement** is passed along a conductor. A fraction of a micro-second after an e.m.f. has been applied to a 10 metre length of conductor, electrons at the far end are starting to move. An analagous situation is when water is flowing slowly and steadily in a pipe. If the water is turned on and off the effects are felt at the remote end almost immediately, whereas the water entering the pipe does not emerge until sometime much later.

EFFECTS OF AN ELECTRIC CURRENT

As an electric current flowing in a conductor cannot be seen, we have to rely on its effects to enable detection. There are three main effects.

(1) Chemical Effect

If a pair of platinum electrodes are placed in an electrolyte of water to which is added a small quantity of sulphuric acid to make it more conductive and a d.c. voltage supply is connected to the electrodes as shown in Fig. 9.3(a), a current will flow between the electrodes. It is observed that gas bubbles are given off at both electrodes. Effectively, a chemical change has taken place with the water in the electrolyte decomposing into its constituent elements of oxygen and hydrogen, a process known as **electrolysis**.

Another example of the chemical effect is in **electroplating**. Here the article to be plated forms the cathode and the metal to be deposited is the anode, with the electrolyte usually consisting of a salt of the metal to be deposited. When a current is passed through the electrolyte the metal anode is dissolved away and deposited on the article to be plated; an example being the silver plating of a baser metal. In some cases, for example in chromium plating, the anode material is insoluble and the chromium is provided by the electrolyte.

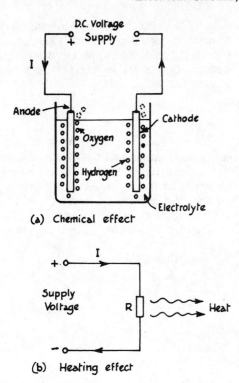

(a) Chemical effect

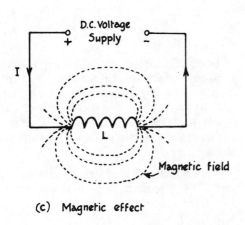

(b) Heating effect

(c) Magnetic effect

Fig. 9.3 Three effects of an electric current.

The reverse process of electroplating is sometimes used where metal is deliberately removed from the work-piece. This is usually done with an alkaline electrolyte when metal is removed from high-points to achieve a highly polished surface and is called **electropolishing**.

A further application is in **electrolytic extraction and refining**, a process used to extract metals such as copper and aluminium from their ores and for the refining of metals such as silver, copper and gold.

(2) Heating Effect

Whenever current flows in a conductor heat is produced, see Fig. 9.3(b). The amount of heat generated not only depends on the magnitude of the current flowing but also on the resistance R which is affected by the conductor dimensions and the material from which it is made.

Typical common applications of the heating effect, of which there are many, are found in electric ovens, fires, irons, toasters and electric lamps. The ability of an electric current to heat a metal to melting point is utilised in electric welding and fuses.

A fuse must be capable of carrying a normal circuit load current without overheating. An abnormal increase in current as a result of a fault or accidental short-circuit will cause the fuse to heat to its melting point and **blow**. This action breaks the circuit to prevent further damage and the risk of fire.

(3) Magnetic Effect

When a current flows in a conductor a magnetic field is set up around the conductor. To enhance the magnetic field the conductor is usually wound in the form of a coil as in Fig. 9.3(c).

If the coil is wound over an iron core, the core becomes magnetised when current flows and behaves like a magnet. Such an arrangement is called an **electromagnet**. The magnetic effect is utilised in electrical relays, motors and generators, electric bells, lifting magnets, transformers and some measuring instruments.

CONDUCTORS AND INSULATORS

Metals that contain very large numbers of free electrons will allow the electrons to move through them when a suitable form of electromotive force is applied. Metals are thus **electrical conductors**; the metals silver, copper and aluminium being among the best. Aside from metals, current may also be conveyed by **ionised gases** such as sodium vapour, mercury vapour and neon which are used in gas discharge lamps. Here current is conveyed by free electrons and positive ions which move in opposite directions. Also, **electrolytes** used in batteries are conductors where current is supported by the movement of both positive and negative ions.

Materials that produce relatively few free electrons at normal room temperature permit electrons to move only with difficulty and few vacancies are created in the atoms to assist in the handing-on of electrons to the next in line, as explained in Fig. 9.2. Such materials are called pure **semiconductors**, examples being silicon and germanium.

In another group of materials there are so few free electrons produced when a normal electromotive force is applied that electrical conduction becomes very difficult to measure. These materials are called **insulators** and very high energy only is required to produce free electrons in sufficient numbers to enable conduction to take place, common examples being glass and nylon.

A list of conductors and insulators is given in Table 9.1.

Conductors	Insulators
Silver	Glass
Copper	Rubber
Gold	Sulphur
Platinum	Polystyrene
Tin	Polypropylene
Steel	Nylon
Lead	Paraffin wax
Iron	Epoxy resin
Nickel	Polyvinylchloride (PVC)
Brass	Wood (dry)
Bronze	Paper
Aluminium	Perspex
Zinc	Cork

Table 9.1 Conductors and insulators.

ELECTRICAL UNITS

Electromotive Force (E.M.F.)

This is the force necessary to produce the flow of current or movement of electrons around an electrical circuit and is usually provided by a power supply or battery in a d.c. circuit. The unit of e.m.f. is the **volt (V)** and the symbol for e.m.f. is E.

Charge

The symbol for the quantity of electrical charge is Q and the unit of electrical charge is the **coulomb (C)**. One coulomb represents the electrical charge of a very large number of electrons or protons; **1 coulomb = 6.289 × 10^{18} electrons or protons**, see Fig. 9.4 Thus a coulomb is a quantity of electrical charge.

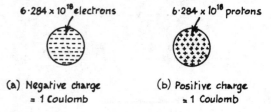

(a) Negative charge = 1 Coulomb   (b) Positive charge = 1 Coulomb

Fig. 9.4 Bodies having an electrical charge of one coulomb.

Current

Electrical current is a measure of **the rate of movement of charge** around a circuit. The unit of current is the **ampere (A)** and the circuit symbol for it is I. **If one coulomb of charge passes a given point in a conductor in one second, then the rate of flow of charge is one ampere**, see Fig. 9.5. Thus

1 ampere = 1 coulomb per second
and $I = Q/t$ ampere or $Q = It$ coulombs.

Problem 1

An electrical charge of 30 coulombs moves past a point in an electrical circuit in one minute. Determine:

(a) The value of the current.
(b) The amount of charge that passes the point in 3·5 minutes if the current remains constant.

Solution

(a) $I = \dfrac{Q}{t}$ amperes

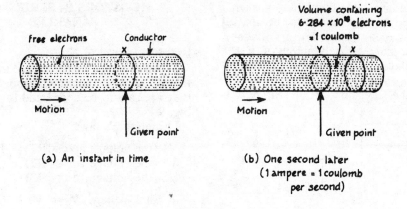

Fig. 9.5 *Diagrams illustrating definition of ampere.*

$$= \frac{30}{60}$$

$$= 0.5A$$

(b) Q = It coulombs
       = $0.5 \times 3.5 \times 60$
       = 105C

Resistance

The opposition to the flow of current around a circuit is called resistance and the unit of resistance is the **ohm** (Ω). When free electrons move in a particular direction through a circuit conductor by the applied e.m.f. some of the free electrons collide with the atoms of which the conductor is made. These collisions impede, or resist, the flow of current and also produce heat in the conductor.

Multiple and Submultiple Units

For some uses in practical systems the basic electrical units may be too large or too small and a range of multiples and submultiples has been developed, as shown in Table 9.2.

Some examples are:

$$
\begin{aligned}
&1 \text{ mV (1 milivolt)} &&= 1/1000\,\text{V} = 10^{-3}\,\text{V} \\
&1 \text{ k}\Omega \text{ (1 kilohm)} &&= 1000\,\Omega = 10^{3}\,\Omega \\
&1 \,\mu\text{A (1 microamp)} &&= 1/1000000\,\text{A} = 10^{-6}\,\text{A} \\
&1 \text{ MV (1 megavolt)} &&= 1000000\,\text{V} = 10^{6}\,\text{V} \\
&1 \text{ nC (1 nano-} &&= 1/1000000000\,\text{C} \\
&\quad\quad\text{coulomb)} &&= 10^{-9}\,\text{C}
\end{aligned}
$$

OHM'S LAW

Ohm's law is a valuable rule for making calculations in circuits where the resistance is

Multiple	Prefix	Symbol	Submultiple	Prefix	Symbol
10^{12}	tera	T	10^{-1}	deci	d
10^{9}	giga	G	10^{-2}	centi	c
10^{6}	mega	M	10^{-3}	milli	m
10^{3}	kilo	k	10^{-6}	micro	μ
10^{2}	hecto	h	10^{-9}	nano	n
10^{1}	deca	da	10^{-12}	pico	p

Table 9.2 *Multiples and submultiples.*

constant. The law states simply that in such a circuit **current is proportional to the applied voltage**. This means that if the voltage is doubled, the current is doubled or if the voltage is reduced to one quarter, the current is reduced to one quarter.

Thus if the resistance R in Fig. 9.6 is

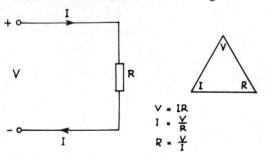

Fig. 9.6 Ohms Law (current ∝ voltage).

constant, the circuit will conform to Ohm's law and we may write that

$$\frac{V}{I} = \text{constant} = R.$$

This equation may be expressed in three ways:

$$I = \frac{V}{R}, \quad V = IR \quad \text{and} \quad R = \frac{V}{I}.$$

Problem 2

(a) If in Fig. 9.6, V = 10V and R = 2Ω, find the value of current flowing.
(b) If in Fig. 9.6, R = 10Ω and I = 2·5A, find the value of the applied voltage.
(c) If in Fig. 9.6, V = 20V and I = 0·5A, find the value of R.

Solution

(a) $I = \dfrac{V}{R} = \dfrac{10}{2} = 5A.$

(b) $V = IR = 10 \times 2 \cdot 5 = 25V.$

(c) $R = \dfrac{V}{I} = \dfrac{20}{0 \cdot 5} = 40Ω$

It should be mentioned that not all circuit components obey Ohm's law. Some devices obey the law fairly accurately but unfortunately others such as diodes, transistors and voltage dependent resistors do not. In the following it will be assumed that the devices do conform to the law.

RESISTORS IN SERIES AND PARALLEL

Resistors in Series

When resistors are connected in a circuit so that the **same current flows through all of them** they are said to be connected in series, as in Fig. 9.7.

Using Ohm's law:

V1 (the voltage across R1) = I.R1
V2 (the voltage across R2) = I.R2
V3 (the voltage across R3) = I.R3

The total voltage V = V1 + V2 + V3 and hence substituting for V1, V2 and V3 we have:

V = I.R1 + I.R2 + I.R3

If we call the effective resistance of the series combination R, then:

V = I.R

thus:

I.R = I.R1 + I.R2 + I.R3

or:

R = R1 + R2 + R3

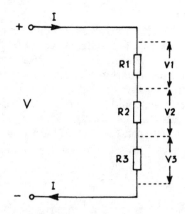

Fig. 9.7 Resistors in series.

Thus for resistors in series the **effective resistance is the sum of the individual resistances.**

Problem 3

In the circuit of Fig. 9.7 if V = 100V and R1 = 3Ω, R2 = 8Ω and R3 = 14Ω, determine:

(a) The effective resistance of the circuit.
(b) The value of the current flowing.

Solution

(a) R = R1 + R2 + R3
$= 3 + 8 + 14 = 25\Omega$

(b) $I = \frac{V}{R} = \frac{100}{25} = 4A$

Resistors in Parallel

When resistances are so connected in a circuit that the **same voltage is developed across all of them**, they are said to be connected in parallel as in Fig. 9.8.

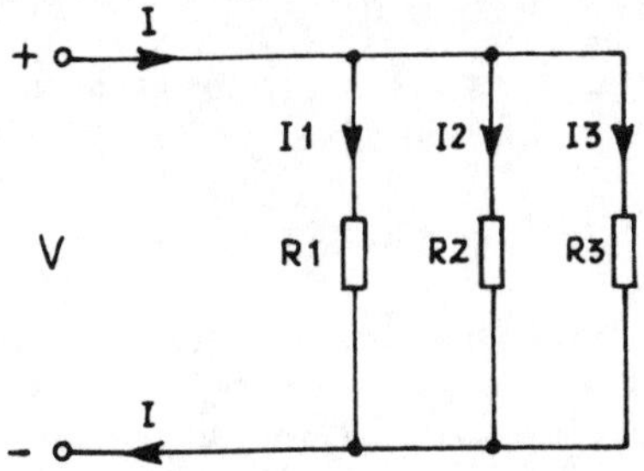

Fig. 9.8 Resistors in parallel.

Using Ohm's law:

I1 (the current in R1) = V/R1
I2 (the current in R2) = V/R2
I3 (the current in R3) = V/R3

The total current I = I1 + I2 + I3

If we call the effective resistance of the parallel combination R, then:

V/R = V/R1 + V/R2 + V/R3

or:

1/R = 1/R1 + 1/R2 + 1/R3.

Thus resistors in parallel are added as reciprocals.

For two resistors in parallel, the effective resistance R is given by:

$$R = \frac{R1 \times R2}{R1 + R2}.$$

With **equal value of resistors** in parallel, the effective resistance is equal to the **value of a single resistor divided by the number of resistors.**

Problem 4

In the circuit of Fig. 9.8, if R1 = 10Ω, R2 = 10Ω, R3 = 20Ω and V = 30V, determine:

(a) The effective resistance of the circuit.
(b) The value of current I.

Solution

(a) The effective resistance of R1 and R2 in parallel = 10/2 = 5Ω.
This resistance is in parallel with R3, thus the final effective resistance

$$R = \frac{5 \times 20}{5 + 20} = \frac{100}{25} = 4\Omega.$$

(b) $I = \frac{V}{R} = \frac{30}{4} = 7{\cdot}5A.$

RESISTANCE AND RESISTIVITY

The resistance of a material depends upon the number of collisions that occur between free electrons and atoms, which is governed by the lattice structure of the material.

In order to compare the resistance of various materials, a quantity known as **resistivity** (symbol p) is used. This is defined as the resistance between opposite faces of a metre-cube of the material, see Fig. 9.9, and has the dimension of ohm-metre. Some typical resistivity values are given in Table 9.3.

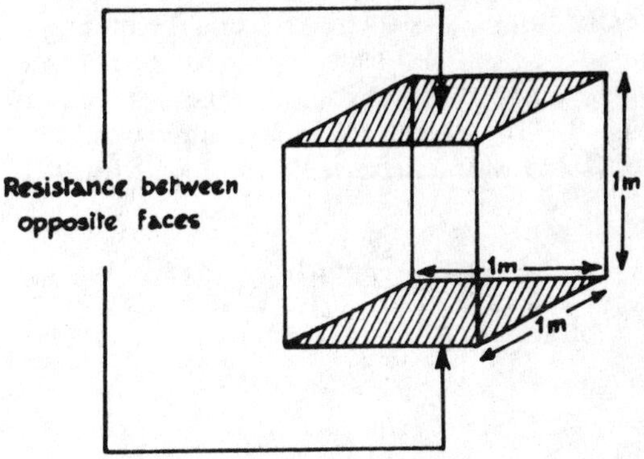

Fig. 9.9 Metre-cube of material.

Good metal conductors such as copper, silver and aluminium are characterised by a very small resistivity. Although silver is the best conductor, copper is extensively used in wire form and for printed circuit connections as it is cheaper. Insulators, on the other hand are identified by their high resistivity value, a feature common to poor conductors of electricity. Some of the poorer conductors such as

Material	Resistivity (ohm-metre)	Features
Silver	1.6×10^{-8}	
Copper	1.7×10^{-8}	Good conductors
Aluminium	2.65×10^{-8}	
Nickel	7.24×10^{-8}	
Iron	9.4×10^{-8}	Used as
Manganin	45×10^{-8}	resistance
Nichrome	108×10^{-8}	elements
Carbon	$33–185 \times 10^{-8}$	
Germanium	0.5	Used in semi-
Silicon	2×10^3	conductor devices
Glass	10^{12}	
Mica	10^{14}	Used in
Polythene	10^{15}	insulators
Polystyrene	10^{16}	

Table 9.3 Resistivity values.

carbon, iron and nickel are used as conductors for special applications.

Apart from resistivity, the resistance of a particular material is also affected by its dimensions, *i.e.* its length and cross-sectional area. Consider a length (l) of a conductor of rectangular cross-sectional area A, having a resistance of 0.1Ω as in Fig. 9.10(a). If three such lengths were joined together, as in Fig. 9.10(b), the effective resistance would be 0.3Ω (resistors in series). Similarly for five

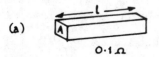

(a)

$0.1\,\Omega$

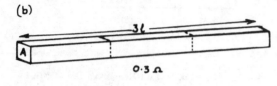

(b)

$3l$

$0.3\,\Omega$

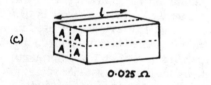

(c)

$0.025\,\Omega$

Fig. 9.10 Effect of conductor dimensions on resistance.

lengths the resistance would be 0.5Ω. Thus we can say that:

Resistance is proportional to conductor length (l)

or $R \propto l$

Suppose now that four of the lengths at (a) are joined together as in Fig. 9.10(c). The effective resistance would be $0.1/4 = 0.025\Omega$ (equal value resistors in parallel). Similarly for eight lengths joined in this manner, the effective resistance would be $0.1/8 = 0.0125\Omega$. Thus we can say that:

Resistance is inversely proportional to cross-sectional area (A)

or $R \propto \dfrac{1}{A}$

The resistance of a conductor is thus proportional to its resistivity and length but inversely proportional to its cross-sectional area. Expressed in equation form:

$$R = \frac{pl}{A} \text{ ohms}$$

where p = resistivity (ohm-m)
       l = length in metres
       A = cross-sectional area in square metres (m^2)

Problem 5

(a) Find the resistance of a 10 metre length of copper wire having a cross-sectional area of 2 square mm ($p = 1.7 \times 10^{-8}$ ohm-m).
(b) Determine the resistance of the wire at (a) if:
   (1) Its length is increased by a factor of five.
   (2) Its cross-sectional area is halved.

Solution

(a) $R = \dfrac{pl}{A} = \dfrac{1.7 \times 10^{-8} \times 10}{2 \times 10^{-6}}$

    $= 0.085\Omega$

(b) (1) By proportion if the length increases by a factor of 5, resistance increases to $5 \times 0.085 = 0.425\Omega$.
    (2) By proportion if cross-sectional area is halved, resistance is doubled to $0.085 \times 2 = 0.17\Omega$.

Problem 6

A length of conductor has a resistance of $0 \cdot 025\Omega$. Find its resistance if:

(a) Its length is reduced to one fifth.
(b) Its cross-sectional area is increased by a factor of four.

Solution

(a) $R \propto l$

Thus resistance $= 0 \cdot 025 \times \dfrac{1}{5} = 0 \cdot 005\Omega$.

(b) $R \propto \dfrac{1}{A}$

Thus resistance $= \dfrac{0 \cdot 025}{4} = 0 \cdot 00625\Omega$.

Effect of Temperature on Resistance

Electrical resistance is affected by temperature variations in two ways. As a result of a temperature rise:

(a) More electrons escape from their parent atoms to become free electrons.
(b) The atoms vibrate more rapidly in the lattice structure resulting in an increase in the number of collisions with free electrons.

These two factors give rise to opposing effects, *i.e.* factor (a) will cause a decrease in resistance but factor (b) will cause an increase in resistance. For most metals it is factor (b) that predominates and in consequence resistance increases with temperature, see Fig. 9.11.

Over the operating temperature range of electrical apparatus, the resistance of electrical metal conductors varies linearly with

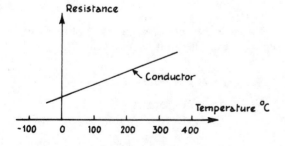

Fig. 9.11 Effect of temperature on resistance of metal conductor such as copper.

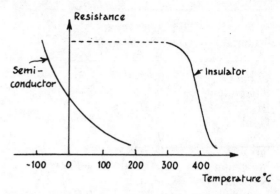

Fig. 9.12 Effect of temperature on resistance of insulators and semiconductors.

temperature. In contrast, insulators and semiconductors are typified by a resistance that falls with increasing temperature, see Fig. 9.12. The resistance of an insulator is very high at normal operating temperatures but falls rapidly at high temperatures leading ultimately to break-down of the insulator.

In all cases, it should be noted that the change in resistance of the material is not due only to a rise in surrounding (ambient) temperature but also because of the self-heating effect as a result of current flowing in the material.

The amount of change in resistance with temperature is called the **temperature coefficient of resistance** (symbol α). It is commonly defined as the change in resistance of 1 ohm of the material at 0°C when the temperature is raised by 1°C. For example, if a length of wire of resistance 1 ohm at 0°C rises to $1 \cdot 004$ ohms when the temperature is raised by 1°C, its temperature coefficient would be $0 \cdot 004$ ohms per ohm per °C.

Some typical values for temperature coefficient are given in Table 9.4. It should be noted that the temperature coefficient of pure metals is not large and always **positive**, *i.e.* the resistance increases with a rise in temperature. In contrast, the temperature coefficient for carbon, semiconductors and insulators is **negative**, *i.e.* the resistance decreases with a rise in temperature.

The temperature coefficient of resistance enables the resistance to be calculated due to a temperature change, if the resistance is known at some reference temperature, *e.g.* 0°C or room temperature. For metals, over the range

Material	Temperature coefficient at 0°C
Copper	0·00426
Aluminium	0·0043
Brass	0·001
Gold	0·0034
Iron	0·0055
Silver	0·0038
Manganin	0·000002 to 0·00005
Nichrome	0·0001
Carbon	− 0·0006 to − 0·0012

Table 9.4 Temperature coefficient of resistance in ohm/ohm/°C.

where the increase in resistance varies linearly with temperature, the increase in resistance is given by:

$$R_{increase} = R_o \alpha t$$

where R_o = resistance at 0°C
α = temperature coefficient
t = rise in temperature in °C

The total new resistance is thus:

$$R_t = R_o + R_o \alpha t$$

or

$$R_t = R_o (1 + \alpha t).$$

Problem 7

A length of iron wire wound in the form of a coil has a resistance of 250Ω at 0°C. What will be its resistance if it is immersed in an oil bath at a temperature of 165°C?

Solution

$$R_t = R_o (1 + \alpha t)$$
$$= 250 (1 + 0·0055 \times 165)$$
$$= 476·875\Omega$$

Temp.Coeff. of iron = 0·0055 see Table 9.4.

Problem 8

A length of copper wire has a resistance of 0·25Ω at 0°C. Determine the increase in its resistance when subject to an ambient temperature of + 25°C.

Solution

$$R_{increase} = R_o \alpha t$$
$$= 0·25 \times 0·00426 \times 25$$
$$= 0·0267\Omega$$

Temp.Coeff. of copper
= 0·00426 see Table 9.4.

ELECTRICAL ENERGY AND POWER

Energy

Energy is the capacity to do work and the unit is the **Joule (J)**. Electrical energy can be produced in a number of ways, for example, through magnetism as with a lifting magnet, through thermo-electric effects as with a thermo-couple or electro-chemically as in a primary or secondary battery.

When energy is expended work is done and in electrical terms:

Work done (Joules) = Electric Charge × Electrical Height

where electrical height is the voltage or potential difference through which the charge moves, see Fig. 9.13.
Thus:

Work done (J) = coulombs × voltage

which means that one Joule of work is done in moving a charge of one coulomb through a potential difference of one volt.

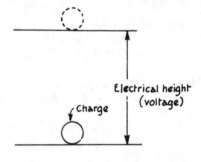

Fig. 9.13 Work done (Joules) = charge × voltage.

Power

Power is the rate of doing work or using up energy and the unit is the **Watt (W)**. Now since:

Work done = voltage × coulombs

Work done per second = voltage × coulombs per second

or

Power (P) = Voltage × Current (Watts or joules/sec)

Therefore

$$P = VI \text{ watts}$$

and since

$$V = IR, P = I^2R \text{ watts}$$

also since

$$I = \frac{V}{R}, P = \frac{V^2}{R} \text{ watts.}$$

Problem 9

A battery receives a charge of 10 coulombs per second from a 12V supply. Determine:

(a) The energy supplied if the battery is charged for one hour.
(b) The power delivered by the supply.

Solution

(a) Energy supplied per second (J)
    = charge × voltage
    = 10 × 12
    = 120 J
   Energy supplied per hour
    = 120 × 60 × 60
    = 432,000 J
(b) Power = V × I
    = V × coulombs per second
    = 12 × 10
    = 120 watts

Problem 10

A 6V battery has an energy reservoir of 4.32×10^6 Joules. A lamp connected to the battery takes 0·5A. Estimate how long the lamp will operate continuously without the need to recharge the battery.

Solution

$$P = V \times I$$
$$= 6 \times 0.5$$
$$= 3W = 3 \text{ Joules per second}$$

Thus 4.32×10^6 Joules will last

$$\frac{4.32 \times 10^6}{3} \text{ seconds}$$

or

$$\frac{4.32 \times 10^6}{3 \times 60 \times 60} \text{ hours}$$

$$= 400 \text{ hours}$$

This time is only an estimate because the current will reduce as the battery runs down.

Kilowatt hour

This is a commonly used unit and is equal to the energy expended when a power of 1 kilowatt (1kW) is used over a period of one hour.

Since 1 kilowatt = 1000 Joules per second
1 kilowatt hour (1kWh) = 1000 × 60 × 60
= 3,600,000 Joules

When being charged for electricity it is the kilowatt hour (often referred to as a **unit of electricty**) for which we pay.

Problem 11

A 240V electric kettle has a power rating of 3kW. How much will it cost to use over a 12 week period if it is operated for 4 mins, 50 times per week when the cost of a unit is 6p.

Solution

Total time for which kettle is operated
= 50 × 4 × 12
= 2400 mins
= 40 hours
Thus the number of kWh (units) used
= 3 × 40 = 120kWh
Total cost (for 12 week period)
= 120 × 6p
= £7.20

EFFECT OF POWER RATING ON COMPONENT SIZE

Heat Generation

Heat energy is generated whenever an electric current flows through electrical resistance. The power or rate at which heat is generated is:

$$P = I^2R \text{ (watts or joules/second).}$$

The total heat energy (W) liberated in a time interval of t seconds is:

$$W = I^2Rt \text{ joules}$$

The resistance in which heat is generated may be in different forms when current flows:

(a) It may be the resistance of connecting wires or strips in which case the resistance is usually small. Thus, unless high currents are involved, the amount of heat generated can usually be ignored.

(b) It may be the resistance of a **resistor**, a circuit component put in to do a specific job, *e.g.* load or bias resistor, and considerable quantities of heat may be generated.

(c) It may be the resistance of a winding, as in a transformer or motor. If there are many turns of fine wire the resistance can be comparatively large and again the amount of heat generated can be considerable.

(d) It may be the resistance of a junction of a semiconductor device. This resistance is often non-linear and difficult to measure in ohms. Thus instead of using $P = I^2R$, we use $P = VI$ where V is the voltage drop across the junction. Again relatively large quantities of heat may be generated.

Temperature Rise

When heat energy is generated within a circuit component or electrical device, the temperature of its body rises. For a given amount of heat the rise in temperature is inversely proportional to the **heat capacity** of the body, *i.e.* a body with a small heat capacity has a larger temperature rise than one with a large heat capacity. An electric lamp filament heats up more quickly than a soldering iron of the same power. Heat capacity depends upon the mass of the body and the material from which it is made.

As soon as the temperature of a body rises above that of its surroundings, the body begins to lose heat. The greater the temperature difference, the greater is the rate of heat loss.

The rate of heat loss depends upon the surface area of the body. When the rate of heat lost is just equal to the rate of heat generation, the temperature of the body stops rising and a steady equilibrium condition is reached. Generally speaking, for a given set of cooling conditions the final steady temperature rise depends upon the surface area of the body. The smaller the surface area, the higher the temperature rise, see Fig. 9.14. Note that a body can only lose heat when its temperature is higher than the **ambient** temperature (surrounding temperature).

Power Rating

The heating effect and consequent rise in temperature must be taken into account in the design of circuit components. If the temperature of a component is allowed to rise excessively, the intended resistance value of the device may alter significantly or the device may fail.

In order to ensure that the temperature rise is not excessive, manufacturers state the maximum power level, *i.e.* **rating** at which a component can be operated safely. The power rating of a component depends upon the cooling conditions, in particular the ambient temperature. Thus manufacturers power rating is usually stated for operation of the component under specified conditions.

If a component is to be operated at a higher ambient temperature than that given by the manufacturer then its rating must be reduced, *i.e.* it must be **derated**. For example, most

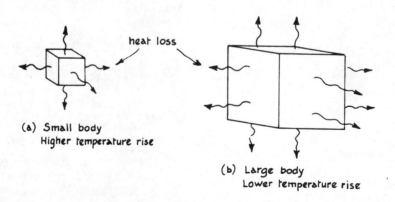

(a) Small body
Higher temperature rise

heat loss

(b) Large body
Lower temperature rise

Fig. 9.14 Comparison of temperature rise for two bodies having same heat energy.

resistors are given two power or wattage ratings, one at 70°C and the other at 40°C. At 40°C a resistor may have a rating of 0·5W but at 70°C it is derated to 0·25W. The lower temperature rating would be appropriate to components used in portable equipment such as a pocket calculator or radio receiver, whereas the higher temperature rating would apply to components used in complex industrial equipment or television receivers.

Resistors are generally available in 0·25W, 0·5W, 1W and 2W ratings and may be of carbon composition, carbon film or metal film types. For resistors of one type, the **higher the power rating the larger the physical size**, see Fig. 9.15. A larger surface area improves the heat loss and reduces the temperature rise.

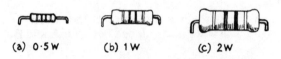

(a) 0·5 W   (b) 1 W   (c) 2W

Fig. 9.15 Comparative physical size of carbon film resistors of different power ratings.

Resistors of larger power ratings from about 3W to 10W are usually wirewound and protected with either a vitreous enamel coating or ceramic body. These coverings have good thermal conductivity and in the case of the ceramic body type provide a high insulation resistance, which is important if high voltages are present. High power resistors must be mounted clear of circuit boards to give proper cooling.

Metal cased power resistors in the range of 10W to 50W are also available. These may be provided with a finned aluminium case which acts as a heat sink to assist in reducing the temperature rise when clamped to the metal frame or chassis of the equipment.

In general, upgrading of physical size with increase in power rating applies to most electrical components. High power wound components such as transformers, smoothing inductors, motors and generators use thicker conductors in their windings resulting in a bulkier structure. Higher power semiconductor devices such as diodes, thyristors and transistors, see Fig. 9.16, may also be identified by their larger physical size.

(a) 300mW   (b) 6W

Fig. 9.16 Physical sizes of small and medium power transistors.

CALCULATIONS IN RESISTIVE CIRCUITS

In this section the following important formulae will be applied:

$$I = \frac{V}{R} \qquad\qquad P = VI$$

$$V = IR \qquad\qquad P = I^2R$$

$$R = \frac{V}{I} \qquad\qquad P = \frac{V^2}{R}$$

$$R_T = R1 + R2 + R3 \text{ (resistors in series)}$$

$$R_T = \frac{R1 \times R2}{R1 + R2} \text{ (2 resistors in parallel)}$$

Problem 12
Using Fig. 9.17 calculate:

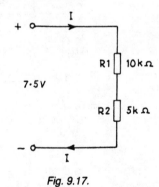

Fig. 9.17.

(a) The value of the current I.
(b) The voltages developed across R1 and R2.

Solution
(a) $R_T = R1 + R2$ (resistors in series)
$\quad\quad = 10 + 5 = 15k\Omega$

$$I = \frac{V}{R}$$

$$= \frac{7\cdot5}{15 \times 10^3} \text{ A}$$

$$= 0\cdot5mA$$

(b) Voltage developed across R1
$$= I \times R1 = 0.5 \times 10^{-3} \times 10^4 V = 5V$$

Voltage developed across R2
$$= I \times R2 = 0.5 \times 10^{-3} \times 5 \times 10^3 V = 2.5V$$

(Note that the sum of the voltages across R1 and R2 = supply voltage).

These voltages may have been arrived at by proportion:

As the current flowing is common to both resistors, the voltage across each resistor is proportional to the resistor value.

The total resistance = 15 kΩ

Therefore the voltage across R1 is

$$\frac{10}{15} \times 7.5V = 5V$$

and the voltage across R2 is

$$\frac{5}{15} \times 7.5V = 2.5V.$$

Problem 13
Using Fig. 9.18 calculate:

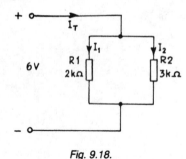

Fig. 9.18.

(a) The effective resistance of the circuit.
(b) The value of the currents I_1, I_2 and I_T.

Solution
(a) R1 and R2 are in parallel (same voltage across them) therefore:

$$R_T = \frac{R1 \times R2}{R1 + R2} = \frac{3 \times 2}{3 + 2} \, k\Omega = 1.2 \, k\Omega.$$

(b) $I_1 = \dfrac{V}{R1} = \dfrac{6}{2 \times 10^3} \, A = 3mA$

$I_2 = \dfrac{V}{R2} = \dfrac{6}{3 \times 10^3} \, A = 2mA$

$I_T = I_1 + I_2 = 3 + 2 = 5mA$

Note that $I = \dfrac{V}{R} = \dfrac{6}{1.2 \times 10^3} \, A$
$$= 5mA \text{ (as before)}$$

Problem 14
Using Fig. 9.19 calculate:

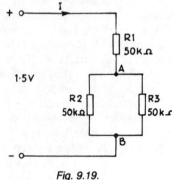

Fig. 9.19.

(a) The effective resistance of the circuit.
(b) The voltage developed between A and B.

Solution
(a) The effective resistance of R2 and R3 in parallel:

$$= \frac{R2 \times R3}{R2 + R3} = \frac{50 \times 50}{50 + 50} = 25 \, k\Omega$$

This resultant resistance is in series with R1

thus $R_T = 50 + 25 = 75 \, k\Omega$.

(b) The current I

$$= \frac{V}{R_T} = \frac{1.5}{75 \times 10^3} \, A = 20 \mu A$$

Voltage between A and B = I × resultant resistance of R2 and R3

$$= 20 \times 10^{-6} \times 25 \times 10^3 V = 0.5V$$

This voltage may also have been obtained by proportion of resistances:

Voltage between A and B:

$$= \frac{25}{75} \times 1.5V = 0.5V \text{ (as before)}$$

Problem 15
Using Fig. 9.20 calculate:

(a) The resistance of R.
(b) The power dissipated in R.

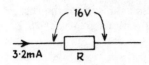

Fig. 9.20.

Solution

(a) $R = \dfrac{V}{I} = \dfrac{16}{3 \cdot 2 \times 10^{-3}} \, \Omega = 5k\Omega$

(b) $P = VI = 16 \times 3 \cdot 2 \times 10^{-3}W = 51 \cdot 2mW.$

Problem 16
Using Fig. 9.21 calculate:

(a) The value of the supply voltage V.
(b) The power dissipated in R1, R2 and R3.
(c) The total power supplied.

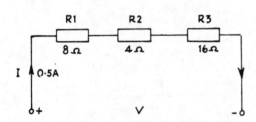

Fig. 9.21.

Solution

(a) Effective resistance of circuit R_T
$= R1 + R2 + R3$
$= 8 + 4 + 16 = 28\Omega$

Therefore $V = I \times R_T$
$= 0 \cdot 5 \times 28V = 14V$

(b) $P = I^2R$ watts
Thus power dissipated in R1
$= (0 \cdot 5)^2 \times 8 = 2W$

power dissipated in R2
$= (0 \cdot 5)^2 \times 4 = 1W$

and power dissipated in R3
$= (0 \cdot 5)^2 \times 16 = 4W$

(c) Total power supplied may be found from:

$P = VI$
$= 14 \times 0 \cdot 5W = 7W$

(which equals the sum of the powers dissipated in R1, R2 and R3).

Problem 17
Using Fig. 9.22 calculate:

(a) The power developed in R3.
(b) The current in R1.
(c) The voltage dropped across R2.
(d) The current taken from the supply.

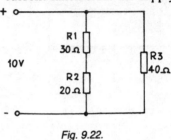

Fig. 9.22.

Solution

(a) The power developed in R3 may be found from:

$$P = \frac{V^2}{R} \text{ watts}$$

$$= \frac{10^2}{40} W = 2 \cdot 5W$$

(b) The total resistance of the series combination of R1 and R2

$= 30 + 20 = 50\Omega$

By proportion the voltage across R1:

$= \dfrac{30}{50} \times 10V = 6V$

therefore the current in R1 (and R2):

$= \dfrac{\text{Voltage across R1}}{\text{Resistance of R1}}$

$= \dfrac{6}{30} = 0 \cdot 2A$

(c) By proportion the voltage across R2:

$= \dfrac{20}{50} \times 10V = 4V$

(d) The current in R3:

$= \dfrac{\text{Supply voltage}}{\text{Resistance of R3}}$

$= \dfrac{10}{40} A = 0 \cdot 25A$

Current taken from supply:
$= \text{Current in R3} + \text{Current in R1}$
$= 0 \cdot 25 + 0 \cdot 2 = 0 \cdot 45A.$

Problem 18
Using Fig. 9.23 calculate:

(a) The voltage drop across the parallel network.
(b) The current in each resistor.

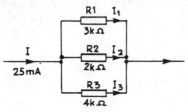

Fig. 9.23.

Solution
(a) We must first find the equivalent resistance of the parallel network. Taking a pair of resistors at a time:

Resultant of R1 and R2 in parallel:

$$= \frac{R1 \times R2}{R1 + R2} = \frac{3 \times 2}{3 + 2} = 1 \cdot 2 k\Omega.$$

This resultant is in parallel with R3

therefore $R_T = \dfrac{1 \cdot 2 \times 4}{1 \cdot 2 + 4} k\Omega \approx 923\Omega.$

Voltage drop across network:

$$= I \times R_T = 25 \times 10^{-3} \times 923V$$

$$= 23 \cdot 075V$$

(b) Current (I_1) in R1

$$= \frac{\text{Voltage across network}}{R1}$$

$$= \frac{23 \cdot 075}{3 \times 10^3} A = 7 \cdot 69 mA$$

Current (I_2) in R2

$$= \frac{\text{Voltage across network}}{R2}$$

$$= \frac{23 \cdot 075}{2 \times 10^3} A = 11 \cdot 54 mA$$

Current (I_3) in R3

$$= \frac{\text{Voltage across network}}{R3}$$

$$= \frac{23 \cdot 075}{4 \times 10^3} A = 5 \cdot 77 mA$$

Note that the sum of the three currents = current entering the network.

QUESTIONS ON CHAPTER NINE

(1) The flow of current in a metal conductor is due to the movement of:
   (a) protons
   (b) electrons
   (c) neutrons
   (d) negative ions.

(2) Which requires the largest amount of energy to produce current flow:
   (a) Nylon
   (b) Aluminium
   (c) Silicon
   (d) Carbon.

(3) Which of the following is **not** a good conductor:
   (a) Platinum
   (b) Gold
   (c) Copper
   (d) Sulphur.

(4) One coulomb is equal to:
   (a) 1 electron
   (b) 10^4 electrons
   (c) $6 \cdot 289 \times 10^{18}$ electrons
   (d) $3 \cdot 142 \times 10^{-12}$ electrons.

(5) Current and charge are related by:
   (a) $I = 1/Q$
   (b) $Q = 1/I$
   (c) $I = t/Q$
   (d) $I = Q/t.$

(6) A charge of $2 \cdot 5$ coulombs moves past a point in 2 seconds. The current flowing is:
   (a) $2 \cdot 5A$
   (b) $1 \cdot 25A$
   (c) $5A$
   (d) $5mA.$

(7) A current of 10mA equals:
   (a) 10^3A
   (b) $10^{-4}A$
   (c) $10^{-2}A$
   (d) $10^{-5}A.$

(8) When 5V is applied across a resistor, a current of 2mA flows. The value of the resistor is:
   (a) 50Ω
   (b) $10k\Omega$
   (c) $1k\Omega$
   (d) $2 \cdot 5k\Omega$

(9) Three resistors of value 5Ω, 6Ω and 7Ω are placed in parallel. The effective resistance will be:
(a) 1·96Ω
(b) 18Ω
(c) 210Ω
(d) 0.37Ω.

(10) The resistivity of a good conductor will be of the order of:
(a) 10^{-8} ohm-metre
(b) 1 ohm-metre
(c) 10^8 ohm-metre
(d) 10^{16} ohm-metre.

(11) The resistance of a length of copper wire is 0·75Ω. If its cross sectional area and length are both doubled its resistance will be:
(a) 3Ω
(b) 1·5Ω
(c) 0·1875Ω
(d) 0·75Ω.

(12) Which of the following materials has a negative temperature coefficient of resistance:
(a) Carbon
(b) Copper
(c) Brass
(d) Iron.

(13) The unit of energy is the:
(a) Volt
(b) Coulomb
(c) Watt
(d) Joule.

(14) The work done when a charge of 4 coulombs moves through a potential difference of 10V is:
(a) 2·5 J
(b) 40 C
(c) 2·5 A
(d) 40 J.

(15) Electrical power (P) is given by:
(a) $P = I R$ watts
(b) $P = I^2 R$ joules
(c) $P = V I$ joules/s
(d) $P = V/R$ watts.

(16) The power dissipated in a 5Ω resistor when 2A flows through it is:
(a) 20W
(b) 10W
(c) 2·5W
(d) 50W.

(17) A kilowatt-hour is equal to:
(a) 1000 J
(b) 1000 J/s
(c) 3 600 000 J
(d) 3 600 000 J/s.

(18) Refer to Fig. 9.24

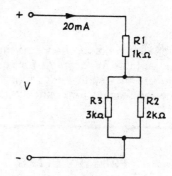

Fig. 9.24.

The current flowing in R2 will be:
(a) 8mA
(b) 12mA
(c) 20mA
(d) 60mA.

(19) Refer to Fig. 9.24. The power dissipated in R1 will be:
(a) 20mW
(b) 0·2W
(c) 0·4W
(d) 2W.

(20) Refer to Fig. 9.24. The voltage of the supply will be:
(a) 240V
(b) 44V
(c) 22V
(d) 120V.

(Answers on page 219.)

CHAPTER TEN

PRIMARY AND SECONDARY CELLS

Objectives

1 Name the common types of primary and secondary cells in use.
2 State suitable applications for each type.
3 Compare the relative advantages and disadvantages of each type.
4 State the reasons for connecting cells in series or parallel.

PRIMARY CELLS

ELECTRICAL CELLS ARE devices for **storing electrical energy**. A primary cell is one which produces electrical energy from chemical changes taking place within the cell, but once the chemical has been expended the cell is of no further use and must be discarded. A **battery** is a collection of cells and circuit symbols are given in Fig. 10.1.

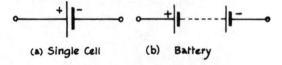

(a) Single Cell   (b)   Battery

Fig. 10.1 Circuit symbols.

All cells consist of two plates or poles, between which there is an electrolyte. For primary cells in common use the electrolyte is in the form of a paste; such cells are commonly referred to as **dry types**.

Leclanché Cell

This is the most common type of dry cell named after its inventor G. Leclanché in 1866. A typical basic construction for a round-type cell is given in Fig. 10.2. It consists of a central carbon rod forming the positive pole of the cell surrounded by a zinc container which constitutes the negative pole. The electrolyte is a thick fluid paste containing ammonium chloride (sal ammoniac) impregnated into a paper lining placed close to the zinc case. Around the carbon rod is placed a depolariser consisting of a mixture of powdered carbon and manganese dioxide. The purpose of the depolariser is to remove hydrogen formed at the carbon rod when the cell is delivering current. If this is not done the hydrogen gas film formed on the rod will reduce the current that can be taken from the cell to a low value. The cell is sealed at the top with bitumen to prevent evaporation of the electrolyte which would render the cell useless.

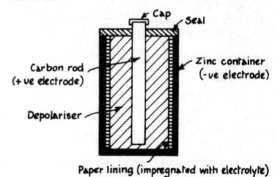

Fig. 10.2 Basic Leclanché cell (zinc-carbon).

The Leclanché cell has an open-circuit (unloaded) e.m.f. of approximately 1·5V. When the cell is delivering current, the active material of the cell is used up and the zinc is eaten away resulting in the e.m.f. falling. The cell construction used in Fig. 10.2 has the disadvantage that if the cell is left in the exhausted state, holes appear in the zinc casing allowing the electrolyte paste to leak out resulting in possible damage to the device or equipment in which the cell is fitted. Also the cell tends to swell making it difficult to remove from its container, *e.g.* a torch. For these reasons, **leak-proof cells** are manufactured where the cell is almost completely enclosed in a steel case which prevents the cell expanding and active chemicals leaking out.

When e.m.fs. greater than 1·5V are required the round-type cells are stacked in series with one another to produce e.m.fs. of 3V (2 cells). 4·5V (3 cells), 6V (4 cells), *etc*.

Another common form of construction for the Leclanché cells is the layer type illustrated in Fig. 10.3(a).

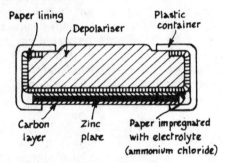

(a) Single Layer Cell

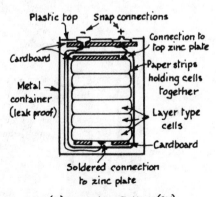

(b) Layer type Battery (9V)

Fig. 10.3 Leclanché layer type cells.

Each cell is of rectangular shape with a size depending on current rating and formed in a plastic container with openings at top and bottom. The negative pole of the cell is formed by the zinc plate which is coated on its lower side by a thin carbon layer. A layer of absorbent paper on the upper side of the zinc plate contains the electrolyte. The depolariser (manganese dioxide and powdered carbon) is contained in a paper lining which prevents it from coming into contact with the zinc plate. It will be seen that the same active materials are used in this type of cell construction as for the round-type of dry cell.

To produce a battery from layer-type cells, the individual cells are stacked in series one on top of the other, as in Fig. 10.3(b) where six cells are used to produce a 9V battery. With this arrangement there is no physical division between the cells and the carbon coating on the zinc plate acts as the positive pole of the cell immediately below it. The bottom cell has the carbon removed from the centre of the zinc electrode to which contact is made for the negative terminal of the battery. The top cell is completed by placing a zinc plate with a carbon coating on the top of the plate to which connection is made to the positive terminal of the battery. Commonly, non-reversible snap connectors are used for the battery connections so that the polarity of the battery voltage is not accidently reversed.

The thickness of each cell does not vary a great deal with different batteries but the cross-sectional area is increased with an increase in the required current output.

Mercuric Oxide Cell

Leclanché cells use an electrolyte (ammonium chloride) which is **acid** based. Mercuric oxide cells, on the other hand, use an **alkaline** electrolyte of potassium hydroxide (caustic potash). These cells are manufactured in the cylindrical and flat-pellet form. Fig. 10.4 shows an example of the flat-pellet or button type construction.

A mercuric oxide button cell basically consists of a zinc negative electrode, a positive electrode of mercuric oxide and graphite and an electrolyte formed from a saturated solution of potassium hydroxide and zinc oxide. The cell is enclosed in a nickel plated steel case

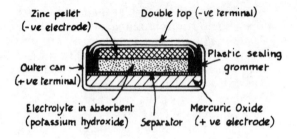

Fig. 10.4 Mercuric oxide cell (button or flat pellet type).

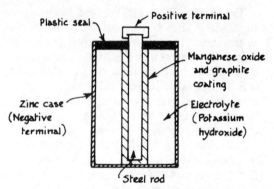

Fig. 10.5 Basic manganese-alkaline cell.

to resist corrosion and sealed by a plastic grommet to prevent leakage of the electrolyte.

These cells have a lower e.m.f. than the Leclanché cell; it being about 1·35V. The cell voltage remains almost constant under load conditions until the cell is nearly exhausted when the voltage rapidly drops. Note that the outer case is the **positive** terminal of the cell.

Miniature cells of this type are intended for low current operation and care should be exercised to avoid accidental discharge paths. If touched by hand, films of perspiration left behind will considerably shorten the cell life. It is, therefore, best to avoid hand contact by fitting or removing cells with the aid of small plastic tweezers. It should also be noted that the electrolyte potassium hydroxide is caustic which is extremely dangerous to the eyes and can dissolve skin. Thus mercury cells (or any other primary cells) should not be opened or punctured or attempts made to recharge them.

Another button cell which is similar in construction to the mercuric oxide cell is the silver oxide cell. In these cells the active electrodes are zinc and silver oxide and the electrolyte is potassium hydroxide (as for the mercuric oxide cell). The e.m.f. of a silver oxide cell is 1·5V, has a good shelf life and the e.m.f. is maintained at a steady level during its discharge life.

Manganese-Alkaline Cell

This cell uses the same alkaline electrolyte of potassium hydroxide as the mercuric oxide cell. It is available in cylindrical and button type construction, a basic cylinder type being illustrated in Fig. 10.5.

The positive electrode is formed by a coating of manganese oxide and graphite which is laid on a central steel rod. The electrolyte of potassium hydroxide is either in liquid or jelly form and the negative electrode is formed by the zinc case. The nominal e.m.f. of the cell is higher than the mercury cell at about 1·5V. Output voltage is more constant during discharge than the Leclanché cell and can provide higher current output. The shelf life of both mercuric oxide and manganese-alkaline cells is much longer than the Leclanché cell but they are more expensive.

The cell is sealed and is usually enclosed in a steel casing fitted with an insulating plastic sleeve. Alkaline cells are made in a large number of sizes and types and for higher voltages the individual cells are connected in series.

Lithium Cell

The basic construction of a lithium cell is illustrated in Fig. 10.6. Lithium being a highly reactive metal cannot be exposed to water (or air), thus it must not be used with an

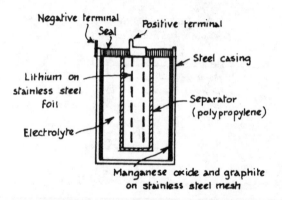

Fig. 10.6 Basic lithium cell (P.C.B. mounting type).

electrolyte in water solution. Commonly the electrolyte consists of a mixture of thionyl chloride and lithium salts.

The positive electrode is formed from lithium on a stainless steel foil, which is separated from the rest of the cell by a porous polypropylene enclosure. The negative electrode is formed from a coating of manganese oxide and graphite on a stainless steel mesh surrounded by a steel casing. The cell is then very carefully sealed.

The chemical reactions within the cell provide it with a high e.m.f. of about 3·4 to 3·7V. It has a very long shelf life (10 years or more) and the output voltage remains practically constant over its useful life. Lithium cells are commonly used for memory back-up and the button type is used to power some pocket calculators.

Lithium cells should never be connected in parallel and series connection is limited to a maximum of two cells.

Comparison and Uses of Primary Cells

Comparison of cell output voltage during discharge for four common types of primary cell is given in Fig. 10.7.

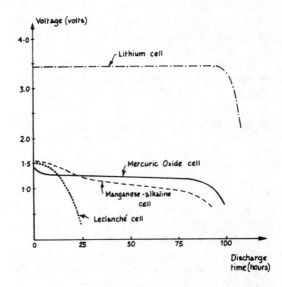

Fig. 10.7 *Comparison of cell output voltage during discharge (continuous load).*

Primary Cell	Voltage (Single Cell)	Shelf Life	Main Uses
Leclanché (Zinc-Carbon)	1·5V	1 year	Torches, lamps, portable radios and tape cassette players, clocks, electronic toys and games
Mercuric oxide	1·35V	2 years	Button variety for use in watches, clocks, cameras and small tools
Silver oxide	1·5V	2 years	
Manganese-Alkaline	1·5V	30 months	Suited to applications where high intermittent current is required, *e.g.* in smoke detector alarms and electric bells. These cells have up to 4 times the energy content of the standard Leclanché cell
Lithium	3·3–3·7V	10 years	P.C.B. mounting types for memory back-up, clock support and other low to medium drain applications. Button variety for use in calculators, memory back-up, process controllers and robotics

Table 10.1 *Typical uses for these non-rechargeable cells*

SECONDARY CELLS

A secondary cell is a device which produces electrical energy from chemical changes taking place within the cell, but by passing a direct current through the cell the chemical changes are reversed and the cell may be restored to its original condition. Thus after the output voltage of a secondary cell has fallen below a certain voltage during discharge it may be **recharged** by connecting the cell to a suitable d.c. voltage or rectified a.c. voltage supply. This charge-discharge process may be repeated many hundreds of times. Secondary cells may be connected together to form secondary batteries.

Lead Acid Cell

The lead acid is the commonest type of secondary cell. It consists of two lead grids in plate form, one covered with lead peroxide and the other containing spongy lead immersed in an electrolyte of dilute sulphuric acid, see Fig. 10.8.

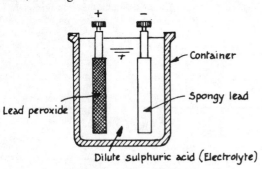

Fig. 10.8 Basic lead-acid secondary cell.

When fully charged the lead acid cell gives an e.m.f. of approximately 2·2V but when in use this falls rapidly to about 2V. The cell is said to be discharged when the voltage has fallen to 1·8V and requires recharging before it is used again. The state of charge of a lead acid cell (or battery) is best determined using an hydrometer to measure the specific gravity of the electrolyte. When fully charged the specific gravity should be about 1·25 and drops to about 1·18 at the end of discharge. The principle of operation of a lead acid cell is illustrated by the diagrams of Fig. 10.9.

During use the water content of the electrolyte evaporates and periodically the cell

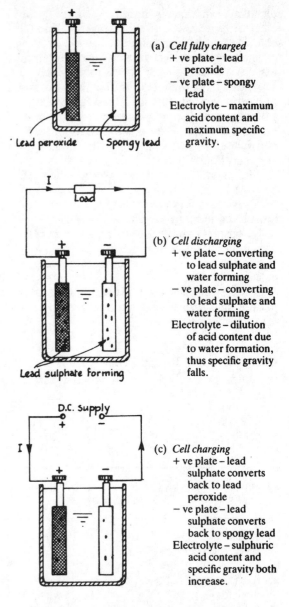

Fig. 10.9 Principle of operation of lead acid cell.

should be topped up with distilled water to the correct level. Additionally, it should be noted that in a vented cell, hydrogen and oxygen (an explosive mixture) are released during charge and may detonate violently if subjected to an electric spark.

Modern lead acid cells are now sealed and rely on better control of charging equipment to avoid excessive build-up of gas pressure than the older vented lead acid cells. In these sealed cells the electrolyte may be liquid or jelly form. With the liquid type a separator is fitted between the cell plates and made from a porous material that absorbs the electrolyte so that the cell may be operated in any position. Additionally, the liquid cells are fitted with a pressure operated vent which will release gas pressure should this build-up during charge. The vent automatically reseals when the gas pressure drops.

To produce higher voltages individual cells may be connected in series resulting in battery voltages of 4V (two cells), 6V (3 cells) or 12V (6 cells). Each complete cell is made up from a sufficient number of positive and negative plates interleaved with each other and connected to their respective terminals via lead group bars, see Fig. 10.10.

The capacity of a cell or battery is given in **Ampere hours (Ah)** and is the product of discharge current and time. The **rated capacity** is specified generally for discharge times of 5 hours, 10 hours or 20 hours. Thus a 100Ah, 5h battery will give 20A for 5 hours. The same battery will give 10A for 10 hours or 5A for 20 hours. This is not true, however, for higher current as the rate of discharge affects the rated capacity, thus the same battery would not give, say, 50A for 2 hours. At this rate the capacity would be reduced from the quoted figure of 100Ah.

Nickel-Cadmium Cells

Essentially a nickel-cadmium cell comprises a positive plate using nickel hydroxide as the active material, a negative plate of cadmium hydroxide as the active material together with an electrolyte of potassium hydroxide in aqueous solution. These rechargeable cells are manufactured in a large number of sizes and are available as open types (vented cells) or sealed types, see Fig. 10.11.

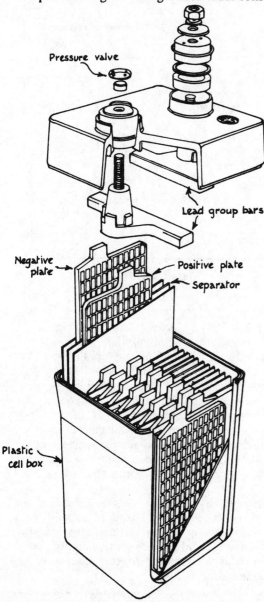

Fig. 10.10 Modern lead-acid cell (sealed type).

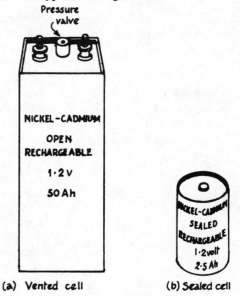

Fig. 10.11 Nickel-Cadmium cells.

Nickel-cadmium (ni-Cd) cells have a nominal voltage of 1·2V but the actual basic e.m.f. is always between 1·25V and 1·3V. Sealed cells and batteries (round and button types) are available with rated capacities of 100mAh to 10Ah with voltages from 1·2V (single cell) to 12V (10 cells) and are commonly used in a wide range of portable electronic equipment. Open type cells are generally of larger capacity, typically in the range of 10Ah to 600Ah and are designed for heavy duty such as engine starting and emergency lighting.

Ni-Cd cells have excellent shelf life and if stored in accordance with manufacturers instructions they suffer no permanent deterioration over many years of storage.

CELLS IN SERIES AND PARALLEL

Internal Resistance of Cell

When a load is connected to the terminals of a cell a current will flow around the circuit. The current flows within the cell and in particular through its electrolyte. This together with other factors depending upon the cell construction will present some resistance to current flow. Thus to represent an actual cell in circuit form we must include this resistance. This is known as the **internal resistance** of the cell and is represented by the resistance **r** in the circuit model of Fig. 10.12, in series with an ideal cell of voltage E (the cell e.m.f.). It should be noted that the only accessible parts of the cell are the two terminals and that the internal resistance is not

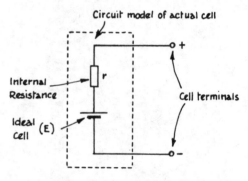

Fig. 10.12 *Internal resistance of a cell.*

Comparison of Uses for Secondary Cells

Secondary Cell	Voltage (Single Cell)	Main Uses
Lead Acid (Sealed types)	2·0V	Medium to Heavy Duty to include: engine starting; battery powered fork-lift trucks and milk floats; emergency standby lighting and power supplies in hospitals, airports and hotels. Standby supplies for fire/intruder alarms and main frame computers.
Nickel-Cadmium (Sealed types)	1·2V	Light to Medium Duty to include: power supplies for domestic equipment such as electric knives, razors, drills and small vacuum cleaners; portable measuring instruments such as gas detectors, electric meters and portable computers; portable communications equipment such as paging devices, cordless phones and radio transceivers.
Nickel-Cadmium (Open types)	1·2V	Medium to Heavy Duty to include: starting of diesel or turbine railway locomotives; power source for ship radio transmitters and receivers and navigation lights; standby supplies for computers and process control equipment; military use in radar, missiles and rockets; aircraft engine starting and emergency lighting.

Table 10.2 *Rechargeable cells and their main uses*

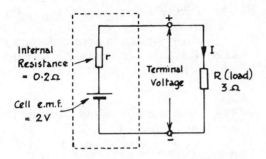

Fig. 10.13 Effect of internal resistance on terminal voltage of cell.

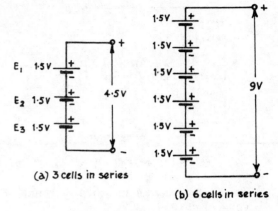

(a) 3 cells in series

(b) 6 cells in series

Fig. 10.14 Cells in series.

an actual resistor within the cell but a representation of the cells opposition to current flow.

The effect of a cell's internal resistance is considered in Fig. 10.13 where a load **R** is connected between the cell terminals. As we now have a complete circuit a current I will flow of magnitude equal to

$$\frac{\text{Cell e.m.f.}}{\text{total resistance of circuit}} = \frac{E}{R+r}$$

For the values given

$$I = \frac{2}{3+0.2} A = 0.625A$$

The voltage across the load $= I \times R = 0.625 \times 3 = 1.875V$
The voltage across r $= I \times r = 0.625 \times 0.2 = 0.125V$

The voltage across the load is the **terminal voltage (or p.d.)** of the cell and is seen to be less than the cell e.m.f. (the open circuit voltage). The difference in voltage between the cell e.m.f. and the terminal voltage is that voltage which appears across the internal resistance of the cell. This voltage is called the 'lost' voltage. Since we do not wish the voltage dropped across the internal resistance of the cell to be very large the internal resistance of a cell is made as small as is possible.

Cells in Series

Many items of analogue and digital portable electronic equipment operate from voltage supplies in the range of 5V to 10V which cannot be provided by the basic e.m.f. of single primary or secondary cells. Thus in

order to provide these **higher supply voltages**, individual cells may be connected in series with one another as shown in Fig. 10.14. The total e.m.f. of series connected cells is the sum of the individual e.m.fs. For the three series connected cells of Fig. 10.14(a) the total e.m.f. $= E_1 + E_2 + E_3 = 4.5V$. Thus the total e.m.f. for the six cells of Fig.10.14(b) is $6 \times 1.5V = 9V$.

Since the internal resistances of the cells are in series, the total internal resistance $= n \times r$ where n is the number of cells and r is the internal resistance of a single cell.

Problem 1

Four cells each having a nominal e.m.f. of 1.5V are connected in series. If the internal resistance of a single cell is 0.1 ohm, determine:

(a) The total e.m.f. of the combination.
(b) The effective internal resistance of the combination.
(c) The terminal voltage of the combination when it is connected to a load of 10 ohm.

Solution
(a) Total e.m.f. $= 4 \times 1.5V = 6V$.
(b) Effective internal resistance $= 4 \times 0.1$ ohm $= 0.4$ ohm.
(c) The equivalent circuit of the four cells in series is as in Fig. 10.15.

The value of the current I $=$

$$\frac{E}{R+r} = \frac{6}{10+0.4} A = 0.577A$$

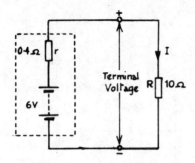

Fig. 10.15 Equivalent circuit.

The voltage across the load (terminal voltage) =
$I \times R = 0.577 \times 10V = 5.77V$
Note that the remaining voltage $(6 - 5.77V) = 0.23V$ is developed across the internal resistance.

Cells in Parallel

If it is required to **increase the energy capacity** of a cell (but not its voltage), cells may be connected in parallel with one another as in Fig. 10.16. This is normally only done for secondary cells such as those used in lead acid batteries.

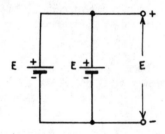

Fig. 10.16 Cells in parallel.

Cells connected in parallel must be of the same nominal e.m.f. and of the same internal resistance. Since the internal resistances are now in parallel, the effective internal resistance is $^1/_n$ where **n** is the number of cells connected in parallel and **r** is the equal internal resistance of each cell.

Problem 2

Two identical cells each having an e.m.f. of 2V and internal resistance of 0.25 ohm are connected in parallel. Determine:

(a) The effective e.m.f. of the combination.

(b) The effective internal resistance of the combination.

(c) The current flowing in each cell when a load of 5 ohm is connected across the combination.

Solution

(a) The effective e.m.f. is the same as the e.m.f. of a single cell, *i.e.* 2V.

(b) The effective internal resistance = $^{0.25}/_2$ = 0.125 ohm.

(c) The equivalent circuit of the combination is as in Fig. 10.17.

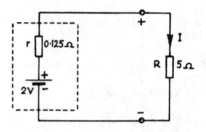

Fig. 10.17. Equivalent circuit.

The value of the current I flowing =

$$\frac{E}{R + r} = \frac{2}{5 + 0.125} = 0.39A.$$

Since the internal resistances of the two cells are the same this current is divided equally between the cells and

$$\frac{0.39}{2} A = 0.195A \text{ flows in each cell.}$$

Note that in the interests of safety it is prudent to follow only manufacturers' instructions for series or parallel connection of cells.

QUESTIONS ON CHAPTER TEN

(1) The e.m.f. of a fresh Leclanché cell is approximately:
  (a) 1.35V
  (b) 1.5V
  (c) 2.0V
  (d) 2.2V.

(2) The electrolyte used in a Leclanché cell is a solution of:
  (a) Potassium Hydroxide
  (b) Sulphuric Acid
  (c) Thionyl Chloride
  (d) Ammonium Chloride.

(3) The e.m.f. of a fresh Lithium cell is about:
  (a) 1·2V
  (b) 1·5V
  (c) 2·2V
  (d) 3·5V.

(4) A primary battery is one which:
  (a) Is topped up with distilled water
  (b) Is rechargeable
  (c) Is not rechargeable
  (d) Has an e.m.f. of less than 2V.

(5) Three 1·2V cells each having an internal resistance of 0·15 ohm are connected in series. The resultant e.m.f. and internal resistance of the combination will be:
  (a) 1·2V and 0·05 ohm
  (b) 3·6V and 0·05 ohm
  (c) 3·6V and 0·45 ohm
  (d) 1·2V and 0·45 ohm.

(6) Which of the following would be found in a secondary battery:
  (a) Nickel-Cadmium cells
  (b) Mercuric Oxide cells
  (c) Silver Oxide cells
  (d) Lithium cells.

(7) Cells are connected in parallel to:
  (a) Increase the internal resistance
  (b) Increase the capacity
  (c) Increase the e.m.f.
  (d) Increase the shelf life.

(8) A typical application for a button type Lithium cell would be:
  (a) Standby lighting supply
  (b) Supply for electronic calculator
  (c) Engine starting
  (d) Supply for electric drill.

(9) A cell of internal resistance 0·1 ohm has an open-circuit e.m.f. of 2V. If the terminal voltage falls to 1·9V when on load, the current flowing in the load will be:
  (a) 1mA
  (b) 100mA
  (c) 500mA
  (d) 1A.

(10) A Manganese Alkaline cell has a shelf life of about:
  (a) 10 years
  (b) 1 month
  (c) 1 week
  (d) 30 months.

(11) A cell has a rated capacity of 60Ah over 5 hours. The cell will deliver:
  (a) 24A for 10 hours
  (b) 1A for 600 hours
  (c) 120A for 2·5 hours
  (d) 300A for 1 hour.

(12) Three primary batteries are selected at random from a box of batteries of the same type. Which of the following gives the only possible combination of voltages that could be obtained:
  (a) 1·5V, 3·0V and 5V
  (b) 3V, 4·5V and 9V
  (c) 4V, 6V and 7·5V
  (d) 1·5V, 2·5V and 3·5V.

(Answers on page 219.)

CHAPTER ELEVEN

BASIC MAGNETISM

Objectives

1 Identify magnetic field patterns around permanent and electromagnets and effects of different materials in the field and core.
2 State the effects of movement of a conductor in a magnetic field, a current carrying conductor in a magnetic field and self/mutual inductance.
3 State the unit of inductance and describe the construction of simple coils and transformers.
4 Describe the elementary principles and applications of simple alternators and motors.

MAGNETIC FIELDS

THE PHENOMENON OF magnetism has been known and used probably longer than any other in electrical science. Magnetism is the property by which forces may be set up at a distance to attract certain materials. The materials which are attracted by the forces of magnetism are called **ferromagnetic** materials and elements in this category include **iron, nickel** and **cobalt**.

Some materials are naturally magnetic; the earliest permanent magnets were made from lumps of magnetite (magnetic iron ore). These natural magnets, however, produce a weak magnetic effect. Strong artificial permanent magnets can be created by using the flow of an electric current.

If a permanent magnet is covered with a sheet of smooth cardboard and sprinkled evenly with iron filings, it is found that after slight tapping of the cardboard the filings set themselves in **curved chains** between the poles, as in Fig. 11.1. The shape and density of the chains enables us to form a mental image of the magnetic condition or **field** around the magnet and lead to the idea of **lines of magnetic flux**.

The path of any chain represents the direction of the magnetic field along that particular chain. Also, the closer the chains or lines of magnetic flux are together the more intense is the magnetic field. The intensity is thus seen to be greatest close to the magnet and in particular immediately around the poles. It is important to realise that the magnetic forces set up are not just confined to the lines of flux but spread into the whole of the space occupied by that flux.

The **direction of the magnetic field** is taken to be that in which the north pole of a compass

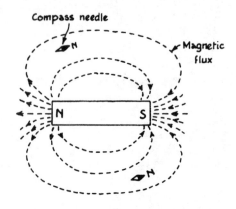

Fig. 11.1 Magnetic field around bar magnet.

needle points when placed in the field, that is from the **NORTH** to the **SOUTH** pole of the magnet. Hence the magnetic flux is assumed to pass through the magnet, emerge from the north pole and return to the south pole.

Magnetic Flux and Flux Density

The total magnetic field, *i.e.* the sum of all the lines of magnetic force, is measured in terms of **magnetic flux** for which the symbol is Φ and the unit is the Weber (Wb).

The magnitude of many electromagnetic effects depends not so much on the total extent of the field as upon its concentration. The concentration of a magnetic field is measured in terms of **magnetic flux density**, symbol B and is the amount of flux per square metre (Wb/m^2). A magnetic flux density of 1 Wb/m^2 is given the special name tesla (T).

Effect of Different Materials in Field of Magnet

If a piece of ferromagnetic material is brought close to the field of a magnet or a magnetic field of any kind, the material tends to **concentrate the flux**, as shown in Fig. 11.2(a), generally in the direction of its longest dimension. It will be noted that poles are **induced** in the material so that it behaves in a similar way to a permanent magnet and will be attracted towards the pole of the magnet. When removed from the magnetic field, **soft** magnetic materials such as iron will lose their induced magnetism whilst **hard** magnetic materials retain much of the induced magnetism.

On the other hand, materials which are non-ferromagnetic such as copper, silver, brass, tin and lead etc are not influenced by the steady forces of magnetism and thus are neither attracted nor repelled by the poles of the magnet, see Fig. 11.2(b). The path of the flux lines is not altered by the presence of the piece of material.

Attraction and Repulsion of Magnetic Poles

Lines of magnetic flux do not really have any physical existence but they form a convenient and useful way of explaining many different magnetic effects and calculating their magnitudes. We have seen that each flux line of the magnetic field forms a closed path and never intersects other flux lines.

If two dissimilar magnet poles are placed near to each other, as in Fig. 11.3(a), it is

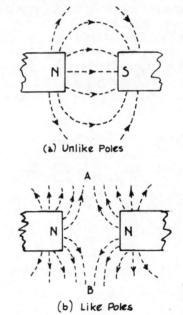

(a) Unlike Poles

(b) Like Poles

Fig. 11.3 *Attraction and repulsion of magnetic poles.*

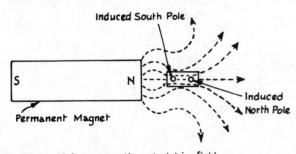

(a) Piece of ferromagnetic material in field

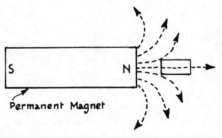

(b) Piece of non-ferromagnetic material in field

Fig. 11.2 *Effect of different materials in field of magnet.*

found that the **unlike poles attract one another**. The magnetic flux lines act like **stretched elastic bands**, always trying to shorten themselves and thereby causing the dissimilar poles to be attracted towards each other.

The opposite effect occurs when similar poles (two North or two South) are placed near to one another, as in Fig. 11.3(b). Here, the **like poles repel one another**. This effect arises when flux lines are parallel to one another and act in the same direction, as they are around points A and B. These flux lines behave as if they exerted a lateral pressure on one another thereby moving the poles apart.

Other Magnetic Field Patterns

Permanent magnets having pole pieces of various shapes are in common use to obtain particular magnetic field patterns and some examples are illustrated in Fig. 11.4.

In the diagram of Fig. 11.4(a) a uniform magnetic field in any plane can be obtained between two flat magnetic poles which may be either the poles of a permanent magnet or an electro-magnet (see later).

The radial magnetic field produced by the poles of the magnet in Fig. 11.4(b) is that required for a moving coil loudspeaker. The moving coil (speech coil) moves up and down in the air gap when a current flows in the coil. A radial field may also be produced by using a soft iron cylinder placed between the curved pole pieces of a permanent magnet as shown in Fig. 11.4(c). This arrangement is used in moving coil measuring instruments. The soft iron cylinder concentrates the magnetic flux to produce an intense field in the air gap.

MAGNETIC FIELD DUE TO AN ELECTRIC CURRENT

All magnetism is due to the movement of electrical charge and when an electric current flows in a conductor a magnetic field is produced, see Fig. 11.5(a). The magnetic field exists **within and around the conductor** and weakens as the distance from the conductor

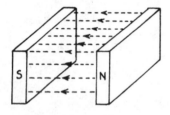

(a) Magnetic field between flat magnetic surfaces

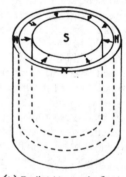

(b) Radial Magnetic Field

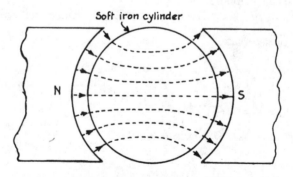

Soft iron cylinder

(c) Radial Magnetic Field

Fig. 11.4 Other magnetic field patterns.

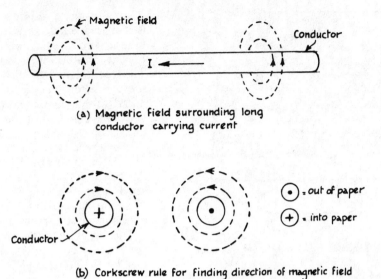

(a) Magnetic field surrounding long
conductor carrying current

(b) Corkscrew rule for finding direction of magnetic field

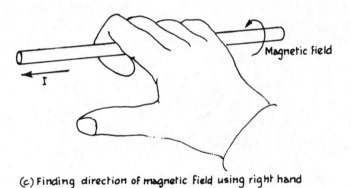

(c) Finding direction of magnetic field using right hand

Fig. 11.5 Magnetic field due to an electric current.

increases. Magnetism attributed to the flow of an electric current is referred to generally as **electromagnetism**.

The direction of the magnetic field may be found by applying the **Corkscrew Rule** as in Fig. 11.5(b) where the conductor is viewed from its ends. The Corkscrew Rule assumes that a right-hand corkscrew is turned into the conductor in the direction of current flow; the corkscrew will thus rotate in the direction of the magnetic field. With current flow into the end of the conductor the magnetic field acts in a clockwise direction. Current flow in the opposite direction (out of the conductor) will cause the direction of the magnetic field to reverse to an anticlockwise direction.

Alternatively, the **Right-Hand Grip Rule** may be applied as in Fig. 11.5(c). Here it is **imagined** that the conductor is gripped with the right hand with the thumb pointing along the conductor in the direction of current flow. The fingers will then curl in the direction of the magnetic field.

If a conductor carrying current is made into a loop as in Fig. 11.6, the magnetic field within the loop will become stronger because of the cumulative effect of current all round the loop. The resultant magnetic field has properties similar to that of a permanent magnet. However, in order to produce an intense magnetic field a very high current (many hundreds of amperes) would be required.

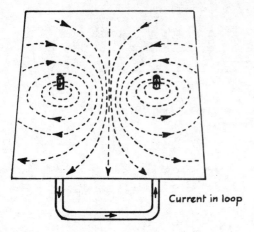

Fig. 11.6 Magnetic field around conductor loop.

As a result of coiling a long conductor, the flux in adjacent turns of the coil reinforce each other to produce a strong magnetic field which is concentrated into a relatively small space. The resemblance of this field pattern to that of the permanent magnet of Fig. 11.1 should be noted); the field emanating from an apparent N-pole at one end of the coil and converging on a S-pole at the other end.

The direction of the magnetic field may be found by applying the **Right Hand Grip Rule** as illustrated in Fig. 11.7(b). Here, the fingers are imagined to curl round the coil in the direction of current flow; the thumb then points in the direction of the magnetic field.

The direction of the magnetic field may also be established using the **End Rule** which enables the North and South ends of a coil to be determined, see Fig. 11.8. It is found that if the current is in a clockwise direction when the coil is viewed at one of its ends, that end is a S-end, but if in an anti-clockwise direction it is

Thus instead, a small current is used, but the conductor is wound in the form of a **coil** or **solenoid** to create many adjacent loops or turns as in Fig. 11.7(a).

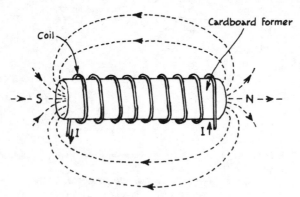

(a) Magnetic field due to current in coil

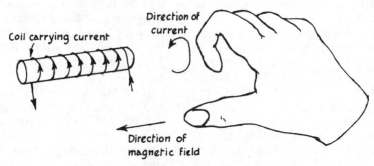

(b) Finding direction of magnetic field using right hand

Fig. 11.7 Magnetic field produced by current in a coil.

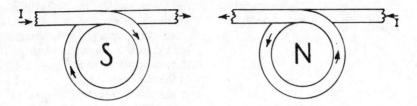

Fig. 11.8 The end rule.

a N-end. In both cases, the extremeties of the letters S and N point in the same direction as the direction of current flow.

Coil with Ferromagnetic Core

The magnetic field inside a coil may be strengthened considerably if a ferromagnetic core such as iron is used, see Fig. 11.9. The iron core becomes magnetised with the polarities shown and behaves like a permanent magnet as long as the current in the coil is maintained; such an arrangement is referred to as an **electromagnet**.

Ferromagnetic cores are used in coils when particularly strong magnetic fields are required, *e.g.* in relays, transformers and in electrical motors and generators. The cores

are made from magnetically soft materials and may be either solid, laminated, iron dust or of the ferrite type. Solid cores which have limited application are used in relays. Laminated cores which use laminations of the core material that are electrically insulated from one another find application in transformers. Iron dust and ferrite cores are used for high frequency applications, *e.g.* in r.f. inductors and transformers.

The strongest magnetic field is obtained inside the coil when the magnetic field is contained entirely in the core material, as with the toroidal coil of Fig. 11.10. This arrangement is used for electron beam deflection in television and VDU display tubes and in audio and video record/playback heads where a small break in the core path is made and filled

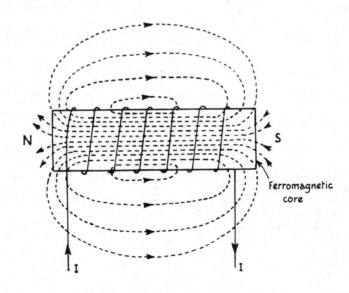

Fig. 11.9 Coil with ferromagnetic core.

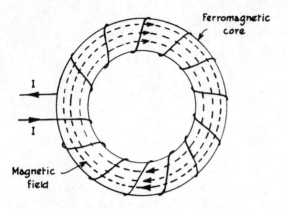

Fig. 11.10 Toroidal coil with ferromagnetic core.

with a non-ferromagnetic material such as glass.

CURRENT CARRYING CONDUCTOR IN MAGNETIC FIELD

When a conductor carrying current is placed in a magnetic field, a **force acts on the conductor**.

Suppose that we have a magnetic field as in Fig. 11.11(a) and a current carrying conductor. This conductor will produce a magnetic

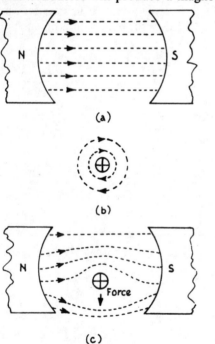

Fig. 11.11 Force on a current carrying conductor in a magnetic field.

field as shown in Fig. 11.11(b) when current is assumed to flow in the direction indicated (into the paper). If the conductor is now placed in the magnetic field of Fig. 11.11(a), the result will be as in Fig. 11.11(c). At the top of the conductor, the magnetic lines of flux are in the same direction and will thus reinforce one another. Below the conductor, however, the flux lines act in opposite directions and thus tend to cancel one another. As a result there is a downward force exerted on the conductor as shown. If the current had been in the opposite direction, an upward force would have been experienced. This is known as the **motor principle** and is fundamental to the operation of all electric motors, some measuring instruments and the moving coil loudspeaker.

The direction of the force acting on the conductor may be found by applying **Fleming's Left-Hand Rule**, see Fig. 11.12. Here, the first finger of the left-hand is placed along the direction of the magnetic field and the second finger in the direction of current flow. The thumb then indicates the direction of the force on the conductor, the thumb and fingers all being at right angles to one another.

The magnitude of the force is given by

$F = B I l$ newtons (N), where
B = flux density (T)
I = current (A)
l = active length of conductor (m)

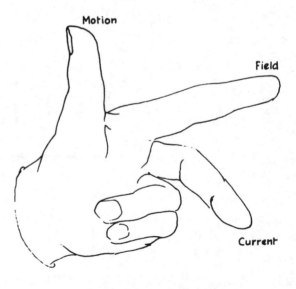

Fig. 11.12 Fleming's left-hand rule.

Simple Motor

The principle of a d.c. motor is illustrated in Fig. 11.13. A strong magnetic field is produced by an electromagnet or a permanent magnet in the case of small motors. The conductor is formed into a loop and mounted so that it is free to rotate in the magnetic field.

If the current direction is as shown, there will be a downward force exerted on conductor A and an upward force on conductor B (found by applying Fleming's Left-Hand Rule). These forces will cause the loop to rotate in an anti-clockwise direction. Unfortunately, the movement will stop when the loop has rotated through a quarter of a turn. Should it tend to rotate further as a result of its momentum, the forcing acting on the conductors will cause movement in the reverse direction.

To obtain continuous rotation in one direction it is necessary to reverse the direction of current flow when the loop reaches the vertical position and at every following half-revolution. This is achieved by the use of a commutator or split ring which rotates with the loop. Current is supplied to the loop via carbon brushes which contact with the commutator. When the loop reaches the vertical position and carries just beyond it due to its inertia, the current in conductors A and B reverses direction. That is after passing through the first quarter turn from the starting position shown in the diagram, current enters the loop via conductor B and leaves via conductor A. After a further half-revolution current will enter the loop via conductor A and leave via conductor B and so on.

In a practical motor many loops are formed with the conductors wound in slots in an iron armature and the commutator is divided into a similar number of segments. The operating principle, however, remains the same.

MOVEMENT OF CONDUCTOR IN MAGNETIC FIELD

Consider a single rigid conductor placed in a powerful magnetic field as in Fig. 11.14. Whenever the conductor is caused to move so that the conductor **cuts the lines of magnetic flux** the voltmeter will give a momentary indication and a current will flow in the circuit. If both the conductor and the magnetic field remain stationary the meter will read zero.

This is an example of **electromagnetic induction** when an e.m.f. appears between the ends of any conductor which is made to move relative to the flux lines of a magnetic field. From Fig. 11.14 the following results may be confirmed:

(a) The polarity of the induced e.m.f. reverses if either the direction of motion or the direction of the field is reversed.

(b) The induced e.m.f. is greatest when the conductor moves at right angles to the magnetic field and is zero if the conductor moves horizontally.

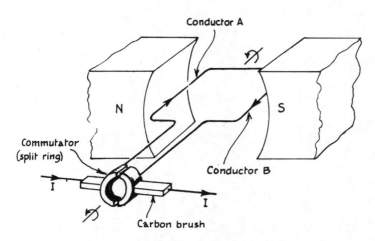

Fig. 11.13 Simple D.C. motor.

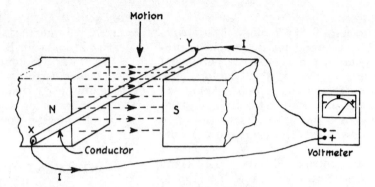

Fig. 11.14 *Conductor moving in a magnetic field.*

(c) The magnitude of the induced e.m.f. (E) is proportional to the velocity (v) of the conductor, to the flux density (B) and to the length (L) of the conductor in the field, *i.e.*

E = v B L volts,

where v is measured in metres/sec,
     B is the flux density (tesla)
and   L is in metres.

The direction of the induced e.m.f. and hence the direction of current flow when a circuit is completed from the conductor may be found by applying **Fleming's Right-Hand Rule**, see Fig. 11.15. Here the thumb of the right hand is made to point in the direction of motion and the first finger in the direction of the magnetic field; the second finger then lies in the direction of current flow. When the rule is applied to Fig. 11.14, end X of the conductor becomes the positive terminal and end Y the negative terminal.

Simple Alternator

One application of the phenomenon of electromagnetic induction is in electrical generators (a.c. and d.c.).

The principle of an a.c. generator or alternator is illustrated in Fig. 11.16. Here a

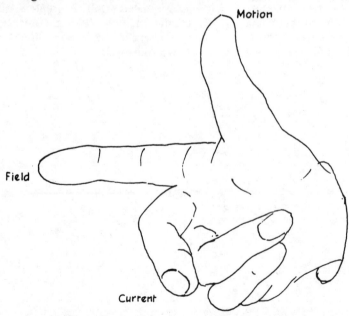

Fig. 11.15 *Fleming's right-hand rule.*

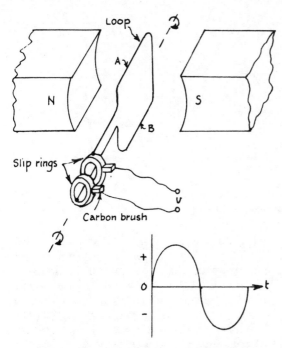

Fig. 11.16 *Principle of A.C. voltage generator.*

loop consisting of two conductors A and B is caused to rotate continuously in a magnetic field. With the loop in the position shown there will be zero e.m.f. as neither conductor is cutting the lines of magnetic flux. If the loop rotates clockwise through 90°, the e.m.f. will increase as the conductors start to cross the lines of magnetic flux reaching a maximum when conductor A is adjacent to the S-pole of the magnet; here the conductors will be cutting the flux at right angles. The output e.m.f. is the sum of the individual e.m.fs. in the two conductors since when they are cutting flux the force on one conductor will be upwards whilst it is downwards on the other.

As the loop rotates through the next 90° the e.m.f. generated decreases reaching zero when conductor A is at the bottom and conductor B is at the top. As the loop rotates through a further 90°, the e.m.f. increases once again but this time the polarity is reversed as the positions of the conductors will have interchanged with conductor A becoming adjacent to the N-pole of the magnet. As before the e.m.f. is a maximum when the conductors cut the flux at right angles. Finally, as the loop rotates through a further 90°, the e.m.f. diminishes and falls to zero when the

conductors are back in their starting position.

It will be seen that the polarity of the generated voltage changes every half-revolution giving an alternating voltage output (sine wave). In order to make contact between the rotating loop and the external circuit, slip rings and carbon brushes are used.

When a load is connected to the alternator output, a current will flow in the conductors. This current will cause a force to be set up opposite to the direction of motion, *i.e.* the force tends to oppose the motion. This is an application of **Lenz's law** which states that the force, current or e.m.f. produced is always in a direction so as to oppose that which is causing it.

INDUCTANCE AND THE TRANSFORMER PRINCIPLE

In the last section it was seen how an e.m.f. was induced in a conductor when it cut a magnetic field. It is not essential for the conductor to move and **an e.m.f. will be induced if the field moves relative to the conductor**.

If a coil is considered as in Fig. 11.17(a) the magnetic field due to the current will be as shown. When the current is decreased as in Figs. 11.17 (b) and (c), it is imagined that the lines of flux become smaller and smaller and finally collapse in the centre of the conductor. When this happens the lines of flux cut the turns of the coil, thus inducing an e.m.f. in them. Therefore, whenever the current in a coil decreases or increases, changes in flux occur and an e.m.f. is induced. No e.m.f. is induced, however, if the current is constant. This property of a coil is known as its **self-inductance** and the unit of inductance is the **henry (H)**. A coil is said to have a self-inductance of 1 henry if, when the current changes at a rate of 1 ampere per second, the induced e.m.f. is 1 volt. Sub-divisions of the henry are commonly used:

1 millihenry (mH) = 10^{-3} henry
1 microhenry (μH) = 10^{-6} henry.

The magnitude of the induced e.m.f. (E) in a coil is given by **E = L × rate of change of current**, where L (the symbol for inductance) measured in henrys and the rate of change of current is in amperes/second. E is then in volts.

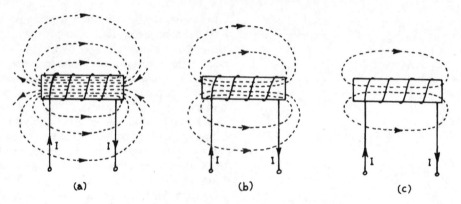

Fig. 11.17. Effect of reducing current in coil.

It should be noted that the induced e.m.f. acts in a direction so as to produce a current flow which opposes the change of flux which caused the induced e.m.f.; this is an example of **Lenz's law**.

The inductance of an air-cored coil is proportional to the (number of turns)^2, the diameter of the coil and a constant that depends upon the ratio of coil length to its diameter. For a coil of a given number of turns and size, the inductance may be increased by using a magnetic core. Inductors found in power and audio frequency applications often use laminated cores and have inductance values in the range of about 5–30 henrys. Inductors used for radio frequency applications may be iron dust, ferrite or air-cored and have much smaller inductance values in the range of a few microhenrys to tens of millihenrys.

If two coils are placed side-by-side as in Fig. 11.18 so that some of the flux set up by the current in coil A cuts or links the turns of coil B, any changes in current in coil A will not only induce an e.m.f. in coil A but also in coil B. This is known as **mutual inductance**, the unit being the **henry** as for self-inductance. The henry has the same significance except that the induced e.m.f. is in coil B (secondary) instead of in coil A carrying the current (primary). The magnitude of the voltage induced into coil B will depend on (a) the number of turns on the secondary, and (b) the fraction of flux passing between the primary and secondary, *e.g.* it will depend on how close the coils are together.

This property is used in the **transformer**. It should be noted that the e.m.f. is proportional to the rate of change of current and does not depend upon the value of the current itself. Thus, if a steady d.c. is passed through coil A, no e.m.f. is induced in coil A or coil B.

In most cases the primary and secondary coils are wound on a magnetic core of iron as in Fig. 11.19. The use of a magnetic core has two effects. Firstly, it increases the inductance of the primary winding and thus reduces the current that flows in the primary and secondly,

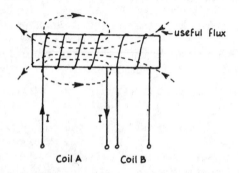

Fig. 11.18 Transformer principle.

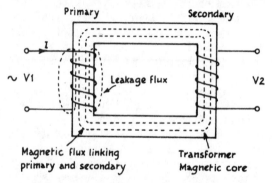

Fig. 11.19 Simple practical transformer.

it concentrates the magnetic flux so that most of its links with the secondary winding (the portion of flux not linking with the secondary is called the **leakage flux**). When an a.c. supply of voltage V1 is applied to the primary, a current I, will flow. Since this current is a.c. the flux in the magnetic core will change inducing a voltage V2 into the secondary winding. By varying the ratio of the primary-to-secondary turns a secondary voltage equal to, greater than or less than the primary voltage may be obtained.

QUESTIONS ON CHAPTER ELEVEN

(1) An example of a non-ferromagnetic material is:
   (a) Iron
   (b) Copper
   (c) Nickel
   (d) Cobalt.

(2) Which of the diagrams in Fig. 11.20 shows the correct direction for the magnetic field when current flows into the end of a conductor?

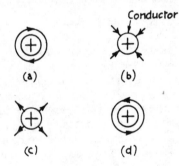

Fig. 11.20.

(3) Which of the following statements is correct?
   (a) The direction of magnetic flux is from South-to-North
   (b) Flux lines always cross one another
   (c) Flux lines are always uniformly spread
   (d) The North pole of a compass points in the direction of the lines of flux.

(4) The unit of inductance is:
   (a) The weber
   (b) The ampere-turn
   (c) The tesla
   (d) The henry.

(5) The direction of the force acting on a conductor carrying current in a magnetic field may be found by applying:
   (a) The corkscrew rule
   (b) Fleming's right-hand rule
   (c) Fleming's left-hand rule
   (d) Lenz's law.

(6) A commutator is used in a d.c. motor to:
   (a) Increase motor speed
   (b) Decrease motor speed
   (c) Reverse the direction of current flow each half-revolution
   (d) Reverse the direction of the magnetic field each revolution.

(7) A voltage is induced into the secondary winding of a transformer only when:
   (a) The primary voltage is changing value
   (b) A large d.c. voltage is applied to the primary
   (c) The flux in the core is constant
   (d) There is a load connected to the secondary winding.

(Answers on page 219.)

CHAPTER TWELVE

CAPACITANCE AND CAPACITORS

Objectives

1 Identify the basic elements of a capacitor and state the effects of each on capacitance. Describe common types of capacitor.
2 State the relationship between charge, capacitance and voltage, and calculate the combined capacitance of capacitors connected in series and parallel.
3 State the importance of voltage rating and precautions to be taken when using electrolytic capacitors.
4 State the effect of component values on the charge and discharge curve of a capacitor and define time constant.

CAPACITANCE

IF A POTENTIAL difference exists between two points in a circuit, such as A and B in Fig. 12.1(a) which are connected together by an electrical conductor, **charge** is set in motion along the conductor and a current I flows in the circuit. The magnitude of the current for a given potential difference is determined by the cross-sectional area of the conductor, its length and the material from which it is made.

Removing the conductor from the circuit will produce an **open-circuit**, but the potential difference will remain as shown in Fig. 12.1(b). If the insulation surrounding the circuit is perfect the resistance between A and B is infinitely large and so no current can flow. However, if the circuit is examined more closely with the aid of sensitive instruments some interesting results are obtained.

The circuit is first modified to that in Fig. 12.1(c) to include a switch S and a resistor R across which is connected to high gain c.r.o. When S is moved to position 1, a small pulse may be observed on the c.r.o. indicating that a pulse of current has flowed through R. If S is now moved to position 2, a similar pulse will be observed but opposite in direction.

This experiment demonstrates that charge is passing in and out of the open-circuit AB. When the p.d. between A and B is equal to the battery voltage (S in position 1) charge flows one way. When the p.d. is reduced to zero (S in position 2) charge flows in the opposite direction.

The above results are of great importance and a special name is given to the property of a circuit which enables **charge to be stored** and current to flow where there is apparently no path. This property is called **capacitance**. symbol C.

The unit of capacitance is the **farad** (F) and a circuit is said to have a capacitance of 1 farad if it is possible to store 1 coulomb of electrical charge when a p.d. of 1 volt exists. As an equation the general result may be written as:

$$C = \frac{Q}{V}$$

where C is in farads, Q in coulombs and V in volts.

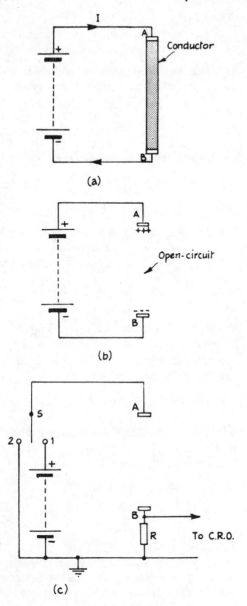

Fig. 12.1 *Investigation of capacitance.*

circuits and is called **stray capacitance** and although it is often small (a few pF) its effects may be very important in high frequency and pulse circuits. Stray capacitance is usually a nuisance. However, if capacitance can be introduced into a circuit in the right places and in the correct amount, it greatly increases the uses to which circuits can be put and for this reason capacitors are made.

Before looking at the construction of various types of capacitors, it is necessary to find out how the capacitance between two points can be calculated. Instead of using two conductors ends, such as A and B of Fig. 12.1(b), where the capacitance is really stray capacitance, a capacitor constructed from two flat parallel metal plates will be considered as illustrated in Fig. 12.2. The metal plates each having an area A are separated from one another by a distance d. The space between the plates is filled with an insulating material known as the **dielectric**. The dielectric may be air or some other gas, or it may be a liquid or solid, but whatever material is chosen it must be a good electrical insulator otherwise charge will be lost by leakage.

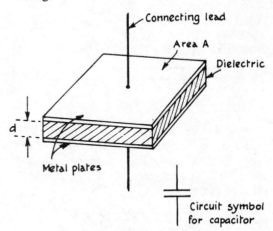

Fig. 12.2 *Parallel plate capacitor.*

In practice the farad is a very large unit and capacitors found in electronic circuits have capacitance values measured in micro-farads (μF), nano-farads (nF) or picofarads (pF).

CAPACITORS

All electrical circuits possess capacitance which exists whenever there is a difference in potential. This capacitance occurs naturally in

It may be verified by experiment that the capacitance C:

(1) Is proportional to the plate area A.
(2) Is inversely proportional to the distance between the plates d.
(3) Depends upon the material used for the dielectric.

If these factors are put in equation form we have:

$$C = \frac{E_o E_r A}{d}$$

where C = capacitance in farads.

    A = area of each plate in square metres.

    d = distance between plates (or dielectric thickness) in metres.

    E_o = a constant, known as the permitivity of free space (or vacuum or dry air approx.) having a value of $8 \cdot 85 \times 10^{-12}$.

    E_r = relative permitivity of the material used for the dielectric.

Table 12.1 Some values for the relative permitivity E_r.

Material	Relative permitivity
Air	1·0006
Glass	5 to 10
PVC	4·5
Perspex	3·5
Mica	5·7 to 6·7
Polystyrene	2·55
Ebonite	2·7 to 2·9
Ceramics	6 to 1000

Problem 1

Find the capacitance of a parallel plate capacitor made of two copper plates each of area $2 \cdot 2 \, cm^2$ separated by a distance of $0 \cdot 1mm$ and filled with a mica dielectric having a relative permitivity of 5·7.

Solution

$$C = \frac{E_o E_r A}{d} \text{ farads}$$

$$= \frac{8 \cdot 85 \times 10^{-12} \times 5 \cdot 7 \times 2 \cdot 2 \times 10^{-4}}{10^{-4}}$$

$$E_r = 5 \cdot 7$$
$$A = 2 \cdot 2 \times 10^{-4} \, m$$
$$d = 10^{-4} \, m$$

$$= 110 \cdot 979 \times 10^{-12} F$$
$$\approx 111pF$$

Problem 2

A parallel plate capacitor has a capacitance of 2·2nF. What will be its capacitance if:

(a) The dielectric thickness is doubled.

(b) The area of each plate is doubled.

Solution

(a) Now $C \propto 1/d$, thus by proportion if d is doubled the capacitance C is halved. Therefore, new capacitance:

$$= \frac{2 \cdot 2}{2} = 1 \cdot 1nF.$$

(b) Now $C \propto A$, thus by proportion if A is doubled the capacitance C is doubled. Therefore, new capacitance:

$$= 2 \cdot 2 \times 2 = 4 \cdot 4nF.$$

Problems Involving Charge, Voltage and Capacitance

From the definition of the farad we arrive at the general equation

$$C = \frac{Q}{V}$$

where C is in farads, Q is in coulombs and V is in Volts.

By transposition we also have:

$$V = \frac{Q}{C} \text{ and } Q = CV$$

Problem 3

A capacitor of value $2\mu F$ has a voltage of 100V across it. How much charge is stored in the capacitor?

Solution

    Q = CV

        $= 2 \times 10^{-6} \times 100$ coulombs

        $= 2 \times 10^{-4}$ coulombs

or   0·2 millicoulombs (0·2mC).

Problem 4

A charge of 2nC is stored in a capacitor of value (a) 50pF and (b) 1000pF. Find the p.d. across the capacitor in each case.

Solution

(a) $V = \dfrac{Q}{C} = \dfrac{2 \times 10^{-9}}{50 \times 10^{-12}} = 40\text{V}$

(b) $V = \dfrac{Q}{C} = \dfrac{2 \times 10^{-9}}{10^3 \times 10^{-12}} = 2\text{V}$

Note that for the same charge stored, the larger value capacitor has the smaller p.d. across it.

Problem 5

A capacitor with a p.d. across it of 50V stores a charge of 5mC. What is its capacitance value?

Solution

$C = \dfrac{Q}{V} = \dfrac{5 \times 10^{-3}}{50}\text{ F}$

$= 0.0001\text{ F} = 100\,\mu\text{F}.$

Problem 6

A capacitor of value $100\,\mu\text{F}$ is charged at a constant rate of 1mA for 5 seconds. Find:

(a) The charge stored at the end of the charge period.
(b) The final p.d. across the capacitor.

Solution

(a) Now $Q = It$ (Chapter 9)

$= 1 \times 10^{-3} \times 5\text{ C}$

$= 5\text{mC (charge stored)}$

(b) $V = \dfrac{Q}{C} = \dfrac{5 \times 10^{-3}}{100 \times 10^{-6}}$

$= 50\text{V (final p.d.).}$

Capacitors in Parallel

When capacitors are connected in parallel, they all have the same voltage or p.d. V across them as in Fig. 12.3, but the charge stored in

each capacitor depends upon the individual capacitor values.

Thus for capacitors in parallel we have:

$$Q_1 = C_1 V$$
$$Q_2 = C_2 V$$
$$Q_3 = C_3 V$$

The total charge stored Q is the sum of the individual charges, thus:

$$\begin{aligned} Q &= Q_1 + Q_2 + Q_3 \\ &= C_1 V + C_2 V + C_3 V \\ &= V(C_1 + C_2 + C_3) \end{aligned}$$

or $\dfrac{Q}{V} = C_1 + C_2 + C_3$

If the resultant capacitance of the combination is C then:

$$C = \dfrac{Q}{V}$$

or $C = C_1 + C_2 + C_3$

Hence for capacitors in parallel the resultant capacitance is the sum of the individual capacitances. These results should be compared with resistors in series.

Problem 7

Three capacitors of values 2nF, 200pF and 5nF are connected in parallel. What is the resultant capacitance?

Solution

$\begin{aligned} C &= C_1 + C_2 + C_3 \\ &= (2 + 0.2 + 5)\text{ nF} \quad (200\text{pF} = 0.2\text{ nF}) \\ &= 7.2\text{ nF} \end{aligned}$

Problem 8

Refer to Fig. 12.4, and calculate:

(a) The resultant capacitance of the circuit.
(b) The charge stored in each capacitor.

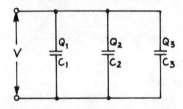

Fig. 12.3 Capacitors in parallel.

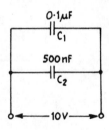

Fig. 12.4.

Electronics Servicing Volume 1

Solution

(a) $C = C_1 + C_2$

$= (0 \cdot 1 + 0 \cdot 5) \, \mu F$ $(500 \, nF = 0 \cdot 5 \, \mu F)$

$= 0 \cdot 6 \, \mu F$

(b) Charge (Q1) stored in C_1 is given by:

$Q1 = C_1 V$

$= 0 \cdot 1 \times 10^{-6} \times 10$

$= 1 \, \mu C$

Charge (Q2) stored in C_2 is given by:

$Q2 = C_2 V$

$= 0 \cdot 5 \times 10^{-6} \times 10$

$= 5 \, \mu C$

Capacitors in Series

When capacitors are connected in series, as shown in Fig. 12.5, the displacement of charge Q is the same in every part of the series circuit.

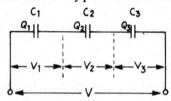

Fig. 12.5 Capacitors in series.

Thus the same amount of charge is stored in each capacitor.

Thus $Q = Q_1 = Q_2 = Q_3$.

However, the total voltage V is divided between the capacitors and:

$V = V_1 + V_2 + V_3$.

Now for a capacitor $V = \dfrac{Q}{V}$

therefore:

$V = \dfrac{Q_1}{C_1} + \dfrac{Q_2}{C_2} + \dfrac{Q_3}{C_3}$

$= Q \left(\dfrac{1}{C_1} + \dfrac{1}{C_2} + \dfrac{1}{C_3} \right)$

or $\dfrac{V}{Q} = \dfrac{1}{C_1} + \dfrac{1}{C_2} + \dfrac{1}{C_3}$

but $\dfrac{V}{Q} = \dfrac{1}{C}$

therefore

$$\frac{1}{C} = \frac{1}{C_1} + \frac{1}{C_2} + \frac{1}{C_3}.$$

It should be noted that for capacitors in series:

(a) The resultant capacitance is always less than the smallest individual capacitance value.

(b) The highest voltage appears across the smallest capacitance.

For two capacitors in series, the resultant capacitance C_t may be found from:

$$C_t = \frac{C_1 \times C_2}{C_1 + C_2}.$$

These results should be compared with resistors in parallel.

Problem 9

Two capacitors of values 5nF and 20nF are connected in series. Find:

(a) The resultant capacitance of the circuit.

(b) The voltage across each capacitor if 100V is applied across the whole circuit.

Solution

(a) $C_t = \dfrac{C_1 \times C_2}{C_1 + C_2} = \dfrac{5 \times 20}{5 + 20} = 4 \, nF$

(b) Charge stored in resultant capacitance is given by:

$Q = CV$

$= 4 \times 10^{-9} \times 100$

$= 0 \cdot 4 \, \mu C$

Voltage across 5nF capacitor:

$= \dfrac{Q}{C_1} = \dfrac{0 \cdot 4 \times 10^{-6}}{5 \times 10^{-9}} = 80V$

Voltage across 20nF capacitor:

$= \dfrac{Q}{C_2} = \dfrac{0 \cdot 4 \times 10^{-6}}{20 \times 10^{-9}} = 20V$

Problem 10

The resultant capacitance of two capacitors in series is $0 \cdot 1 \, \mu F$. If one capacitor has a value of $0 \cdot 5 \, \mu F$, what is the value of the other?

Solution

$$\frac{1}{C} = \frac{1}{C_1} + \frac{1}{C_2}$$

therefore:

$$\frac{1}{0 \cdot 1} = \frac{1}{0 \cdot 5} + \frac{1}{C_2} \quad \text{(working in } \mu F)$$

or $\quad \dfrac{1}{C_2} = \dfrac{1}{0 \cdot 1} - \dfrac{1}{0 \cdot 5}$

$$= 10 - 2$$

$$= 8$$

thus $C_2 = \dfrac{1}{8} = 0 \cdot 125 \, \mu F$

Problem 11

Refer to Fig. 12.6. Find the resultant capacitance of the circuit.

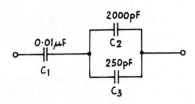

Fig. 12.6.

Solution

Resultant capacitance of C_2 and C_3 in parallel:

$$= C_2 + C_3$$
$$= 2000 + 250 = 2250 \, pF$$

This capacitance is in series with C_1, thus total capacitance of circuit is:

$$\frac{2 \cdot 25 \times 10}{2 \cdot 25 + 10} \text{ (values in nF)} = 1 \cdot 84 \, nF.$$

Charge and Discharge of a Capacitor

When a capacitor is connected to a source of voltage in a practical circuit there is always some resistance present; this may be simply the low resistance of the connecting leads, or the resistance of resistive components forming an essential part of the circuit. The presence of resistance in a circuit affects the growth and decay of voltage across the capacitor and, therefore, the time taken to complete the charge or discharge process.

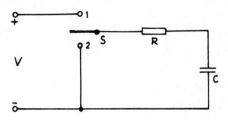

Fig. 12.7 Charge and discharge of a capacitor.

Consider the circuit of Fig. 12.7 where a source of d.c. voltage V is applied via a changeover switch S to a series circuit consisting of a resistance R and a capacitor C. With S in the position shown the capacitor will be uncharged. If S is set to position 1 then C will be able to charge towards the voltage V via R. The effective circuit will then be as in Fig. 12.8(a).

Initially on setting S to position 1 all of the applied voltage will appear across R, therefore $V_R = V$ and $V_C = 0$; the charging current I is then given by V/R. As current flows around the circuit, the capacitor commences to charge and a voltage V_C builds up across the capacitor. However, as V_C rises the voltage across R (V_R) falls since at all times $V = V_C + V_R$. Therefore, with less voltage across R, the charging current I decreases and **the rate at which V_C rises will decrease**. In consequence, the voltage across the capacitor rises in a non-linear manner and the current I falls in a non-linear manner as shown in Fig. 12.8(b). When the capacitor is fully charged the current I will be zero, the voltage across R will be zero and V_C will be equal to V.

If S of Fig. 12.7 is now set to position 2, the effective circuit will be as in Fig. 12.9(a). The capacitor previously charged will, therefore, have across it a voltage V_C equal to V. As we have a complete circuit, a discharge current I will flow, but note that it is in the opposite direction to that when the capacitor was charging. At the commencement of discharge, the fully charged voltage V is across R and the initial discharge current magnitude is given by V/R. However, when current flows charge is lost from C and the p.d. across it falls. As a result, the discharge current reduces in value as time progresses and the voltage across the capacitor falls in a non-linear manner as does the discharge current. When the capacitor is fully discharged, $V_C = 0$ and $I = 0$.

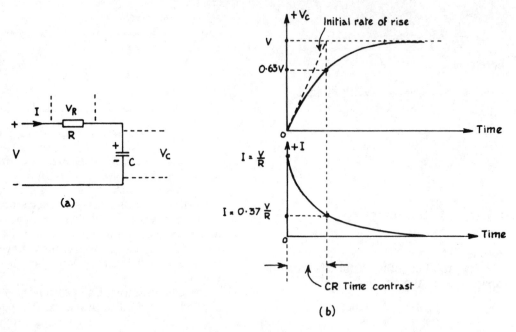

Fig. 12.8 Capacitor charging.

The **time constant** of the circuit may be defined as the time taken for the capacitor voltage to reach the final value V, if the initial rate of rise of V_C had been maintained, see Fig. 12.8(b). In practice it is found that the capacitor voltage only reaches approximately 0·63V during this time. Thus **time constant** may alternatively be defined as the time taken for the capacitor voltage to reach 0·63 of the final value.

We may state that:

time constant = C R seconds

where C is in farads and R is in ohms.

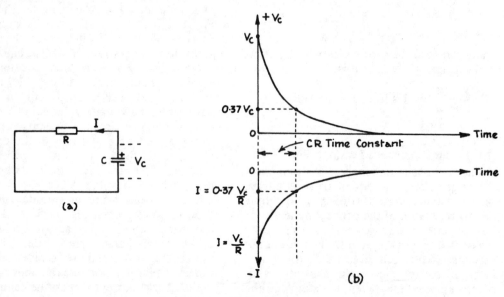

Fig. 12.9 Capacitor discharging.

Problem 12

A capacitor of value $0.1\,\mu\text{F}$ is charged via a $1\,\text{k}\Omega$ resistor. If the supply voltage is 20V determine:

(a) The time constant of the circuit.
(b) The voltage across the capacitor after a time period equal to the time constant.

Solution

(a) Time constant = C R seconds
$$= 0.1 \times 10^{-6} \times 10^{3}\,\text{s}$$
$$= 0.1\text{ms}$$

(b) After a period equal to the time constant the capacitor voltage will have risen to $0.63 \times 20\text{V} = 12.6\text{V}$.

The diagrams of Fig. 12.10 show the effect of component values on the charge and discharge curves. With, for example, C = 100nF and R = 100kΩ the resulting time constant would be $100 \times 10^{-9} \times 10^{5}\text{s} = 1\text{ms}$.

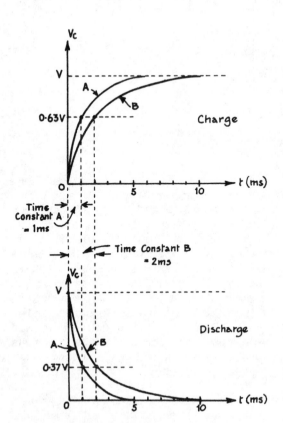

Fig. 12.10 *Effect of CR values on charge and discharge curves.*

Thus the voltage across C would rise to 0.63V during charge and fall to 0.37V during discharge in a period of 1ms, see curves marked A. If the time constant is increased to, say, 2ms either by doubling the value of C or R, the capacitor voltage would rise to 0.63V during charge, or fall to 0.37V during discharge in a period of 2ms, see curves B. Thus increasing the time constant will increase the time required to charge and discharge the capacitor. For practical purposes, the voltage across the capacitor will reach the final value of V during charge or 0V during discharge in a time period equal to 5 × time constant from the commencement of charge or discharge.

TYPES OF CAPACITOR

Capacitors available for use in electronic applications have capacitance values ranging from about 2pF to around $50{,}000\mu\text{F}$. In order to obtain any reasonable value of capacitance the area of the plates must be large, the relative permitivity of the dielectric should be high and the dielectric thickness small.

Because the space available on modern printed circuit boards for components is limited, the physical size or volume of a capacitor in relation to its capacitance value is also important. To achieve a good capacitance-to-volume ratio, the conducting plates and dielectric must be made thin to create a component of small volume. A further consideration is that if a thin dielectric is used it must withstand the voltage applied across the capacitor without the dielectric breaking down. Thus the **dielectric strength** of the chosen material is also important.

Paper Capacitors

Two common forms of construction are shown in Fig. 12.11. Here thin sheets of paper dielectric impregnated with oil or wax, to prevent the absorption of moisture and to increase the dielectric strength, are wound with interleaving aluminium foil strips to form a roll. A relatively large plate area can be created by this method at the same time keeping the physical size reasonable. In the extended-foil type of Fig. 12.11(a) the aluminium foil plates are exposed at either end to which electrical contact is made by welding

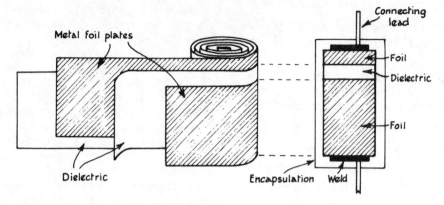

(a) Extended - foil

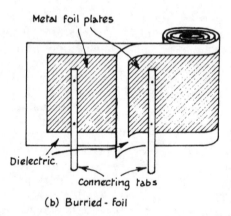

(b) Burried - foil

Fig. 12.11 Common types of wound capacitor structure.

end caps to the foil. This technique permits contact to be made along the entire length of the foil, thereby ensuring a low-inductance capacitor.

With the buried-foil design of Fig. 12.11(b), connecting tags are welded at one place on each foil strip. An undesireable feature of this form of construction is that the capacitor has a larger inductance than the extended-foil type, which may be important if the capacitor is to be used in high frequency applications. In both types, the capacitor is encapsulated in resin or sealed in a metal container.

Plastic Film Capacitors

These types often adopt a similar construction to the paper capacitors but use a plastic film dielectric, such as polystyrene, in place of the paper dielectric, interleaved with aluminium foil strips and wound into a roll. End caps are then fitted and the assembly encapsulated in either resin or a clear lacquer.

An alternative form of construction is the **metallised-film type**. Here a very thin metallic layer is formed on one side of the plastic dielectric by exposing the dielectric to a metal vapour (aluminium). Two of the metallised plastic strips are then rolled together as shown in Fig. 12.12. Each end of the roll is sprayed with copper to contact the metallised film and then wires are attached. Capacitors of this type use polyester or polycarbonate dielectric films.

Plastic films can be made very thin giving a double advantage of increased capacitance and reduced volume for a given plate area. Metallisation also reduces the thickness of the

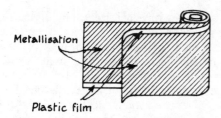

Metallisation

Plastic film

Fig. 12.12 Metallised plastic film capacitor.

plates and thus aids in the miniaturisation of wound capacitors. Another benefit of metallisation is its self-healing effect, when the dielectric **breaks-down**. If a short occurs between the metallised plates the thin metal film is vaporized, or converted into an insulating oxide by the heat developed in the short circuit, and so the fault clears itself.

Ceramic Capacitors

The relative permitivity of ceramics varies widely and ceramic capacitors are usually divided into two classes (a) the low-loss, low permitivity types and (b) the high-permitivity types. The use of high permitivity ceramic dielectrics enables capacitors to be made with remarkably small dimensions. One form of construction known as the **disc type** is shown in Fig. 12.13(a). This consists of a ceramic disc which has a thin film of silver deposited on opposite faces. Connecting leads are soldered to the silver coating and the capacitor is given a coating of enamel or plastic.

For the tubular construction of Fig. 12.13(b), the ceramic dielectric tube has silver coatings applied internally and externally to which connecting leads are soldered prior to encapsulation. Other forms of construction are possible depending upon the capacitance size required.

By using various ceramic materials it is possible to construct capacitors with known temperature coefficients, either positive or negative. Such capacitors are used to compensate for the effects of temperature on other components in a circuit, commonly in tuned or timing circuits.

Another important factor to be considered with a capacitor is its loss. Energy loss occurs in the dielectric and the choice of a low-loss ceramic capacitor would be a consideration in tuned circuit applications.

Silver-Mica Capacitors

Because of its plate-like crystal structure, mica can be laminated into very thin slices. Mica is an extremely stable material of high permitivity, thus capacitors made from it give good performance with small loss.

The basic form of construction for mica dielectric capacitors is shown in Fig. 12.14(a), where a slice of mica is metallised with silver on both surfaces. To increase the capacitance several silvered mica slices are stacked together as in Fig. 12.14(b). Mica plates are then fitted at either end and the assembly is

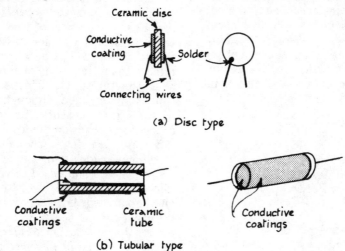

Ceramic disc

Conductive coating

Solder

Connecting wires

(a) Disc type

Conductive coatings

Ceramic tube

Conductive coatings

(b) Tubular type

Fig. 12.13 Ceramic capacitors.

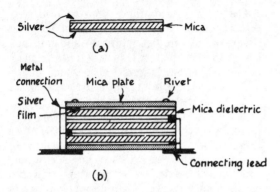

Fig. 12.14 Silver mica capacitor.

riveted together before being moulded in plastic or dipped in resin. Silver mica capacitors are employed as fixed tuning capacitors in tuned circuits offering close tolerance ($\pm 1\%$) and good stability ($\pm 1\%$).

Variable Capacitors

An arrangement of interleaved parallel plates is commonly used for variable capacitors which are employed as tuning capacitors in radio receivers and transmitters. The example shown in Fig. 12.15 uses air as the dielectric. One set of plates (or vanes) is fixed and attached to the frame by suitable insulators. The other set is attached to a spindle so that its vanes may be moved in and out of mesh with the fixed plates. In this way the **overlap area** between the fixed and moving vanes may be varied, and hence the capacitance altered. Such a variable capacitor may have a maximum capacitance of about 500pF (vanes fully meshed) and a minimum capacitance of about 50pF (vanes out of mesh). It is common practice to use two or more variable sections ganged together on a common spindle.

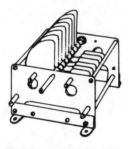

Fig. 12.15 Variable capacitor.

To reduce the physical size a solid dielectric may be used. This takes the form of thin plastic sheets placed between the vanes of the capacitor and fixed so that the moving vanes slide over them. In this way the capacitance is increased approximately by the relative permitivity of the plastic dielectric. Miniature variable capacitors of this type have been extensively used in a.m/f.m. transistor radio receivers.

Miniature variable trimmer capacitors are also available, see Fig. 12.16, and may employ a plastic (polypropylene) or ceramic dielectric. These are used for fine adjustment of oscillator, tuning and timing circuits, and produce small capacitance variations, *e.g.* 0·8pF–5pF, 2pF–22pF or 5pF–65pF.

Fig. 12.16 Trimmer capacitor.

Electrolytic Capacitors

When capacitors with large capacitance values ($1\mu F$–$50,000\mu F$) are required electrolytic capacitors are used. There are two main types of electrolytic capacitor; aluminium and tantalum.

The construction of the aluminium electrolytic is very similar to the paper capacitor, see Fig. 12.17. It consists of two aluminium foil strips separated by paper tissues which are wound together. The paper tissues are saturated with an electrolyte of either ammonium borate or ethylene glycol in the form of a paste (this is the **dry** type, although there must be some moisture present). The operation of this capacitor depends on the formation of a very thin layer (a few nanometres thick) of aluminium oxide on the anode by electrolytic action when a suitable d.c. voltage is maintained between the two foil plates. The aluminium oxide layer acts as the dielectric of the capacitor and because it is extremely thin, the resultant capacitance is large for the area of the plates. To further increase the capacitance the oxide coated plate may be etched to increase its surface area. Note that the

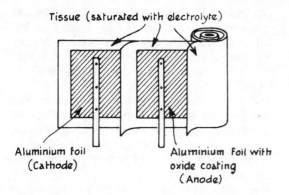

Fig. 12.17 Aluminium electrolytic capacitor (dry type).

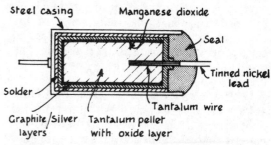

Fig. 12.19 Tantalum electrolytic capacitor (solid type).

absorbent tissue layers are conductors and do not act as a dielectric.

Since the formation and retention of the oxide layer on the anode foil plate depends on the d.c. potential between the plates the voltage applied to the capacitor terminals should not be reversed, otherwise the oxide will be removed from the anode and a large current will flow as oxide is formed on the cathode foil. The resulting large current may cause damage to other components in the circuit in which the capacitor is fitted. Also, gases may build-up inside the capacitor possibly causing it to explode. Thus electrolytic capacitors (with some exceptions) are **polarised** and must be fitted into circuit so that the correct polarity of voltage is maintained across the capacitor as illustrated in Fig. 12.18 (b) and (c).

The structure of a solid tantalum electrolytic capacitor is given in Fig. 12.19. The capacitor anode is formed by a pellet of tantalum which is coated with a layer of tantalum oxide. This

very thin oxide layer serves as the dielectric of the capacitor. The capacitor cathode is formed by layers of graphite and silver in contact with each other. The electrolyte is a solid coat of manganese dioxide deposited on the tantalum oxide pellet. The assembly is fitted in a steel casing over which is placed an insulating plastic sleeve.

Tantalum oxide has a higher relative permitivity than aluminium oxide, thus high capacitance can be produced in a small size. Additionally tantalum capacitors offer a lower leakage, a smaller capacitance tolerance and higher reliability than aluminium electrolytics, but are more costly. As for the aluminium electrolytics, tantalum electrolytics are polarised and must be fitted into circuit to achieve correct polarity.

Voltage Rating

It is important in a capacitor that the material chosen for the dielectric is able to withstand the potential difference applied to its plates when being charged. If the p.d.

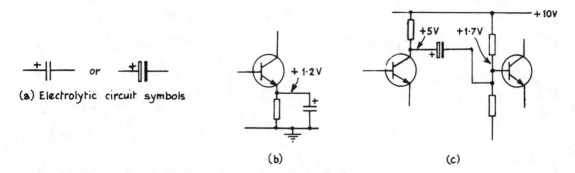

Fig. 12.18. Fitting an electrolytic into circuit with correct polarity.

applied is too large, the electric field set up between the plates may tear some of the electrons out of the atoms of the dielectric, causing its insulation resistance to drop; the insulation of the dielectric is then said to **break-down**.

Dielectric materials differ in the maximum voltage that they are able to withstand and this depends upon the **dielectric strength** of the material, measured in kV/mm. For example, air has a dielectric strength of 1kV per mm thickness, whereas for mica it is between about 40–100kV per mm thickness. Increasing the thickness of the dielectric will, of course, increase the maximum voltage that can be withstood. However, to obtain large capacitance values thin dielectrics are used. Thus for all capacitors there is a **maximum working voltage** a capacitor is able to withstand. If this voltage is exceeded the dielectric is liable to break-down.

Manufacturers often quote voltage ratings for d.c. and a.c. operation and generally the a.c. voltage rating is **several times less** than the d.c. voltage rating. For example, a capacitor may be given a d.c. voltage rating of 600V d.c. but an a.c. voltage rating of 250V a.c. This does not normally apply to polarised electrolytics for which only a d.c. voltage rating is given.

Table 12.2 Comparison Table for Common Capacitors.

Capacitor Type	Range of Values	Tolerance	Stability	Uses
Paper (foil/metallised)	10nF–10μF	$\pm$10%	Moderate	Mains interference suppression and motor start.
Plastic Film Polystyrene (foil)	10pF–10,000pF	$\pm$1%	Excellent	Tuned circuits, filters and timing applications.
Polyester (metallised)	0·01μF–1·0μF	$\pm$5%	Moderate	Coupling and decoupling.
Polycarbonate (metallised)	1μF–10μF	$\pm$5%	Good	Timing applications.
Ceramic Low-k	5pF–10nF	$\pm$10%	Good	Tuned circuits and temperature compensation.
High-k	5pF–1μF	$\pm$20%	Moderate	Decoupling.
Silver-Mica	2pF–10,000pF	$\pm$1%	Excellent	Tuned circuits and filters.
Aluminium Electrolytic Plain/Etched foil	1μF–100,000μF	−20% +50%	Moderate	Reservoir and smoothing in power supplies. L.F. decoupling.
Tantalum Electrolytic Solid	0·1μF–1000μF	$\pm$5%	Excellent	Timing applications.

QUESTIONS ON CHAPTER TWELVE

(1) The capacitance of a parallel plate capacitor is 5nF. If the dielectric thickness is doubled, the new capacitance will be:
(a) 1·25nF
(b) 2·5nF
(c) 10nF
(d) 20nF.

(2) A capacitor of 600pF uses a dielectric with a relative permitivity of 2. If the relative permitivity is increased to 6, the new capacitance will be:
(a) 100pF
(b) 200pF
(c) 1800pF
(d) 3600pF.

(3) A capacitor of 0·1μF has 100V across it. The charge stored will be:
(a) 10μC
(b) 10mC
(c) 100mC
(d) 10C.

(4) Three 25nF capacitors are connected in series. The resultant capacitance will be:
(a) 25nF
(b) 8·33nF
(c) 75nF
(d) 2·25nF.

(5) Capacitors with values of 0·001μF and 1nF are placed in parallel. The resultant capacitance will be:
(a) 2000pF
(b) 0·011μF
(c) 1·001nF
(d) 0·011nF.

(6) A 25V d.c. supply is applied across a resistor and capacitor connected in series. After a period equal to the time constant from switch-on, the voltage across the capacitor will be:
(a) 12·5V
(b) 15·75V
(c) 9·25V
(d) 25V.

(7) The time constant of a 100pF capacitor and a 100kΩ resistor is:
(a) 100μs
(b) 1ms
(c) 0·001s
(d) 10μs.

(8) Which of the diagrams given in Fig.12.20 shows the electrolytic capacitor connected the correct way round?

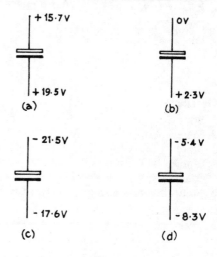

Fig. 12.20.

(9) Which of the following capacitor types would be chosen for a tuned circuit application requiring high stability?
(a) Paper
(b) High-k ceramic
(c) Silver-Mica
(d) Polyester.

(10) The type of capacitor used as the reservoir capacitor in a power supply would be:
(a) Polystyrene
(b) Polycarbonate
(c) Electrolytic
(d) Low-k ceramic.

(Answers on page 219.)

CHAPTER THIRTEEN

HEAT, MECHANICAL UNITS AND LIGHT

Objectives
1 State ways in which heat is transferred and identify heat dissipation devices.
2 State effects of temperature changes on solids, liquids and gases.
3 State SI units for force, mass and work.
4 State relationship between light wavelength, frequency and velocity.
5 Identify ray paths and effects of simple lenses.
6 State the colour spectrum of white light and identify the result of additive colour mixing.

HEAT

WHEN A BODY is heated to a temperature above that of its surroundings it can lose heat in one or more of the following ways:

(a) Thermal Conduction

In solid bodies heat flows from a **region of high temperature to a region of low temperature** by **thermal conduction**. When heat is applied to one end of a copper rod as in Fig. 13.1, the heat is soon transferred to the other end by conduction along the rod.

Materials which are good electrical conductors are usually good thermal conductors. Silver, copper and gold are good heat conductors, iron, lead and tin are moderate

Fig. 13.1 Conducted heat.

conductors whilst glass, paper, rubber and most plastics are very poor thermal conductors.

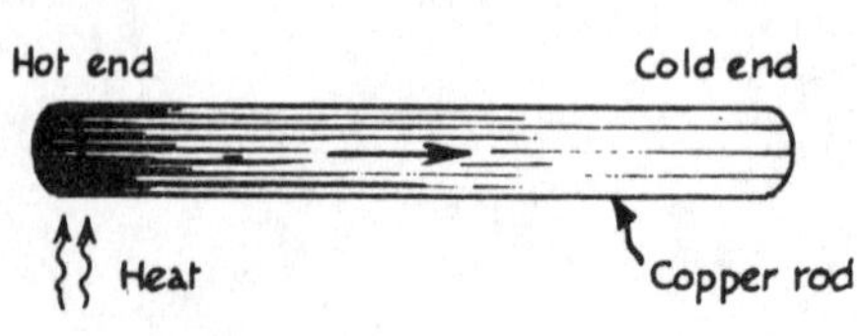

Heat conduction can occur between bodies provided they are in close contact over a wide area. For example, the heat generated in the element of a soldering iron is conducted through the insulation (mica) to the bit, and provided this is clean to the soldered connection. The heat generated in a semiconductor junction (diode or transistor) is conducted by the main bulk of the device to the outer casing. A heat sink, clipped to the lead of a semiconductor device during soldering will conduct heat away from the device to prevent over heating.

(b) Convection

Convection is the transfer of heat by the movement of a gas or liquid over a heated body. A high wattage resistor, for example, transfers heat from the surface of its encapsulation to the layers of air immediately surrounding it. As the temperature of this air increases, it expands and becomes less dense.

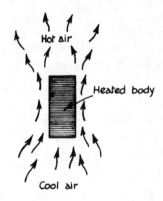

Fig. 13.2 Natural convection.

The warm air thus rises and is replaced by cooler air, a process which is repeated giving rise to convection currents in air as in Fig. 13.2.

The process by which the air is set in motion by the transfer of heat from a heated surface is called **natural convection**. To improve the convection when large amounts of heat need to be removed, a fan or pump may be used to stimulate the movement of the cooling medium; this is called **forced convection**.

The domestic central heating system of Fig. 13.3 is a good example of heat transfer by convection. Heat is transferred from the boiler unit to the radiator panels using forced convection by stimulating flow with the water pump. Natural convection is used to transfer heat to the room from the radiator panels.

(c) Radiation

Unlike conducted or convected heat, radiant heat does not need a medium to enable its transfer and will readily pass through a vacuum. When a body is heated its surface molecules vibrate generating electromagnetic waves which travel away at the speed of light causing the surface to become cooler. When these waves meet some other material they produce a disturbance in its surface molecules causing its temperature to increase.

At temperature differences up to about, say 50°C heat from a body is mainly transferred by convection and conduction (if there is a good conducting path). As the temperature difference increases, the amount of radiant heat transferred increases. Radiant heat produces a large spread of electromagnetic waves but the larger part of the energy lies in the infra-red part of the electromagnetic spectrum. If the temperature of a body is raised high enough the body begins to glow and energy is radiated as light as well as radiant heat (the body is red or white-hot). Radiant heat is the mechanism by which heat from the sun reaches the earth and by which heat is transferred from an electric bar fire. The majority of energy produced by an electric light filament is radiated as heat.

The radiation of heat from a body also depends upon the surface finish. A polished metal surface is a poor radiator for heat energy whilst a matt black one is the best radiator. When exposed to radiation, the matt black one is the most effective absorber of heat energy but the polished metal surface absorbs the least. Thus polished metal surfaces reflect heat best and are used as reflectors on electric bar fires.

For the temperatures found in electronic

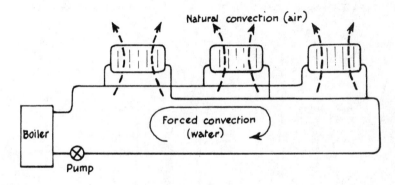

Fig. 13.3 Central heating system.

equipment, radiation does not play a large part in the transfer of heat.

Heat Dissipation

When electrical power is dissipated in a circuit component it produces a rise in temperature and this must be taken into account in the design of the component as discussed in Chapter 9. An excessive temperature rise may cause the device to fail or produce a significant change in the resistance value of the component, for example. Heat of varying amounts depending upon wattage rating is dissipated in **resistors**, **semiconductor devices** and **windings** in **transformers**, **smoothing inductors**, **motors** and **generators**.

To ensure adequate removal of heat from components so that the temperature stabilises and does not rise above the rated temperature the following steps may be taken:

(1) Provide the component with a sufficiently large surface area to increase the rate of heat loss. High wattage components are made physically larger than small wattage ones.

(2) Maintain a temperature difference between components and their surroundings. This may be promoted by providing ventilation holes or slots in the casing and between sections of the equipment so that natural convection will allow the flow of cooler air over components. If this is inadequate, forced convection using an electric fan may be necessary.

(3) Mount high wattage components away from other components and position close to cool air source. Remember that warm air rises and if components are positioned in elevated warm regions in an enclosure they will have difficulty in getting rid of their heat.

(4) Often, particularly with high power semiconductor devices, the casing of the device is insufficient alone to give good heat transfer and a **heat sink** may be used, see Fig. 13.4. This is made from a metal of good thermal conductivity and is usually finned to increase its surface area for the minimum space provided. A matt black surface will improve the radiation heat loss. For the highest power finned heat sinks, forced air or liquid cooling can be used.

Effect of Temperature on Solids, Liquids and Gases

(a) Solids

Solids have a definite shape and particular volume. If a solid block of material such as copper is heated its volume will increase and the length of each of its sides will increase as

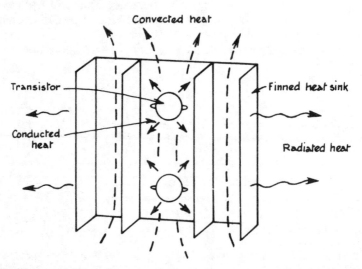

Fig. 13.4 *Heat removed from power transistors by convection, conduction and radiation.*

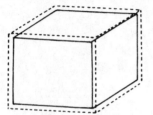

Fig. 13.5 *Expansion of heated solid block.*

shown in Fig. 13.5. Each of the block dimensions will be found to increase by the same fraction of its original length. This leads to the idea of the **coefficient of linear expansion**, which is a measure of the linear expansion that takes place for each unit length for every °C rise in temperature.

Thus when subjected to a temperature rise, expansion takes place in solids. If the body is allowed to cool it will contract and assume its original shape, provided that the increase in temperature was not so great as to cause permanent deformation of its shape.

Expansion and contraction can be a nuisance but must be allowed for in engineering. The tension in overhead power lines must be considered; in cold weather the conductors will contract producing undue stress whereas in hot weather they will sag, reducing the clearance to ground. Bridges with long spans must be designed to allow for a change in length between summer and winter. Expansion bends are incorporated into steam pipelines to allow bending movement without damaging the pipes. The expansion of a heated metal ring may be used when it is to be fitted over some other part, since when it cools it ensures a tight grip. This is known as **shrink fit** and is used for fitting steel tyres to the rims of locomotive wheels.

(b) Liquids

A liquid has no definite shape but flows until it assumes the shape of the container into which it was placed. When subjected to a temperature rise most liquids expand at a constant rate over a particular temperature range and their volume increases. The thermometer of Fig. 13.6 depends upon the expansion of mercury in its glass tube. A full container of liquid will overflow when heated. Conversely if the liquid is allowed to cool the liquid level will fall as it contracts.

Fig. 13.6 *Mercury-in-glass thermometer.*

Water, however, behaves unexpectedly at low temperatures. Its volume decreases as the temperature is lowered to about 4°C and then the volume **increases** as the temperature is reduced to 0°C and ice is formed. It is this effect which is responsible for the bursting of frozen water pipes.

(c) Gases

Unlike a solid or liquid, a gas has no definite volume at any given temperature. A gas always fills any container into which it is placed. If a gas is heated it will expand (become less dense) if it is allowed to do so, but if this is prevented by the rigidity of the container an increase in pressure results.

A balloon filled with a given mass of air as in Fig. 13.7(a) will cause the balloon to expand as the air is heated so that the gas occupies a larger volume as in Fig. 13.7(b). The gas is now less dense but its pressure will be the same.

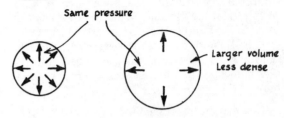

(a) One temperature   (b) Higher temperature

Fig. 13.7 *Temperature of air in balloon increased.*

MECHANICAL UNITS

Mass

The mass of a body is the amount or quantity of matter which makes up the body.

The form (solid, liquid or gas) that makes up the body is not important and the volume is determined by how close together the molecules of the body are packed.

The SI unit of mass is the **kilogramme** (kg) and is the mass of a particular lump of platinum in the International Bureau of Weights and Measures in Paris. Replicas of the standard kilogramme are used all over the world to standardise weighing instruments.

Multiple and sub-multiples of the kilogramme are commonly used:

$$1 \text{ Tonne (t)} = 1000 \text{ kg}$$
$$1 \text{ gramme (g)} = 0.001 \text{ kg} = 10^{-3} \text{kg}$$
$$1 \text{ milligramme (mg)} = 0.001 \text{ g}$$
$$= 10^{-3} \text{g} = 10^{-6} \text{kg}$$

The **mass** of a body determines its reluctance to accelerate when a force is applied to it whereas the **weight** of a body depends upon the force of gravity exerted by the earth and this varies from place to place. The standard kilogramme mass will weigh less on the moon (where the force of gravity is considerably less) than the same standard mass does on earth.

Force

If a body is left to itself it will either remain at rest or continue to move with constant velocity in a straight line. Anything which tends to change these conditions is a **force**. Everyday experiences, like riding a bicycle inform us that we have to apply a force to the pedals to set the machine in motion or apply a force to the hand brakes to stop the machine.

The SI unit of force is the **newton** (N) and is the force required to produce an acceleration of 1 metre per second per second (m/s^2) in a mass of 1 kg.

This may be expressed as:

$$F = \text{mass} \times \text{acceleration}$$
or $\quad F = ma$

where m is in kilogrammes and a is in m/s^2.

Example
What force must be applied to a mass of 5.6 kg to give it an acceleration of $0.8 \, m/s^2$?

Solution

$$F = ma$$
$$= 5.6 \times 0.8$$
$$= 4.48 \, N$$

Work

When a force is applied to a body it will move if it is free to do so in the direction of the force. In moving the body, the force has **done work** on it. Work done is thus the product of force and distance.

Work =
Force × Distance moved in direction of force.

The SI of work is the **joule** (J) and is the work done when a force of one newton moves a distance of one metre.

Example
Determine the work done when a force of 50N moves an object through a distance of 10.5 m.

Solution

$$W = \text{Force} \times \text{Distance}$$
$$= 50 \times 10.5$$
$$= 525 \, J$$

LIGHT

Light rays, radio waves, X-rays and cosmic rays like radiant heat travel through space in the form of electromagnetic waves and with high velocity (3×10^8 metres per second in a vacuum). These different types of radiation are all essentially of the same form but have different properties, *e.g.* radio waves can pass around opaque objects but light waves are blocked. The properties of the different types of e.m. radiation are determined by their frequency or wavelength, see Fig. 13.8. For convenience the spectrum is often divided into sections but the sections have no precise boundaries as the behaviour of e.m. waves does not change sharply at given frequencies.

Visible light occupies a very small section in the e.m. spectrum with wavelengths corresponding to approximately 400–800

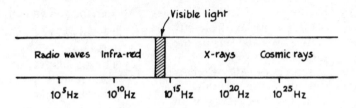

Fig. 13.8 *The electromagnetic spectrum.*

nanometres (nm). When all of the frequencies present in the visible spectrum reach the eye simultaneously we see **white** light.

The wavelength (λ) of an e.m. wave may be found from:

$$\lambda = \frac{v}{f}$$

where f is the frequency (Hz), v = velocity of light (3×10^8 m/s) and λ is in metres.

Example 1

What is the wavelength of a light radiation at 6×10^{14} Hz?

Solution

$$\lambda = \frac{v}{f} \text{ metres}$$

$$= \frac{3 \times 10^8}{6 \times 10^{14}}$$

$$= 0.5 \times 10^{-6} \text{m}$$

$$= 500 \text{ nm}$$

Example 2

What is the frequency of a 750 nm light radiation?

Solution

$$f = \frac{v}{\lambda} \text{ metres}$$

$$= \frac{3 \times 10^8}{750 \times 10^{-9}} \text{ Hz}$$

$$= 4 \times 10^{14} \text{ Hz}$$

Properties of Light

(a) Rectilinear Propagation

By considering the shadow cast by an object placed in the path of a beam of light as in Fig. 13.9, it is evident that light must travel in straight lines and not bend round the object.

Straight line travel or **rectilinear propagation** at it is sometimes called still holds good over great distances as is evident by the shadow cast by the moon on earth during the eclipse of the sun, for example.

It should be mentioned that although Fig. 13.9 shows the light rays travelling in straight lines, this is only approximately true. On closer examination it is found that some of the light passes into the geometric shadow of the object. This is the result of the diffraction of light which occurs when light passes the edge of an object.

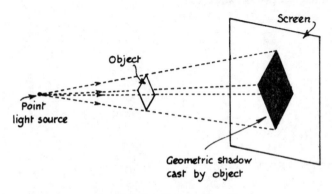

Fig. 13.9 *Rectilinear propagation.*

(b) Reflection

When we see an object, light passes directly from the object into our eyes and sets up the sensation of vision. Objects are only visible if they are themselves sources of light or reflect light from a source into the eye. Nearly all that we see about us is the result of reflection of light. Most bodies of everyday life, *e.g.* paper, cloth, flowers and people *etc.* reflect light in an irregular manner, see Fig. 13.10(a). This is because these types of objects have surfaces that are rough on a microscopic scale and cause the light to be reflected in an irregular way. At each point the laws of reflection are obeyed but the angle of the reflected ray varies.

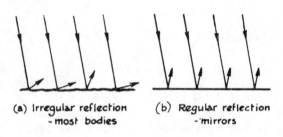

(a) Irregular reflection   (b) Regular reflection
    - most bodies   - mirrors

Fig. 13.10 Reflection.

On the other hand, smooth surfaces like polished metal or glass with a metallic coating on the back or front surface reflect light in a regular way and are used as mirrors. The angle of the reflected light is now the same at every point as in Fig. 13.10(b).

A ray of light such as **CO** in Fig. 13.11 falling on the surface of a flat mirror makes an angle **i** with the normal **NO** to the mirror called the **angle of incidence**. The angle **r** made with the normal by the reflected ray is called the **angle of reflection**.

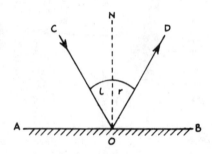

Fig. 13.11 Reflection at mirror surface.

It may be shown experimentally that:

(1) The angle of incidence equals the angle of reflection.
(2) The incident ray, the reflected ray and the normal at the point of incidence all lie in the same plane.

These are the two laws of reflection.

The diagram of Fig. 13.12(a) shows how an image is formed in a mirror from a small point object emitting rays in all directions. At each incident point on the mirror, **B, C, D** *etc.* the laws of reflection are obeyed. To an observer the rays appear to come from **A'** (at the same distance as **A** to the mirror but on the other side of it) where there appears to be an image of the object **A**. Image **A'** is a **virtual image** since light does not pass through the image point but only appears to do so.

A person looking in a mirror and combing their hair with the left hand appears to be using

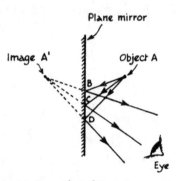

(a) Formation of a point
    image in a mirror

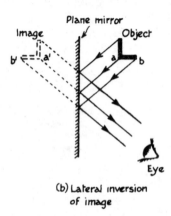

(b) Lateral inversion
    of image

Fig. 13.12 Mirror images.

the right hand. This is lateral inversion of the image, see Fig. 13.12(b). The image of point **a** on the object is at **a′** at an equal distance behind the mirror. Point **b** on the object which is to the right of **a** produces an image at **b′** on the left of **a′**, *i.e.* the right hand side of the object becomes the left hand side of the image. Thus the object is **laterally inverted** to an observer.

The lines shown in the previous diagrams representing rays give the direction that light energy is travelling. It should be appreciated that a light ray has a finite width and a collection of rays is known as a **beam**. Rays which are being received from a point on a most distant object, *e.g.* the sun are substantially parallel, see Fig. 13.13(a). The light coming from a lamp forms a divergent beam as in Fig. 13.13(b), whereas a light source and a lens can provide a convergent beam, see Fig. 13.13(c).

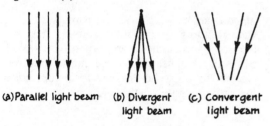

(a) Parallel light beam   (b) Divergent light beam   (c) Convergent light beam

Fig. 13.13 Light beams.

(c) Refraction

When light passes from one medium to another, say from air to glass or from glass to air, the rays are **bent** unless the rays strike the boundary at right angles. This causes the rays to travel in a different direction and are said to be **refracted**.

In the diagram of Fig. 13.14 the incident ray **AO** is refracted at the air to glass boundary and travels in a new direction **OB** through the glass medium. As some reflection always accompanies refraction, a reflected ray has also been shown. If the light ray is reversed it will travel along its original path. The laws of refraction are:

(1) At the point of incidence, the incident and refracted rays and the normal all lie in the same plane.

(2) For the two media concerned:
$$\frac{\sin i}{\sin r}$$

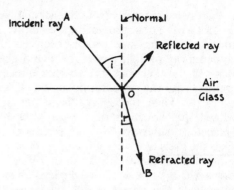

Fig. 13.14 Refraction of light at plane surface.

is a constant where i is the angle of incidence and r is the angle of refraction. This constant is called the **refractive index** (n) for the two media. As the magnitude of the constant depends upon the wavelength of the light, it is usually specified as that obtained with yellow light. The refractive index for air-to-glass is about 1·5 and for air-to-water about 1·33.

Refraction is a consequence of the fact that **light travels more slowly through water or glass than through air** which is less dense. It may be shown that:

$$v = \frac{c}{n}$$

where n is the refractive index, c is the velocity of light in a vacuum and v is the velocity of light in the medium.

It should be noted that when a ray of light passes from air to a denser medium of glass, the ray is **bent towards the normal** as in Fig. 13.15(a). On the other hand if the ray is passing from glass to a less dense medium of

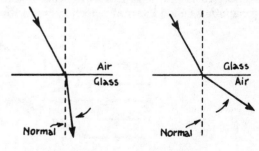

(a) AIR-GLASS
Bending towards normal

(b) GLASS-AIR
Bending away from normal

Fig. 13.15 Refraction on entering and leaving glass.

air, the ray is **bent away from the normal**, see Fig. 13.15(b). These properties are helpful in understanding the basic action of lenses.

When a ray of light passes through a glass block with parallel sides, the ray that emerges is parallel with the ray entering the block, see Fig. 13.16. Thus the glass block has not changed the direction of the ray but has displaced it sideways. If the incident ray strikes the glass block at right angles there will be no displacement. Thus if an object is viewed via a glass section which is placed obliquely to the object it will appear to be displaced.

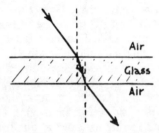

Fig. 13.16 Refraction through a glass block.

A further aspect of refraction is considered in Fig. 13.17. When a ray travelling in glass makes a small angle x with the normal at the glass-to-air boundary as in Fig. 13.17(a), only a small portion of the light is reflected; most of the light is refracted away from the normal. As the incident angle is increased a situation is reached where the refracted ray travels along the glass-to-air boundary, but the portion of light reflected is still quite small as in Fig. 13.17(b). If the angle of incidence is now increased above the **critical angle y**, there is no refraction at the boundary and all of the light is reflected as in Fig. 13.17(c). This phenomenon is called **internal reflection** and is the

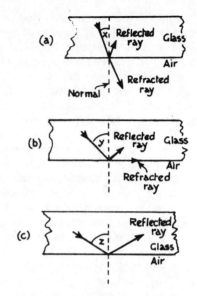

Fig. 13.17 Total internal reflection.

mechanism by which light is propagated along optical fibres. It should be noted that this phenomenon cannot occur when light travels from a less dense to a more dense medium, *e.g.* air-to-glass. For a glass-to-air boundary the critical angle is about 42°.

Simple Lenses

In photography and other optical systems, a lens unit normally consists of a combination of thin glass lenses. There are two main types of lenses which act upon a narrow parallel beam of light falling on the lens in the following manner:

(1) A converging or **convex** lens causing the light to converge to a point as in Fig. 13.18(a).

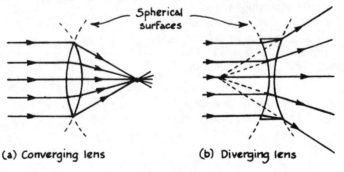

Fig. 13.18 Main lens types.

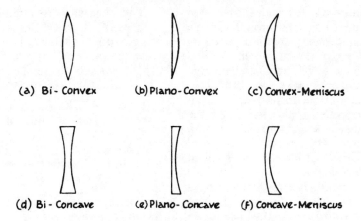

(a) Bi-Convex   (b) Plano-Convex   (c) Convex-Meniscus

(d) Bi-Concave   (e) Plano-Concave   (f) Concave-Meniscus

Fig. 13.19 Six shapes of a simple lens.

(2) A diverging or **concave** lens causig the light to diverge on the far side of the lens as if it were originating from an apparent point on the side of the light source as in Fig.13.18(b).

As light enters and leaves the lens, it is refracted at the air-to-glass and glass-to-air boundaries. In order for the rays to converge or appear to diverge from the same point it is necessary to progressively alter the slope of the incident and exit faces of the glass. This is achieved by providing the lens with spherical surfaces as shown.

Each of the two main lenses exists in three forms as shown in Fig. 13.19. The upper row are all converging lenses and are capable of forming real images on their own. The lower three are diverging lenses and may be found along with converging lenses in camera lenses made up of several elements. A converging lens is always thicker at its centre than at its edges; the reverse is true for a diverging lens.

Focal Length

The focal length for converging and diverging lenses is shown in Figs. 13.20(a) and (b).

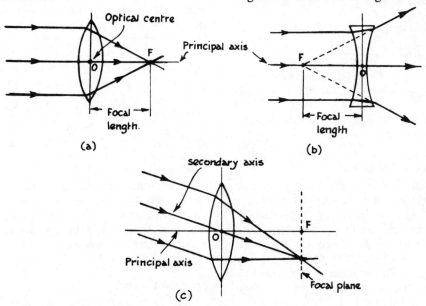

Fig. 13.20 Focal length and focal plane.

The **optical centre** (O) for each lens is that point in the centre of the lens through which a ray can pass and emerge without it being deviated. The point (F) at which parallel incident rays converge or appear to converge from is called the **principal focus** of the lens. There are two principal focus points, equi-distant on either side of each lens since the light may be incident from either side. In both cases, the distance **OF** between the optical centre and the principal focus point is called the **focal length** of the lens.

The rays of a parallel beam arriving on a secondary axis as in Fig. 13.20(c) are refracted so that they pass through a point which lies on a plane through the principal focus point perpendicular to the principal axis, this is called the **focal plane**.

The more strongly the curvature of the lens, the shorter is the distance **OF** and the shorter the focal length, see Fig. 13.21.

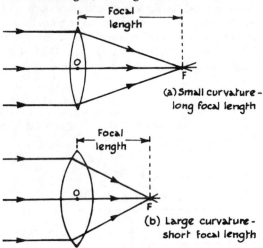

Fig. 13.21 Effect of lens curvature on focal length.

Image formed by a Lens

Only parallel rays have been considered so far; when light from a point on a distant object falls on a lens the rays are substantially parallel. Such is the case for light rays from the sun. Thus in Figs. 13.20 (a) and (c), light from the sun would be refracted by the lens to form a sharp image in the focal plane at **F**. It is this effect used with a lens to burn holes in a piece of paper by positioning the lens so that it is at a distance **OF** from the paper.

The diagrams of Fig. 13.22 show how images of an object are produced when the object-to-lens distance is not large in which case the rays arriving are no longer parallel. The position of the image may be determined by drawing two rays from the top of the object:

(a) One ray is drawn parallel to the principal axis which is refracted through the prin-cipal focus point **F**.
(b) A second ray is drawn through the optical centre which passes undeviated through a thin lens as shown.

For a convex lens with the object at a distance greater than $2 \times$ focal length as in Fig. 13.22(a), a **real image** is formed as shown but is smaller than the object and inverted. Systems of this type are used in cameras.

When the object-to-lens distance is exactly equal to $2 \times$ focal length, a real inverted image is formed having the same size as the object, see Fig. 13.22(b). Systems of the type produc-ing an image of the same size are used in photo-copying machines.

With the object-to-lens distance between 2F and F, a real inverted image is again formed but is a magnified version of the object, see Fig. 13.22(c). Systems producing a magnified image are used in projectors and enlargers.

When the object-to-lens distance is less than the focal length as in Fig. 13.22(d), a **virtual image** is formed. This is magnified, non-inverted and on the same side of the lens as the object. This is the case of a magnifying glass.

Finally if the object is placed at the focal point as in Fig. 13.22(e), the rays emerging from the lens are parallel and the image is said to be formed at infinity, *i.e.* it cannot be seen. This type of arrangement may be used to produce a parallel beam of light as with a spotlight, when used with a light source emitting a divergent beam.

A concave lens, see Fig. 13.23 always forms a virtual image that is a diminished version of the object. The non-inverted image is always nearer the lens than the object and closer to the lens than the principal focus **F**. This arrangement is employed in spectacle lenses.

Spectral Colours

When a beam of white light as in Fig. 13.24 is allowed to fall on a glass prism, the ray that

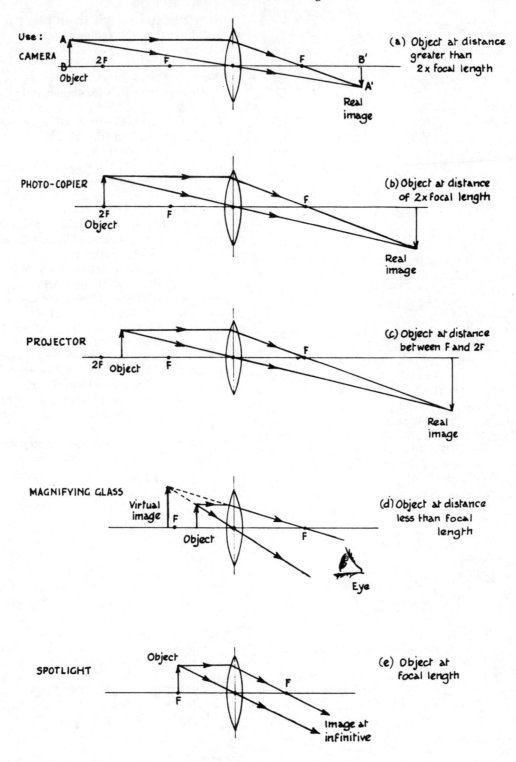

Fig. 13.22 Images formed by a convex lens.

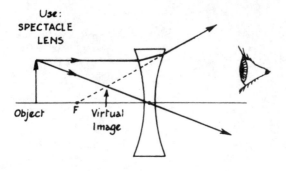

Fig. 13.23 *Image formed by concave lens.*

emerges is no longer a beam of white light but a divergent beam containing all the colours of the rainbow and their intermediate tints. This experiment shows that white light is not the purest kind of light but on the contrary is a mixture of a vast range of colours. Each colour has a specific wavelength but the difference in wavelength between adjacent colours of the spectrum is so small that the vast range of colours are not distinguishable by the human senses. Instead, we see a gradual blending of the numerous colour radiations which produces a graduation of distinct hues called **spectral colours**. These are **Red, Orange, Yellow, Green, Blue, Indigo**, and **Violet**. As an aid to memory the initial letters spell the name **ROY. G. BIV**.

Note that the amount of bending or refraction that occurs is greater for the shorter wavelengths, *i.e.* more at the **blue** end of the spectrum than the **red** end.

Additive Colour Mixing

The principle of all colour printing, colour photography and colour television is based on the mixing of usually three colours to obtain all of the colours in the original. In colour television, the three primary colours are red (615nm), green (532nm) and blue (470nm). By suitable mixing of these so called **primary colours** it is possible to produce nearly all of the colours that occur in nature.

There are two ways that colours can be mixed: by mixing coloured lights (the additive system); or by mixing colured pigments, *e.g.* paints, inks and dyes (the subtractive system).

Here we are concerned with **additive mixing which is employed in colour television**. If two of the television primaries are projected from lamps on to a white screen so that they partly overlap, the colour that we see in the overlap area is the result of additive mixing. The diagrams of Fig.13.25 show the result when various colours are additively mixed. Note that when all three primaries are additively mixed (in suitable proportions) the result is white.

In addition, white is also produced when the following lights are additively mixed:

Blue + Yellow = **White**
Green + Magenta = **White**
Red + Cyan = **White**

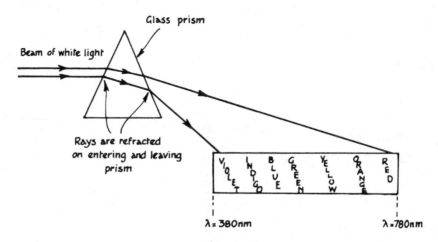

Fig. 13.24 *Spectral colours.*

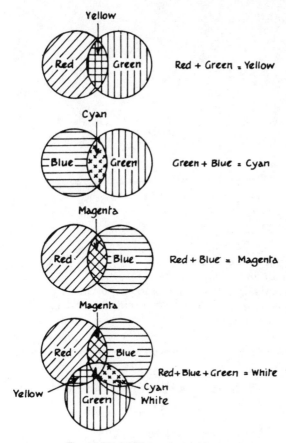

Fig. 13.25 Additive colour mixing.

Red + Green = Yellow

Green + Blue = Cyan

Red + Blue = Magenta

Red + Blue + Green = White

QUESTIONS ON CHAPTER THIRTEEN

(1) An example of a good thermal conductor is:
   (a) Silver
   (b) Glass
   (c) Paper
   (d) Plastic.

(2) The heat that is felt on touching the metal handle of a hot saucepan is the result of:
   (a) Radiation
   (b) Conduction
   (c) Natural convection
   (d) Forced convection.

(3) When a balloon filled with air is heated the following will occur:
   (a) Air pressure will fall but volume will increase
   (b) Volume will increase but pressure will remain the same

(c) Air pressure will rise and volume will increase
(d) Volume will increase and density of air will increase.

(4) The SI unit of work is the:
   (a) kilogramme
   (b) newton
   (c) coulomb
   (d) joule.

(5) The relationship between wavelength, velocity and frequency of light is given by:
   (a) $\lambda = v \times f$
   (b) $v = \lambda \times f$
   (c) $f = \dfrac{\lambda}{v}$
   (d) $\lambda = \dfrac{f}{v}$.

(6) The angle of incidence formed when light strikes the surface of a flat mirror is 32°. The angle of reflection will be:
   (a) 16°
   (b) 32°
   (c) 64°
   (d) 58°.

(7) When a ray of light passes from glass-to-air, the ray:
   (a) Reverses direction
   (b) Is bent away from the normal
   (c) Continues in a straight line path
   (d) Is refracted towards the normal.

(8) An object placed at a distance greater than twice the focal length from a convex lens will result in a:
   (a) real inverted image and magnified
   (b) non-inverted virtual image and diminished
   (c) inverted virtual image and magnified
   (d) real inverted image and diminished.

(9) When red and green light is additively mixed the result will be:
   (a) Blue
   (b) Cyan
   (c) Yellow
   (d) Magenta.

(10) The result of additively mixing blue and yellow light is:
   (a) Magenta
   (b) Cyan
   (c) White
   (d) Pink.

(Answers on page 219.)

CHAPTER FOURTEEN

CALCULATIONS

Objectives

Perform practical electrical calculations involving the following:
1 Decimal numbers, percentages, ratios, averages and tolerances.
2 Significant figures, decimal places, powers of 10 and standard form.
3 Transposition of formulae, squares, square roots, SI prefixes and standard form.
4 Addition and subtraction of binary numbers and conversion between binary and decimal.
5 Plot and interpret linear, exponential and inverse graphs.

THIS CHAPTER IS concerned with basic calculations to find the size of circuit parameters such as electrical power, voltage, current, resistance and resistivity *etc*. Electronic engineers at all levels must be able to work with mathematics, appropriate to their needs, quickly and accurately. Many of the calculation examples given here relate to the science background topics found in other chapters.

DECIMAL NUMBERS

In the **decimal** or **denary** system (base 10) of which we are most familiar, we use 10 digits:

$$0\ 1\ 2\ 3\ 4\ 5\ 6\ 7\ 8\ 9$$

Using these digits we can construct a number of any magnitude using the columns below:

Addition and Subtraction

Suppose that the calculated voltage across R1 and R2 in Fig. 14.1 are as shown. To find the total voltage we add the decimal numbers 4·87 and 3·21 together. Adding (or subtracting) decimal numbers is done exactly the same

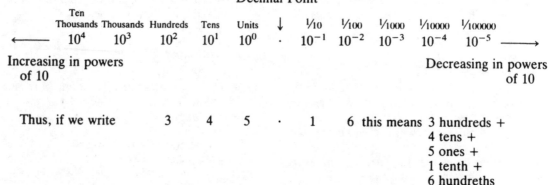

Decimal Point

Ten Thousands	Thousands	Hundreds	Tens	Units	↓	¹/₁₀	¹/₁₀₀	¹/₁₀₀₀	¹/₁₀₀₀₀	¹/₁₀₀₀₀₀
10^4	10^3	10^2	10^1	10^0	.	10^{-1}	10^{-2}	10^{-3}	10^{-4}	10^{-5}

← Increasing in powers of 10

Decreasing in powers of 10 →

Thus, if we write   3   4   5   ·   1   6 this means 3 hundreds +
4 tens +
5 ones +
1 tenth +
6 hundreths

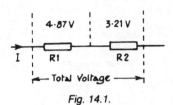

Fig. 14.1.

as for whole numbers. Care must be taken to write down the decimal points directly below one another so that the digits appear in the correct columns.

Thus we have:

$$\begin{array}{r} 4\cdot87 \\ + \ 3\cdot21 \\ \hline 8\cdot08 \end{array} \qquad \text{Ans} = 8\cdot08\text{V}$$

Example 1

Find the sum of three currents having values of 12·4mA, 0·75mA and 3·25mA. Thus we have:

$$\begin{array}{r} 12\cdot4 \\ + \ \ 0\cdot75 \\ + \ \ 3\cdot25 \\ \hline 16\cdot40 \end{array} \qquad \text{Ans} = 16\cdot4\text{mA}$$

Example 2

Find the sum of three voltages having values of 12·2V, 0·15V and 10mV. The values must be in the same units and using volts:

$$10\text{mV} = 0\cdot01\text{V}$$

Thus the sum is given by:

$$\begin{array}{r} 12\cdot2 \\ + \ \ 0\cdot15 \\ + \ \ 0\cdot01 \\ \hline 12\cdot36 \end{array} \qquad \text{Ans} = 12\cdot36\text{V}$$

Example 3

Find the voltage developed across R1 in Fig. 14.2.

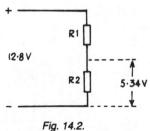

Fig. 14.2.

The voltage across R1 is the **difference** between the supply voltage and the voltage across R2. Thus we subtract 5·34V from 12·8V:

$$\begin{array}{r} 12\cdot8 \\ - \ \ 5\cdot34 \\ \hline 7\cdot46 \end{array} \qquad \text{Ans} = 7\cdot46\text{V}$$

Example 4

A capacitor holds a charge of 1·76mC. If it loses 0·17mC, what charge remains?

$$\begin{array}{r} 1\cdot76 \\ - \ 0\cdot17 \\ \hline 1\cdot59 \end{array} \qquad \text{Ans} = 1\cdot59\text{mC}$$

Multiplication

An advantage of decimal numbers is the ease with which they may be multiplied (or divided) by powers of 10, *e.g.* consider the number 5·7185:

Now 5·7185 × 10   = 57·185
     5·7185 × 100   = 571·85
     5·7185 × 1000 = 5718·5

It will be noted that the figures have not changed in these examples; only the position of the decimal point. Multiplying by 10 results in the decimal point being shifted one place to the right. Multiplying by 100 results in the decimal point moving two places to the right and so on.

Example 5

Multiply 0·563 by 1000

$$0\cdot563 \times 1000 = 563$$

(the decimal point has been moved three places to the right).

Example 6

Multiply 0·00124 by 10000

$$0\cdot00124 \times 10000 = 12\cdot4$$

(the decimal point has been moved four places to the right).

To deal with a multiplication such as 23·7 × 4·306 we use **long multiplication**. The decimal points are first disregarded and 237 is multiplied by 4306.

```
        237
   ×    4306
     948000
      71100
       1422
    1020522
```

The total number of figures following the decimal points in the two numbers are then counted, *i.e.* 1 + 3 = 4. Count this number of figures from the right in the result above and insert the decimal point.

The product is then 102·0522 = Ans

Example 7
A current of 1·28A flows in a resistor of 16·8Ω. Determine the voltage developed across the resistor.

$$\text{Now } V = I \times R$$
$$= 1·28 \times 16·8$$

Using long multiplication and disregarding the decimal points:

```
      128
   × 168
    12800
     7680
     1024
    21504
```

Total number of decimal places = (2 + 1) = 3. Counting from the right 3 figures and inserting the decimal point gives 21·504

$$\text{Ans} = 21·504V$$

Example 8
A current of 2·85mA flows for 3·7 seconds. Determine the charge (Q) that is transferred.

$$\text{Now } Q = I \times t \text{ (coulombs)}$$
$$= 2·85 \times 3·7 \text{ (millicoulombs)}$$

```
      285
   ×  37
     8550
     1995
    10545
```

Inserting the decimal point 3 figures from the right gives 10·545

$$\text{Ans} = 10·545\,mC$$

Division
When dividing a decimal number by powers of 10, the decimal point is moved the appropriate number of places to the left, thus:

$$67·453 \div 10 \quad = 6·7453$$
$$67·453 \div 100 \quad = 0·67453$$
$$67·453 \div 1000 = 0·067453$$

For division by 10 the decimal point is moved one place to the left. Dividing by 100 the decimal point is moved two places to the left and so on.

Example 9
Divide 12·36 by 10000.

$$12·36 \div 10000 = 0·001236$$

(the decimal point has been moved four places to the left).

Example 10
The current flowing in a circuit is 2·5mA. Express the current value in amperes.

$$\text{Now } 1mA = 10^{-3}A = \frac{1}{10^3}\,A$$

Thus we must divide 2·5 by 1000 to express the current value in amperes.

$$2·5 \div 1000 = 0·0025 \qquad \text{Ans} = 0·0025A$$

To find the value of 48·32 ÷ 1·6 we use **long division**. When dividing one number by another and one or both contain a decimal point, a convenient method is to move the decimal point in both numbers by the same number of places until the dividing number becomes a whole number. If the decimal point in both numbers is moved by the same number of places in the same direction, the answer will be the same.

Thus 48·32 ÷ 1·6 gives the same result as 483·2 ÷ 16

```
        30·2
   16) 483·2
        48
         3 2
         3 2
            0        Ans = 30·2
```

Example 11
Solve 30·98 ÷ 2·5

negative powers follows the same rules previously outlined, *e.g.*

$$10^6 \times 10^{-3} = 10^{(6-3)} = 10^3$$

and $\dfrac{10^6}{10^{-3}} = 10^{[6-(-3)]} = 10^{(6+3)} = 10^9$

note that $-(-3) = +3$

Positive powers of 10 are used as multiples and negative powers of 10 are used as sub-multiples in engineering and science units as set out in Table 9.2 of Chapter 9, *e.g.*

10^6 prefix mega
10^3 prefix kilo
10^{-3} prefix milli
10^{-9} prefix nano

Example 15

Evaluate: $\dfrac{10^{12} \times 10^{-2} \times 10^{-3}}{10^4}$

$$\dfrac{10^{12} \times 10^{-2} \times 10^{-3}}{10^4} = \dfrac{10^{(12-2-3)}}{10^4}$$

$$= \dfrac{10^7}{10^4} = 10^{(7-4)} = 10^3 \text{ Ans}$$

Standard Form

It is possible to express any decimal number as a value between 1 and 10 multiplied by a power of 10. A number expressed in this way is said to be in **standard form**. This means having only one figure before the decimal point and adjusting the overall value by multiplying with a suitable power of 10, *e.g.*

492·3 in standard form is $4·923 \times 10^2$
18·5 in standard form is $1·85 \times 10$
3000000 in standard form is 3×10^6
0·572 in standard form is $5·72 \times 10^{-1}$
0·000391 in standard form is $3·91 \times 10^{-4}$

Example 16

Find the resistance of a 5 km length of copper wire with a cross sectional area of 4 square mm if the resistivity of copper is $1·7 \times 10^{-8}$ ohm-m.

Now $R = \dfrac{pl}{A}$ p in ohm-m
                     l in metres
                     A in square metres

$$= \dfrac{1·7 \times 10^{-8} \times 5 \times 10^3}{4 \times 10^{-6}}$$

$$= \dfrac{1·7 \times 5 \times 10^{-5}}{4 \times 10^{-6}}$$

$$= \dfrac{1·7 \times 5}{4} \times 10$$

$$= 2·125 \times 10 \text{ ohms (in standard form)}$$

$$= 21.25 \text{ ohms}$$

RATIO, AVERAGE AND PERCENTAGE

Ratio

A **ratio** is a comparison of the magnitudes of two quantities whether they be lengths, areas, volumes, heights, voltages, resistances, or time intervals *etc.*

For example, in Fig. 14.3 the amplitude of waveform A is 4V whereas the amplitude of waveform B is 1V and as a ratio of A to B this would be 4 to 1 (written as 4:1). Similarly, the ratio of waveform B amplitude to that of waveform C would be 1:2 since C is twice the amplitude of B.

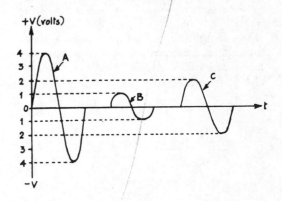

Fig. 14.3.

It is important that before we can state the ratio, the units must be the same. Thus to state the ratio of two voltages of, say, A = 50V and B = 100mV we must first get them into the same units.

Since 100mV = 0·1V, the ratio of A to B is:

$$\dfrac{50}{0·1} = 500:1$$

Example 17

State the frequency ratio of two sine waves, one having a frequency of 2kHz and the other a frequency of 100Hz.

$$\text{Ratio} = \frac{2000}{100} = \frac{20}{1} = 20{:}1$$

(highest-to-lowest)

Example 18

State the capacitance ratio of two capacitors, one having a value of 100nF and the other a value of 25pF.

Using the same units, say pF

$$100\text{nF} = 100 \times 10^3 \text{pF}$$

$$\text{therefore Ratio} = \frac{100 \times 10^3}{25}$$

$$= \frac{4 \times 10^3}{1} = 4000{:}1$$

Average

The **average** or **mean** value of a quantity is found by adding up all the values of the quantity and dividing by the number of values.

$$\text{Average} = \frac{\text{Sum of values}}{\text{Number of values}}$$

For example, the voltage measured across a particular circuit resistor by 4 different voltmeters was 1·08V, 1·06V, 1·02V and 0·98V. What is the average voltage reading?

$$\text{Average} = \frac{1{\cdot}08 + 1{\cdot}06 + 1{\cdot}02 + 0{\cdot}98}{4}$$

$$= \frac{4{\cdot}14}{4}$$

$$= 1{\cdot}035\text{V} \quad \text{Ans}$$

Example 19

The voltage amplitudes at instants a, b, c, d, e and f for the sine wave half-cycle shown in Fig. 14.4 are 0·259V, 0·707V, 0·966V, 0·966V, 0·707V and 0·259V. What is the average value correct to 2 decimal places?

Average value: =

$$\frac{0{\cdot}259 + 0{\cdot}707 + 0{\cdot}966 + 0{\cdot}966 + 0{\cdot}707 + 0{\cdot}259}{6}$$

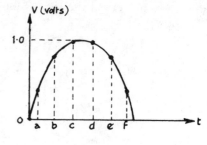

Fig. 14.4.

$$= \frac{3{\cdot}864}{6} = 0{\cdot}644 = 0.64\text{V}$$

(correct to 2 decimal places)

(note the average value for half a sine wave is actually 0·636 × peak).

Example 20

Refer to Fig. 14.5.

(a) Determine the average value of the repetitive waveform.

(b) Give the mark-to-space ratio.

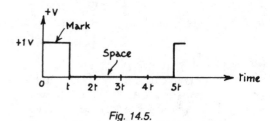

Fig. 14.5.

Solution

(a) During the interval of the 5 equal time periods we have 1 period at +1·0V and 4 periods at 0V.

$$\text{Average value} = \frac{1{\cdot}0 + 0 + 0 + 0 + 0}{5}$$

$$= \frac{1}{5} = +0{\cdot}2\text{V} \quad \text{Ans}$$

(b) Mark-to-space ratio = 1:4   Ans.

Example 21

Find the average value of the repetitive waveform given in Fig. 14.6.

During the interval of the 3 equal time periods, we have 2 periods at +1·0V and 1 period at −0·5V.

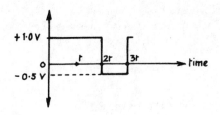

Fig. 14.6.

$$\text{Average value} = \frac{1 + 1 - 0.5}{3}$$

$$= \frac{1.5}{3}$$

$$= +0.5\text{V} \quad \text{Ans}$$

Percentage

A fraction can be expressed as a percentage if the denominator is made 100, *e.g.*

$$\frac{3}{4} = \frac{75}{100} = 75\%$$

$$\text{and } \frac{1}{2} = \frac{50}{100} = 50\%$$

To convert a fraction to a percentage we multiply the fraction by 100, *e.g.*

$$\frac{5}{8} = \frac{5}{8} \times 100 = \frac{500}{8} = 62.5\%$$

$$\frac{1}{5} = \frac{1}{5} \times 100 = \frac{100}{5} = 20\%$$

$$0.4 = 0.4 \times 100 = 40\%$$

$$0.132 = 0.132 \times 100 = 13.2\%$$

To convert a percentage into a fraction we divide by 100, *e.g.*

$$25\% = \frac{25}{100} = \frac{1}{4} \text{ (or } 0.25)$$

$$49\% = \frac{49}{100} = 0.49$$

To find the percentage of a quantity we express the percentage as a fraction and multiply the quantity by it.

What is 15% of 60?

$$15\% \text{ as a fraction } = \frac{15}{100}$$

therefore 15% of 60:

$$= \frac{15}{100} \times 60 = \frac{900}{100} = 9 \quad \text{Ans}$$

Example 22

A resistor has a value of 25Ω. If due to a temperature rise its resistance increases by 1·5%, what is the final value of the resistance?

Increase in resistance:

$$= \frac{1.5}{100} \times 25 = 0.375\Omega$$

Final value $= 25 + 0.375 = 25.375\Omega$ Ans

Tolerance

In engineering, all components are manufactured to a tolerance which specifies how reliable is a measured or calculated value. For example, the length of a small component may be quoted as 56±1mm. This shows that we can rely on the length being between 55mm and 57mm. Alternatively, the tolerance may be quoted as a percentage; this is frequently used with electronic components such as resistors and capacitors.

For example, a resistor may be quoted as 10kΩ±10%, which means that it is true value lies between:

$$\frac{90}{100} \times 10^4 = 9\text{k}\Omega$$

$$\text{and } \frac{110}{100} \times 10^4 = 11\text{k}\Omega.$$

Example 23

A polystyrene capacitor is quoted as 68pF±1%. Calculate the capacitance range in which the true value lies.

The capacitance tolerance:

$$= \frac{1}{100} \times 68 = 0.68\text{pF}.$$

Thus the true value lies in the range of:

$$68 - 0.68 = 67.32\text{pF}$$
$$\text{and } 68 + 0.68 = 68.68\text{pF}.$$

Ans   67·32pF to 68·68pF.

Example 24

The scale reading of a moving-coil voltmeter has a tolerance of 2%. If the voltmeter pointer indicates 5·6V, what is the possible range of values of the voltage being measured?

$$\text{Voltage error} = \frac{2}{100} \times 5\cdot6 = 0\cdot112\text{V}$$

Therefore, voltage being measured lies in the range of:

$$5\cdot6 - 0\cdot112 = 5\cdot488\text{V}$$
and $5\cdot6 + 0\cdot112 = 5\cdot712\text{V}$

Ans 5·488V to 5·712V

SQUARE, SQUARE ROOT AND RECIPROCAL

Square

When a number is multiplied by itself once we say that the number is raised to a **power of 2** or it is **squared**. For example:

$$10 \times 10 = 10 \text{ raised to the power of 2}$$
$$= 100 = 10^2$$

$$3 \times 3 = 3 \text{ raised to the power of 2}$$
$$= 9 = 3^2$$

$$13 \times 13 = 13 \text{ raised to the power of 2}$$
$$= 169 = 13^2$$

$$6\cdot4 \times 6\cdot4 = 6\cdot4 \text{ raised to the power of 2}$$
$$= 40\cdot96 = (6\cdot4)^2$$

Square root

The square root of a number is that value which when multiplied by itself produces the number, *e.g.*

Square root of 25 ($\sqrt{25}$) = 5 since $5 \times 5 = 25$

Square root of 81 ($\sqrt{81}$) = 9 since $9 \times 9 = 81$

Square root of 0·25
($\sqrt{0\cdot25}$) = 0·5 since $0\cdot5 \times 0\cdot5 = 0\cdot25$

The square root of a number may also be written as an indice, *e.g.*

$$\sqrt{25} = 25^{1/2} \text{ or } 25^{0\cdot5}$$
$$\sqrt{3\cdot7} = 3\cdot7^{1/2} \text{ or } 3.7^{0\cdot5}$$

This is in keeping with the rules for indices since for example:

$$\sqrt{25} \times \sqrt{25} = 5 \times 5 = 25$$
and $25^{0\cdot5} \times 25^{0\cdot5} = 25^{(0\cdot5 + 0\cdot5)} = 25^1 = 25$

Reciprocal

The expression ⅛ is called the reciprocal of 8; other examples are:

$\dfrac{1}{256}$ is the reciprocal of 256

$\dfrac{1}{15}$ is the reciprocal of 15

$\dfrac{1}{10\cdot56}$ is the reciprocal of 10·56

Also, note that the reciprocal of 2^4

$$= \frac{1}{2^4} = 2^{-4}.$$

Example 25

Find the power dissipated in a 6·8kΩ resistor when a current of 5mA flows through it.

$$\begin{aligned}
\text{Now } P &= I^2 R \text{ (watts)} \\
&= (5 \times 10^{-3})^2 \times 6\cdot8 \times 10^3 \,\text{W} \\
&= 25 \times 10^{-6} \times 6\cdot8 \times 10^3 \\
&= 25 \times 6\cdot8 \times 10^{-3} \\
&= 170 \times 10^{-3} \,\text{W} \\
&= 170\text{mW} \quad \text{Ans}
\end{aligned}$$

Example 26

The power dissipated in a 15Ω resistor is 2·5W. Determine the voltage across the resistor correct to 2 decimal places.

$$\begin{aligned}
\text{Now } P &= \frac{V^2}{R} \\
\text{or } V^2 &= PR \\
\text{and } V &= \sqrt{PR} \\
&= \sqrt{15 \times 2\cdot5} \\
&= \sqrt{37\cdot5} = 6\cdot1237 \\
&= 6\cdot12\,\text{V}
\end{aligned}$$
correct to 2 decimal places   Ans

TRANSPOSITION OF FORMULAE

In many cases with formulae used in engineering one quantity is expressed in terms of other quantities, *e.g.*

$$I = \frac{V}{R} \quad \text{and} \quad Q = CV$$

In these two formulae, the quantities I and Q are called the **subject** and appear on their own on the left-hand side of the equation. We can make any of the other quantities the subject by transposing the formulae. The rules used in transposition are the same as used in the solution of equations. Briefly, the rules state that **an equation can be modified in any way provided the same modification is made to both sides**.

Suppose that we wish to make R the subject of the formulae:

$$I = \frac{V}{R}$$

Multiplying both sides by R

then $R \times I = \dfrac{V}{R} \times R$

(note that $^R/_R = 1$ on right-hand side)

therefore $\quad R \times I = V$

or $\qquad\qquad V = IR$

Suppose that we wish to make C the subject of the equation

$$Q = CV$$

Dividing both sides by V

then $\qquad \dfrac{Q}{V} = \dfrac{CV}{V}$

therefore $\dfrac{Q}{V} = C$

or $\qquad C = \dfrac{Q}{V}$

Suppose that we wish to make I the subject of the formulae

$$P = I^2 R$$

Dividing both sides by R

then $\qquad \dfrac{P}{R} = \dfrac{I^2 R}{R}$

and $\qquad I^2 = \dfrac{P}{R}$

Taking the square root of both sides

$$I = \sqrt{\frac{P}{R}}$$

Most of the formulae that you will meet will be of the kind given above where transpositions can be done by multiplication or

division of both sides. Practice is required in spotting the correct factors to bring the formulae to the desired form.

Example 27

(a) Make f the subject of the formulae $\lambda = \dfrac{v}{f}$

(b) Make R the subject of the formulae

$$P = \frac{V^2}{R}$$

(a) $\lambda = \dfrac{v}{f}$

Dividing both sides by v

then $\qquad \dfrac{\lambda}{v} = \dfrac{v}{f \times v}$

or $\qquad \dfrac{1}{f} = \dfrac{\lambda}{v}$

thus $\qquad f = \dfrac{v}{\lambda}$

(taking reciprocals of both sides)

(b) $P = \dfrac{V^2}{R}$

Dividing both sides by V^2

then $\qquad \dfrac{P}{V^2} = \dfrac{V^2}{R \times V^2}$

and $\qquad \dfrac{1}{R} = \dfrac{P}{V^2}$

thus $\qquad R = \dfrac{V^2}{P}$

(taking reciprocals of both sides)

GRAPHS

Often in electronic circuits and devices the value of one quantity involved is determined by the value of another and such quantities are usually expressed in equation form. It is useful, however, if the quantities can be shown in diagram form since there are many sets of values which will satisfy the equation. The most common form of diagram used is the graph.

To plot a graph we take two lines or axes at right angles to each other which intersect at point 0, the origin as in Fig. 14.7. In plotting a

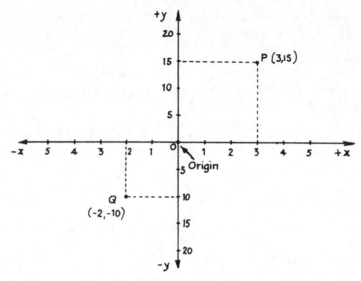

Fig. 14.7 Graph axes.

graph we may have to use positive and negative values thus the horizontal and vertical axes are scaled with positive and negative numbers as shown. The horizontal axis is called the **x-axis** and the vertical axis the **y-axis** (other symbols may be used depending upon the quantities involved).

A point P has been plotted for x = +3 and y = +15. The values +3 and +15 are said to be the **rectangular co-ordinates** of point P. Similarly −2 and −10 are the rectangular co-ordinates of point Q. Other points may likewise be plotted to lie in any of the four quadrants.

Linear Graph

If we consider an equation such as:

$$y = 4x$$

Since y is the subject of the equation, its value is dependent on the value of x, thus y is called the **dependent variable**. Since we can give x any value we choose, x is called the **independent variable**.

Consider now the circuit of Fig. 14.8 for

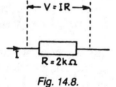

Fig. 14.8.

which we wish to plot a graph of the voltage dropped across R (2kΩ) against current for values of current from zero up to 5mA in 1mA steps.

The equation is V = IR **where R is a constant** (since its value is fixed). V is the subject of the equation thus V is the **dependent variable** and will form the **vertical axis** of the graph. Since **I** is the **independent variable** it will form the **horizontal axis**. Before we can plot the graph we must set out a **table of values**.

I (mA)	0	1	2	3	4	5
V = IR (volts)	0	2	4	6	8	10

Table of values

In the above, the value for V is computed from V = IR where R = 2kΩ and I is the various values of current.

We may now plot the six points as shown in Fig. 14.9 after selecting and marking the axes, choosing the largest possible scale to suit the graph paper. The line connecting the six points forms a **straight line** or **linear** graph. It will be noted that the points have been plotted using the positive values for V and I which is the normal convention when the current does not change direction. Negative values of V and I would be required if the current direction in Fig. 14.8 was reversed.

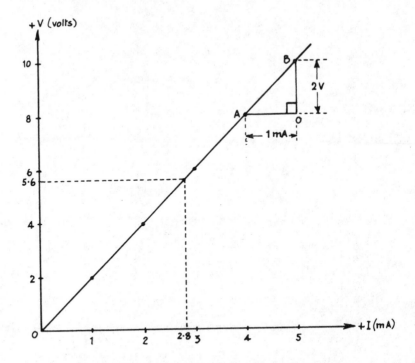

Fig. 14.9 Linear graph of voltage against current for circuit of Fig. 14.8.

If one quantity is directly proportional to another (as in this case) a straight line graph always results passing through the origin. We can find from the graph a value for V not given in the table, *e.g.* when I = 2·8mA we can see from inspection that V = 5·6V.

If instead of being given the circuit of Fig. 14.8 we are given the graph of Fig. 14.9, we can determine the value of the circuit resistor by finding the **slope** or **gradient** of the graph (which for a straight line graph is constant).

$$\text{The gradient} = \frac{0B}{0A} = \frac{2}{1 \times 10^{-3}} = 2000$$

$$\text{Thus } R = 2k\Omega.$$

The graphs of Fig. 14.10 show the effect of altering the value of R in Fig. 14.8. We can see that for any given value of current, the voltage drop increases as the value R increases. Also, we note that as the value of R is reduced (to 1kΩ), the slope or gradient is reduced, whilst if R is increased (to 4 kΩ) the slope or gradient is increased. For all three straight line graphs, the value of R may be determined by finding the slope of the graph.

Inverse Graph

Consider the circuit of Fig. 14.11 for which we wish to plot a graph of current against resistance for various values of R, with constant voltage applied. The equation is:

$$I = \frac{V}{R} \text{ where V is a constant (10V)}$$

Since I is the subject it will form the vertical axis and the independent variable R will form the horizontal axis. A table of values is given below.

R (ohms)	0.5	1	2	3	4	5	6	7	8	9	10
$I = \dfrac{V}{R}$ (A)	20	10	5	3·33	2·5	2	1·67	1·43	1·25	1·1	1

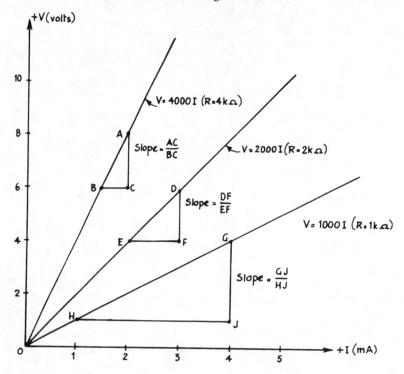

Fig. 14.10 *Effect of slope of graph of altering the value of R in Fig. 14.8.*

The value for I is computed from I = V/R where V = 10V and R is the various values given in the table. If these points are plotted, the graph given in Fig. 14.12 is obtained.

This is the **reciprocal curve** of the equation I = 10/R where positive values for R have been plotted (negative values for R are not practically feasible here). It should be noted that for extreme values of R the curve becomes nearer and nearer to the graph axes but never actually touches them. A general reciprocal curve giving positive and negative values is shown insert. The curve is often called a **rectangular hyperbola** and is an example of a **non-linear** graph.

We can find a value for I not given in the table *e.g.* from inspection of the graph we see that I = 3·8A when R = 2·6 ohms.

Exponential Graph

Consider the charging circuit of Fig. 14.13(a) for which we wish to plot a graph showing how the voltage across the capacitor (V_C) grows with time. A table of values is given below:

Time (ms)	0	0·25	0·5	1	2	3	4	5
V_C (volts)	0	2·21	3·93	6·32	8·65	9·5	9·8	9·9

If we plot these values, the graph shown in Fig. 14.14 is obtained. This is an **exponential**

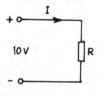

Fig. 14.11.

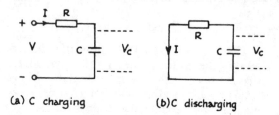

(a) C charging   (b) C discharging

Fig. 14.13 *Charge and discharge of a capacitor through a resistor.*

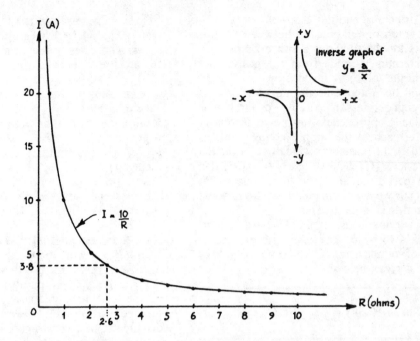

Fig. 14.12 *Inverse graph of current against resistance (voltage constant).*

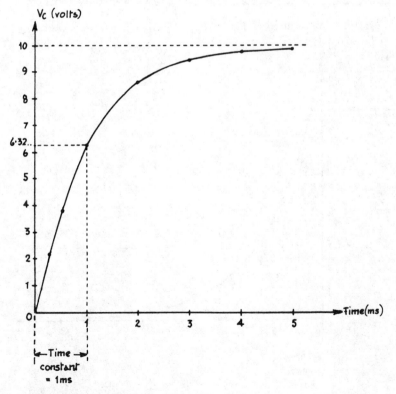

Fig. 14.14 *Exponential graph showing growth of voltage against time as C charges.*

graph which is another example of a **non-linear** graph or relationship between quantities. As for the previous graph examples we can determine a value from the graph (not given in the table) by inspection.

It will be noted that the curve starts off steeply but gets less steep as time progresses as it gradually approaches (but never in theory actually reaches) the supply voltage (in this case 10V). In particular we can see that the voltage across C reaches $0.632 \times 10 = 6.32$V in a time period equal to the time constant of 1ms. Thus we may conclude that the product of C and R is equal to 1ms.

We will now consider the discharge circuit of Fig. 14.13(b) for which we wish to plot the decay of voltage across C with time. A table of values is given below.

Time (ms)	0	0·25	0·5	1	2	3	4	5
V_C (volts)	10	7·79	6·06	3·68	1·35	0·49	0·18	0·06

These values are plotted to form the graph given in Fig. 14.15. This graph follows the law of **exponential decay** and is **non-linear**. We can see that the voltage in the capacitor falls to 0.368×10V = 3.68V in a time interval corresponding to the time constant of 1ms. The curve falls steeply at the commencement of discharge and then less steeply as time progresses as the voltage gradually approaches zero (but never in theory actually reaches it).

Both the charge and discharge curves show that the steady level is reached, for practical purposes, in a time period equal to $5 \times$ time constant.

Another **exponential curve** is given in Fig. 14.16 showing how the resistance of a **negative temperature coefficient (n.t.c.) thermistor** varies with temperature. It will be seen that the resistance decreases with an increase in temperature and that the resistance changes very greatly in a **very non-linear manner**.

From the table of values given it will be seen that the resistance change from 0°C to 50°C is 321000Ω, while for a 50° change above 250°C it is only 130Ω.

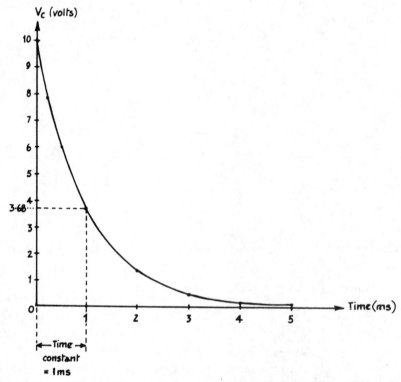

Fig. 14.15 *Exponential graph showing decay of voltage against time as C discharges.*

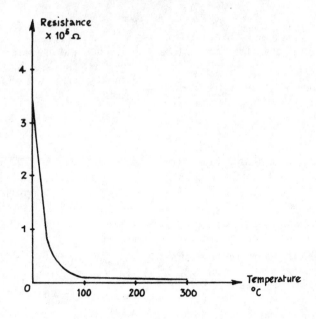

Fig. 14.16 *Exponential graph of resistance against temperature for N.T.C. thermistor.*

T (°C)	0	25	50	100	150	200	250	300
R (Ω)	355000	100000	34000	6000	1650	580	240	110

BINARY NUMBERS

In the binary number system we use only two digits:

0 and 1

When writing down a binary number we use columns (as for decimal) which are based on **powers of 2** (base 2):

Binary Point
↓

32s	16s	8s	4s	2s	1s		½s	¼s	⅛s	1/16s	1/32s
2^5	2^4	2^3	2^2	2^1	2^0	.	2^{-1}	2^{-2}	2^{-3}	2^{-4}	2^{-5}

← Increasing in powers of 2

Decreasing in powers of 2 →

Thus, if we write   1   0   1   1   this means 1 eight +
0 fours +
1 two +
1 unit

= 11 in decimal

Binary Fractions

If we move the **binary point** to the left or right it decreases or increases the number by a factor of 2, *e.g.*

Binary Number		Decimal Equivalent
1000·0	=	8
100·0	=	4
10·0	=	2
1·0	=	1
0·1	=	0·5
0·01	=	0·25
0·001	=	0.125
	etc	

Thus the binary number 1101·11 is 13·75 in decimal.

It should be noted that a fractional decimal number cannot be expressed accurately in binary unless it consists of a sum of ½s, ¼s, ⅛s, 1⁄16s, *etc.*

Binary addition

Binary numbers are added together according to the following rules:

2-Digit
$$0 + 0 = 0$$
$$0 + 1 = 1$$
$$1 + 0 = 1$$
$$1 + 1 = 0 \ (\text{Carry } 1)$$

3-Digit
$$0 + 0 + 0 = 0$$
$$0 + 0 + 1 = 1$$
$$0 + 1 + 0 = 1$$
$$0 + 1 + 1 = 0 \ (\text{Carry } 1)$$
$$1 + 0 + 0 = 1$$
$$1 + 0 + 1 = 0 \ (\text{Carry } 1)$$
$$1 + 1 + 0 = 0 \ (\text{Carry } 1)$$
$$1 + 1 + 1 = 1 \ (\text{Carry } 1)$$

Example 28

Find the result of 1101 + 0110

$$
\begin{array}{r}
1101\ + \\
0110 \\
\hline
= \quad 10011 \quad \text{Ans}
\end{array}
$$

Example 29

Find the result of 1101 + 1111 + 0110.

When adding three or more binary numbers together they are best added by adding two together and then adding the next on to the result:

$$
\begin{array}{r}
1101\ + \\
1111 \\
\hline
= \quad 11100\ + \\
0110 \\
\hline
= \quad 100010 \quad \text{Ans}
\end{array}
$$

Example 30

Find the result of 1101·01 + 1000·11.

Compound numbers are added in the same way:

$$
\begin{array}{r}
1101·01\ + \\
1000·11 \\
\hline
= \quad 10110·00 \quad \text{Ans}
\end{array}
$$

Binary Subtraction

Subraction is just as simple if we remember to add 2 to a column in order to subtract from a lower number and carry 1 over to the next column. For example:

Find the result of 100011 − 1101

$$
\begin{array}{cc}
\begin{array}{r}
1 \ 0^2 0^2 0^2 1 \ 1 \\
- \ 0_{/} \ 0_{/} \ 1_{/} \ 1 \ 0 \ 1 \\
\hline
\text{Ans} \quad 0 \ 1 \ 0 \ 1 \ 1 \ 0
\end{array}
&
\begin{array}{r}
3 \ 5 \\
\text{or} \quad - \ 1 \ 3 \\
\hline
2 \ 2
\end{array}
\end{array}
$$

Example 31

Find the result of 1111·01 − 1001·10.

$$
\begin{array}{cc}
\begin{array}{r}
1 \ 1 \ 1 \ 1^2 \cdot \ 0^2 1 \\
- \ 1 \ 0 \ 0_{/} \ 1_{/} \cdot \ 1 \ 0 \\
\hline
\text{Ans} \quad 0 \ 1 \ 0 \ 1 \cdot \ 1 \ 1
\end{array}
&
\begin{array}{r}
15·25 \\
\text{or} \quad - \ 9·5 \\
\hline
5·75
\end{array}
\end{array}
$$

Example 32
Find the result of $10001 - 1011$.

$$
\begin{array}{llll}
1\ 0^2\ 0^2\ 0^2\ 1 & & 17 \\
-\ 0,\ 1,\ 0,\ 1\ 1 & \text{or} & -\ 11 \\
\hline
\text{Ans} \quad 0\ 0\ 1\ 1\ 0 & & 6 \\
\hline
\end{array}
$$

Conversion between Binary and Decimal

Decimal-to-Binary
To convert a decimal number to binary we find the **powers of 2** contained in it. This may be achieved using the following steps:

(1) If the decimal number is **even** write 0 but if **odd** write 1.
(2) Divide by 2 (ignoring any remainder).
(3) If the result is **even** write 0 but if **odd** write 1.
(4) Go back to step 2 and repeat until the number is reduced to unity.

The binary number is then formed by writing the 1s and 0s from left-to-right starting with the **last** number obtained. For example to convert 28_{10} to binary:

$$
\begin{array}{rr|r}
 & 28 & 0 \\
\div 2 & 14 & 0 \\
\div 2 & 7 & 1 \\
\div 2 & 3 & 1 \\
\div 2 & 1 & 1 \\
\end{array}
$$
$\uparrow$ read

Ans $28_{10} = 11100_2$

Example 33
Convert 339_{10} to binary

$$
\begin{array}{rr|r}
 & 339 & 1 \\
\div 2 & 169 & 1 \\
\div 2 & 84 & 0 \\
\div 2 & 42 & 0 \\
\div 2 & 21 & 1 \\
\div 2 & 10 & 0 \\
\div 2 & 5 & 1 \\
\div 2 & 2 & 0 \\
\div 2 & 1 & 1 \\
\end{array}
$$
$\uparrow$ read

Ans $339_{10} = 101010011_2$

Binary-to-Decimal
This is readily carried out from inspection of the binary number by remembering the column weightings, *e.g.* the binary number:

$$1\ 1\ 0\ 1\ 1$$

consists of 1 unit +
1 two +
1 eight +
1 sixteen
= 27 in decimal

Thus $11011_2 = 27_{10}$

Example 34
Convert 100011 to decimal. From inspection of the column weightings the binary number consists of:

$$
\begin{array}{l}
1 \times 1\ + \\
1 \times 2\ + \\
1 \times 32 \\
\hline
=\quad 35 \\
\hline
\end{array}
$$

Ans $10011_2 = 35_{10}$

Example 35
Convert 1001001000 to decimal. From inspection of the column weightings, the number consists of:

$$
\begin{array}{l}
1 \times\ \ 8\ + \\
1 \times\ 64\ + \\
1 \times 512 \\
\hline
=\quad 584 \\
\hline
\end{array}
$$

Ans $1001001000_2 = 584_{10}$

QUESTIONS ON CHAPTER FOURTEEN
(1) A current of 5·1mA flows in a resistor of $100k\Omega$. The p.d. across the resistor is given by:
(a) $10^5 \times 5\cdot1 \times 10^{-3}V$
(b) $5\cdot1 \times 10^3 \times 10^5V$
(c) $5\cdot1 \times 10^{-6} \times 10^5V$
(d) $5\cdot1 \times 10^{-3} \times 10^{-5}V.$

(2) A current of 5·4556A expressed correct to 2 decimal places is:
(a) 5·5A
(b) 5·45A
(c) 5·55A
(d) 5·46A.

(3) A voltage of 25·375V expressed correct to 2 significant figures is:
(a) 25V
(b) 25·38V
(c) 25·37V
(d) 26V.

(4) The result of $\dfrac{10^7}{10^{-4}}$ is:
(a) 10^{11}
(b) 10^3
(c) 10^{-3}
(d) 10^{-11}.

(5) The number 534·65 is written in standard form as:
(a) $0·53465 \times 10^3$
(b) $5·3465 \times 10^2$
(c) $53·465 \times 10$
(d) $5346·5 \times 10^{-1}$.

(6) The ratio of two voltages, one of 30V and the other of 3mV is:
(a) 10:1
(b) 600:1
(c) 900:1
(d) 10000:1.

(7) When measured, nominal 500 Ω resistors are found to have resistances in the range of 490 Ω to 510 Ω. The resistance tolerance is:
(a) ±1%
(b) ±2%
(c) ±5%
(d) ±10%.

(8) The decimal equivalent of the binary number 1010101·01 is:
(a) 1000·01
(b) 31·0875
(c) 85·25
(d) 68·75.

(9) Which of the diagrams shown in Fig. 14.17 is a reciprocal graph?

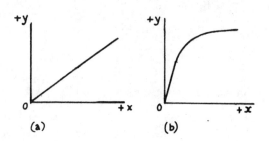

(a)   (b)

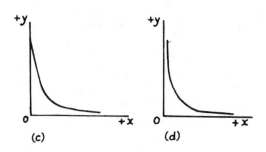

(c)   (d)

Fig. 14.17.

(10) If I is made the subject of the formulae $P = I^2 R$, the equation is:
(a) $I = \dfrac{P}{R}$
(b) $I = \dfrac{P^2}{R}$
(c) $I = \sqrt{\dfrac{P}{R}}$
(d) $I = P\sqrt{R}$.

(Answers on page 219.)

CIRCUIT SYMBOLS

GENERAL

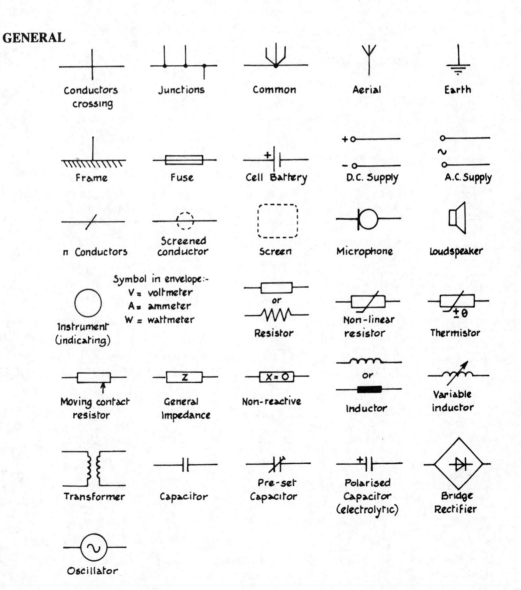

Conductors crossing	Junctions	Common	Aerial	Earth
Frame	Fuse	Cell Battery	D.C. Supply	A.C. Supply
n Conductors	Screened conductor	Screen	Microphone	Loudspeaker
Instrument (indicating)	Symbol in envelope:- V = voltmeter A = ammeter W = wattmeter	Resistor (or)	Non-linear resistor	Thermistor
Moving contact resistor	General Impedance	Non-reactive	Inductor (or)	Variable inductor
Transformer	Capacitor	Pre-set Capacitor	Polarised Capacitor (electrolytic)	Bridge Rectifier
Oscillator				

ELECTRONIC DEVICES

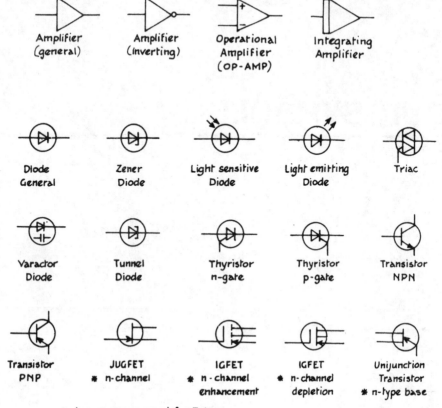

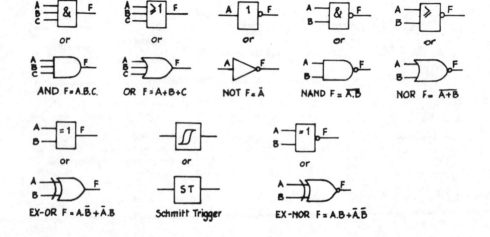

LOGIC SYMBOLS

COMPONENT COLOUR CODES

RESISTORS

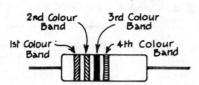

Fig. B.1 Resistor colour coding bands.

Colour	1st Band (1st digit)	2nd Band (2nd digit)	3rd Band (Multiplier)	4th Band (Tolerance)
Black	0	0	1	–
Brown	1	1	10	$\pm 1\%$
Red	2	2	10^2	$\pm 2\%$
Orange	3	3	10^3	–
Yellow	4	4	10^4	–
Green	5	5	10^5	–
Blue	6	6	10^6	–
Violet	7	7	10^7	–
Grey	8	8	10^8	–
White	9	9	10^9	–
Silver	–	–	0.01	$\pm 10\%$
Gold	–	–	0.1	$\pm 5\%$
				None $\pm 20\%$

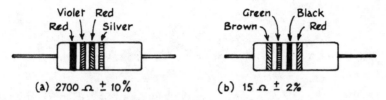

(a) 2700 Ω $\pm$ 10%   (b) 15 Ω $\pm$ 2%

Fig. B.2 Examples of resistor colour coding.

Preferred Values

E12 Series ($\pm 10\%$ tolerance range)

1·0	1·2	1·5	1·8	2·2	2·7	and multiples of 10
3·3	3·9	4·7	5·6	6·8	8·2	

E24 Series (± 5% tolerance range)

1·0	1·1	1·2	1·3	1·5	1·6	1·8	2·0	2·2	2·4	2·7	3·0	and multiples of 10
3·3	3·6	3·9	4·3	4·7	5·1	5·6	6·2	6·8	7·5	8·2	9·1	

CAPACITORS (Candy stripe)

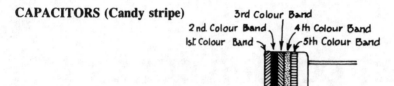

Fig. B.3 Polyester capacitor colour coding.

Colour	1st Band (1st digit)	2nd Band (2nd digit)	3rd Band (Multiplier)	4th Band (Tolerance)	5th Band (Working Voltage)
Black	0	0	–	± 20%	–
Brown	1	1	–	–	–
Red	2	2	–	–	250V d.c.
Orange	3	3	× 0·001 μF	–	–
Yellow	4	4	× 0·01 μF	–	400V d.c.
Green	5	5	× 0·1 μF	–	–
Blue	6	6	–	–	–
Violet	7	7	–	–	–
Grey	8	8	–	–	–
White	9	9	–	± 10%	–

Resistor and Capacitor Letter and Digit Code

Resistance Value	Marked
0·47Ω	R47
1Ω	1R0
4·7Ω	4R7
47Ω	47R
470Ω	470R
1kΩ	1K0
4·7kΩ	4K7
10MΩ	10M

Capacitance Value	Marked	
0·68 pF	p68	
6·8 pF	6p8	Values up to 999 pF marked in pF
15 pF	15p	Values from 1000 pF to 990,000 pF in nF
1000 pF	1n0	Values from 1000 nF upwards in μF
47 nF	47n	
1000 nF	1 μ0	
1·5 μF	1μ5	
50 μF	50μ	

ANSWERS TO QUESTIONS

Chapter 1
No. 1 (b)
2 (c)
3 (a)
4 (d)
5 (d)
6 (b)
7 (b)
8 (a)
9 (a)
10 (b)

Chapter 2
No. 1 (a)
2 (d)
3 (a)
4 (b)
5 (d)
6 (c)
7 (d)
8 (b)
9 (c)
10 (a)
11 (b)
12 (b)

Chapter 3
No. 1 (b)
2 (b)
3 (a)
4 (c)
5 (c)
6 (b)
7 (d)
8 (b)
9 (c)
10 (b)

Chapter 4
No. 1 (c)
2 (a)
3 (d)
4 (d)
5 (a)
6 (b)
7 (b)
8 (d)
9 (c)
10 (a)
11 (d)
12 (b)
13 (c)
14 (c)
15 (b)

Chapter 5
No. 1 (b)
2 (d)
3 (a)
4 (a), (c) and (d)
5 (b)
6 (b)
7 (b)
8 (b)
9 (a)
10 (b)

Chapter 6
No. 1 (a)
2 (b)
3 (c)
4 (b)
5 (d)
6 (d)
7 (b)
8 (a)

Chapter 7
No. 1 (d)
2 (a)
3 (c)
4 (a)
5 (b)
6 (d)
7 (d)
8 (b)
9 (b)
10 (d)
11 (b)
12 (d)
13 (b)
14 (a)
15 (d)
16 (b)
17 (a)
18 (b)
19 (d)
20 (a)

Chapter 8
No. 1 (b)
2 (a)
3 (d)
4 (c)
5 (b)
6 (b)
7 (d)
8 (b)
9 (c)
10 (a)
11 (d)
12 (d)
13 (b)
14 (d)
15 (b)
16 (b)
17 (b)
18 (a)

Chapter 9
No. 1 (b)
2 (a)
3 (d)
4 (c)
5 (d)
6 (b)
7 (c)
8 (d)
9 (a)
10 (a)
11 (d)
12 (a)
13 (d)
14 (d)
15 (c)
16 (a)
17 (c)
18 (a)
19 (c)
20 (b)

Chapter 10
No. 1 (b)
2 (d)
3 (d)
4 (c)
5 (c)
6 (a)
7 (b)
8 (b)
9 (d)
10 (d)
11 (a)
12 (b)

Chapter 11	Chapter 12	Chapter 13	Chapter 14
No. 1 (b)	No. 1 (b)	No. 1 (a)	No. 1 (a)
2 (a)	2 (c)	2 (b)	2 (d)
3 (d)	3 (a)	3 (b)	3 (a)
4 (d)	4 (b)	4 (d)	4 (a)
5 (c)	5 (a)	5 (b)	5 (b)
6 (c)	6 (b)	6 (b)	6 (d)
7 (a)	7 (d)	7 (b)	7 (b)
	8 (d)	8 (d)	8 (c)
	9 (c)	9 (c)	9 (d)
	10 (c)	10 (c)	10 (c)

INDEX